Portsmouth Water 1857 - 2007

150 Years of Service

Portsmouth Water 1857 - 2007

150 Years of Service

by Andy Neve and Mike Hedges

Portsmouth Water 1857 - 2007
150 Years of Service

ISBN 978 0 9556045 0 8

First published July 2007
by Portsmouth Water Ltd
West Street
Havant
Hampshire
PO9 1LG

Designed and produced by Designline Graphics Limited

Contents

Terry Lazenby, Chairman, Portsmouth Water, 2007

Foreword

In 1857 Queen Victoria had been on the throne for 20 years and Palmerston was Prime Minister. 150 years on and Queen Elizabeth II has been on the throne for 55 years and Blair has recently finished his term as Prime Minister. The intervening period has seen enormous change, both socially and in the standard of living that we now enjoy. Technology and engineering have played a key role in this change. In a similar manner, the Directors, management and staff of Portsmouth Water have worked unstintingly to maintain the supply of clean, cheap water to the area, to underpin the growth that the change has demanded. This book is a tribute to their endeavour.

Andy Neve and Mike Hedges are to be congratulated in compiling the detail in this book, building on the work of David Halton Thomson, who produced the centenary edition in 1957. They have built on their 42 years' combined experience with the Company, with an in-depth investigation of the archives to give a faithful account of our activities, successes and difficulties over the 150 years of our existence.

I commend this book to all our friends who will, no doubt, be intrigued by the interplay of issues the Company has faced over the years. The success we have had could not have been achieved without the dedication and loyalty of the staff involved, in whatever capacity, throughout the years. Their commitment has provided a solid platform, on which the Company can face the future as one of the most efficient providers of water in England and Wales; we thank them all for that.

Terry Lazenby
Chairman
Portsmouth Water

Acknowledgements and Authors' Note

This book has drawn heavily on information and photographs provided by many people, but the first acknowledgment must be to the work of David Halton Thomson who, having retired as Engineer to the Company in 1950, wrote *A History of the Portsmouth and Gosport Water Supply*. That book was published to mark the Company's centenary in 1957 and has been abridged to form our chapters about the original Portsmouth and Gosport Companies.

We are also grateful to the Board of Portsmouth Water for the use of its photographic archives and minutes as first-hand sources of information. In addition, much research has been needed into the history of the undertakings absorbed since 1957 and thanks are due to the West Sussex Record Office, the Hampshire Record Office, Portsmouth City Museum and the Chartered Institution of Water & Environmental Management (CIWEM) for access to the records they hold. CIWEM also kindly permitted the use of photographs and information from its journals.

First-hand accounts and stories have been freely provided by many people. The late George Slater, who worked for the Company for 47 years, including service as Chief Engineer, Director and Chairman, wrote an entertaining account of life at the Company in the 1950s and 1960s.

Alfred Burgess, now aged 102, told us about his time at Portsmouth Water and as Engineer & Manager of Chichester Corporation Water Department, including recollections of the discovery of Fishbourne Roman Palace.

Ken Bailey recalled his time as an apprentice at Havant Pumping Station during and after the Second World War.

Alan Twort, former President of the Institution of Water Engineers & Scientists, provided reminiscences about the Bognor Regis undertaking in the 1930s and 1940s, along with photographs.

We have also drawn on articles about the Bognor Regis water undertaking written by the late Russ Burstow, who became Distribution Manager for the Company's East District.

There is very little archive material about Selsey Water Company, but this problem was resolved magnificently by Ruth Mariner, Chairman of the Selsey Society, who obtained photographs of Selsey Water Company staff from friends and acquaintances (acknowledged below), arranged an interview and provided many other pieces of information.

We are grateful to Hazel Ousley, daughter of the late Clem Rose, manager of Selsey Water Company, who agreed to be interviewed about her father and provided some fine insights into his working life, as well as some photographs.

Peter Ogden of the Selsey Society lent us his research notes on the parish history, providing useful information about Selsey Water Company in the 1920s and 1930s.

Diane Bourne and David Riddle in the Company's Drawing Office worked hard to scan archive photographs and produce maps for this book. Colleagues Paul Barfoot, Alan Day, Chris Hudson, Terry Lazenby, Anne McDonald and David Rock carried out valuable proof-reading.

Other present and former staff gave us information about their time at the Company. They are Fred Bailey, John Batty, Dave Bridger, Pete Bridger, Jean Broad, John Cogley, Doug Corbin, Maurice Croxon, Pete Dulson, the late Roy Etherington, Norman Hudson, Len Jones, Dennis Keates, John King, Stan Leggett, Brenda Monnery, Dave Morris, Tony Perry, John Peters, John Polkinghorne, John Reed, Nick Roadnight, Dave Robertson, Des Rutter, Neville Smith, John Stein, Norman Trivett and Chris Whatley.

Other people have been kind enough to lend photographs and provide information: Gillian Cole, Tom Creedy, Gina Fitch-Roy (Dando Drilling International) and the late Allan Pierce.

Authors' Note

Throughout the book, we have referred to units of measurement of the period concerned, ie imperial measurements before the mid-1970s and metric units thereafter. The imperial units are defined in the Glossary at the end of the book.

We have structured the chapters to cover each predessor body separately. Thus there are separate chapters on the water supplies to Portsmouth, Gosport, Fareham, Bognor Regis, Chichester Corporation, Chichester Rural District Council and Selsey Water Company, followed by a chapter on the period 1955 - 1960. After amalgamation with the West Sussex undertakings in 1963, the Company's area of supply has been largely unchanged; each subsequent chapter therefore deals with the history of the whole Company by decade.

Andy Neve and Mike Hedges, July 2007

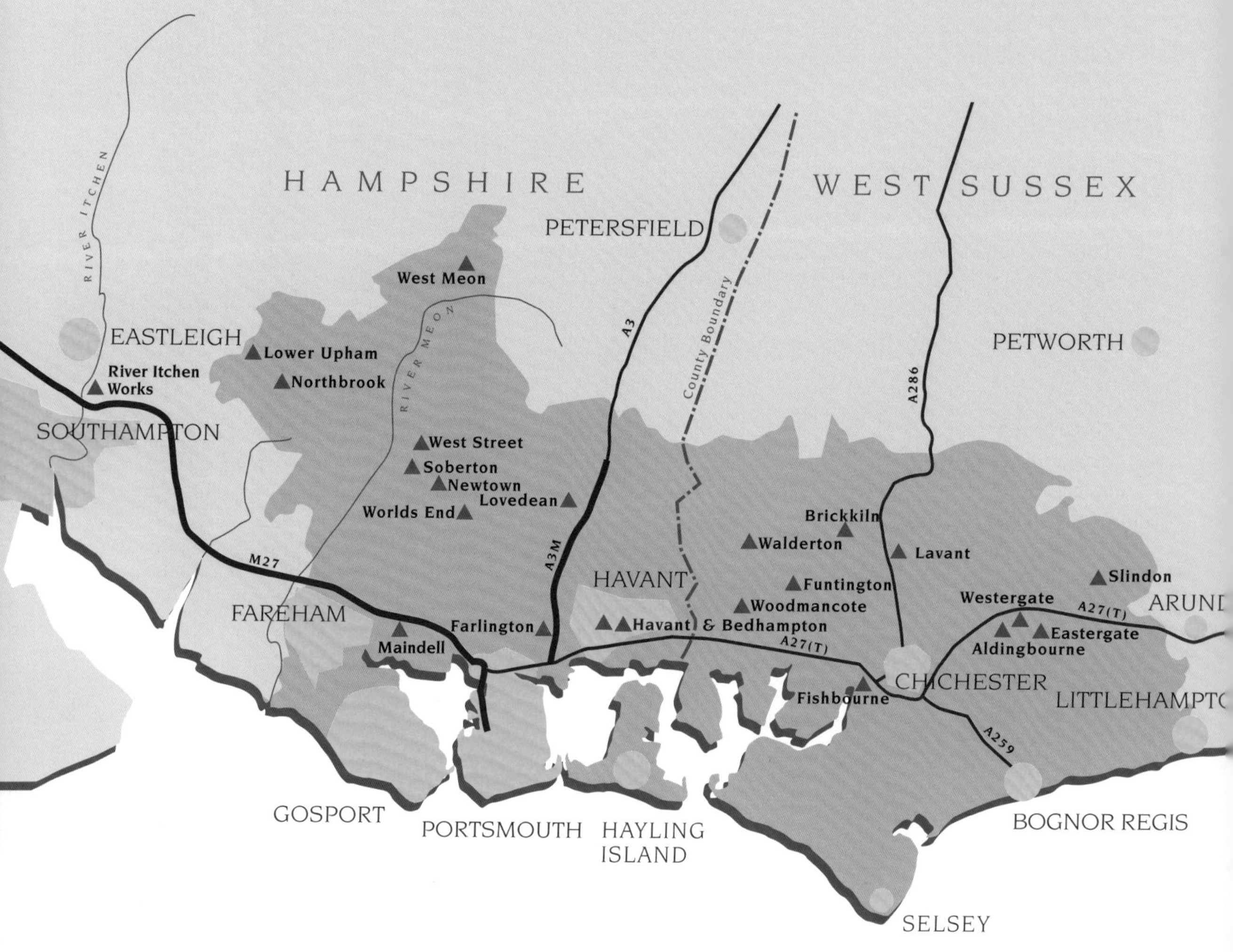
HAMPSHIRE
WEST SUSSEX
RIVER ITCHEN
PETERSFIELD
West Meon
RIVER MEON
County Boundary
A3
EASTLEIGH
Lower Upham
Northbrook
River Itchen Works
PETWORTH
A286
SOUTHAMPTON
West Street
Soberton
Newtown
Lovedean
Worlds End
Brickkiln
Walderton
Lavant
M27
A3M
HAVANT
Funtington
Slindon
Woodmancote
Westergate
A27(T)
ARUND
FAREHAM
Farlington
Havant & Bedhampton
Eastergate
Aldingbourne
Maindell
A27(T)
CHICHESTER
Fishbourne
LITTLEHAMPT
A259
GOSPORT
PORTSMOUTH
HAYLING ISLAND
BOGNOR REGIS
SELSEY
Water Treatment Works
Area of Supply

Introduction

This book celebrates the 150th anniversary of Portsmouth Water by looking back at its origins and how it grew to its present size. It also celebrates the achievement of its Directors and staff over 150 years in providing its customers with that most basic of public health needs, a continuous supply of clean drinking water. This has not happened by accident and has required engineering and technical skill, careful financial management, foresight and the ability to identify and take opportunities.

Portsmouth Water is one of 23 water companies in England and Wales. It supplies an average of 180 million litres of water every day to a population of 660,000, together with 18,000 businesses, in an area of 868 square kilometres that straddles the border between Hampshire and West Sussex. The area of supply ranges from Fareham and Bishop's Waltham in the west to Ford and Middleton-on-Sea in the east, and inland as far as the highest points of the South Downs. The majority of the population lives on the coastal plain in the urban areas of Fareham, Gosport, Havant, Waterlooville, Portsmouth, Chichester and Bognor Regis.

Portsmouth Water has always been independently owned and much of the history of the changing owners is covered in this book. Today the Company employs around 215 people, most of whom are based at its Head Office site in Havant, although a small number of supply staff operate from water treatment works sites at the River Itchen, Farlington, Soberton and Fishbourne.

Although it is one of the smaller companies, Portsmouth Water has had the lowest water charges in England and Wales for many years. It is consistently rated by Ofwat as one of the most efficient companies, with high levels of service to its customers.

Portsmouth Water is also one of the oldest water companies in the UK. On 13th July 1857, an Act of Parliament established the Borough of Portsmouth Waterworks Company, which supplied most of Portsmouth. Since then, the Company has gradually expanded, first in the 1930s to supply rural areas north of Portsmouth and then with a takeover of the Hayling Island supply in 1950. Expansion gathered pace in the 1950s with a merger with Gosport Waterworks Company in 1955 and an amalgamation with the Fareham undertaking in 1959. Finally, in 1963, came the most substantial addition, when the water undertakings of Chichester Corporation, Chichester Rural District Council, Selsey Water Company and Bognor Regis Urban District Council were purchased.

Research for this book has revealed the Company's never-ending quest for improvements to the supply system, driven by a desire to provide its customers with the very highest levels of service, whilst maintaining charges as low as possible. As events have evolved over the years, there has been unwaveringly shrewd foresight from those directing the future, coupled with an immense sense of pride and determination in serving the people of Portsmouth and the surrounding areas. A desire to ensure that the Company remains in control of its destiny has been a recurring theme throughout its history.

As a water supply company, it is inevitable that much of the history is related to the engineering achievements, which have maintained public water supplies. Those achievements would not have been possible without the staff from other disciplines that play their individual part in attempting to ensure that the supply of safe and secure drinking water can be taken for granted by the people of Portsmouth. Accountants, customer billing, computer and many other support staff played their part in that history too. Sadly there is not enough space to be able to recognise them all.

ANNO VICESIMO & VICESIMO PRIMO

VICTORIÆ REGINÆ.

Cap. xlv.

An Act for better supplying with Water the Inhabitants of the Borough of *Portsmouth* in the County of *Southampton.* [13th *July* 1857.]

WHEREAS by an Act passed in the Fourteenth Year of the Reign of King *George* the Second, and intituled *An Act for enabling* Thomas Smith *Esquire, Lord of the Manor of* Farlington *in the County of* Southampton, *to supply the Town of* Portsmouth *and Parts adjacent with good and wholesome Water at his own proper Costs and Charges, Thomas Smith* Esquire, Lord of the Manor of *Farlington* in the County of *Southampton*, his Heirs and Assigns, were authorized and empowered to convey Water from certain Springs arising on his Estate at *Farlington* by Pipes to and through the Town of *Portsmouth*, and through every Street and Lane and Alley thereof, to the Extremity of a Street called "the *Point*," and by and through certain Streets and Buildings called "the *Common*," lying near to the said Town: And whereas the Company of Proprietors of the *Portsmouth and Farlington* Waterworks, Limited (herein-after called "the *Farlington* Company"), being or claiming to be the Assigns of the said *Thomas Smith*, and entitled to the Benefit of the recited Act, have made and maintained Waterworks, and by means thereof supply Water to some Parts of the Borough of *Portsmouth*, but those Waterworks are not sufficient 14 G. 2. c. xliii.

[*Local.*] 7 G adequately

The story of Portsmouth Water is one in which sound, prudent leadership and dedicated, committed staff have combined to ensure 150 years of successful service.

Origins, Successions & Amalgamations

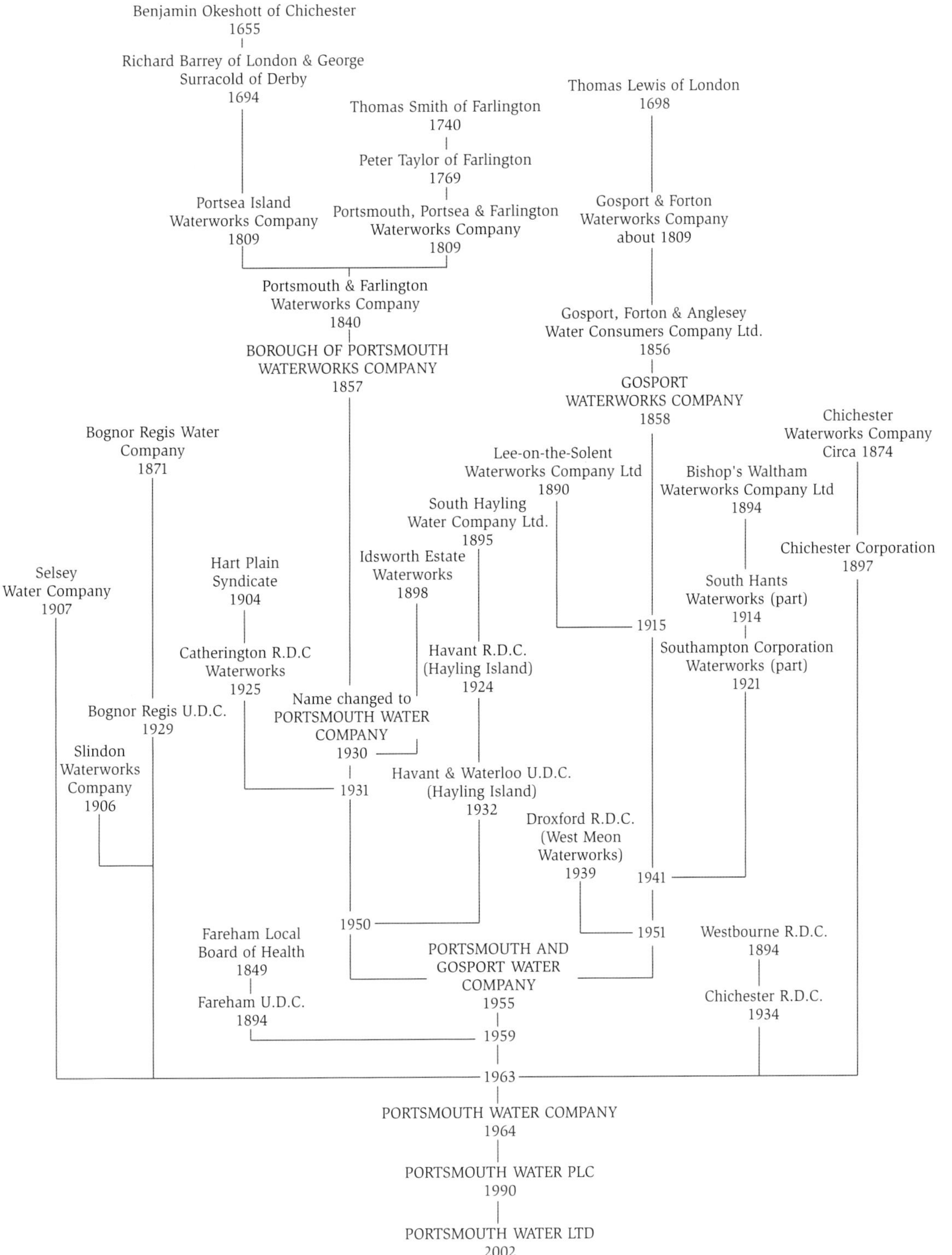

Background

The northern part of the area of supply comprises chalk downland with a scattering of villages, while further south the chalk dips under the clays of the Hampshire Basin. North of Portsmouth, the chalk outcrops in the high ridge of Portsdown Hill, which stretches from Bedhampton westwards to Fareham. Where the chalk first appears at the surface, in Havant and Bedhampton, a prolific series of natural springs appears. These springs have been used by the Company since 1860 and are reputed to be the largest group of springs used for public water supplies in Europe.

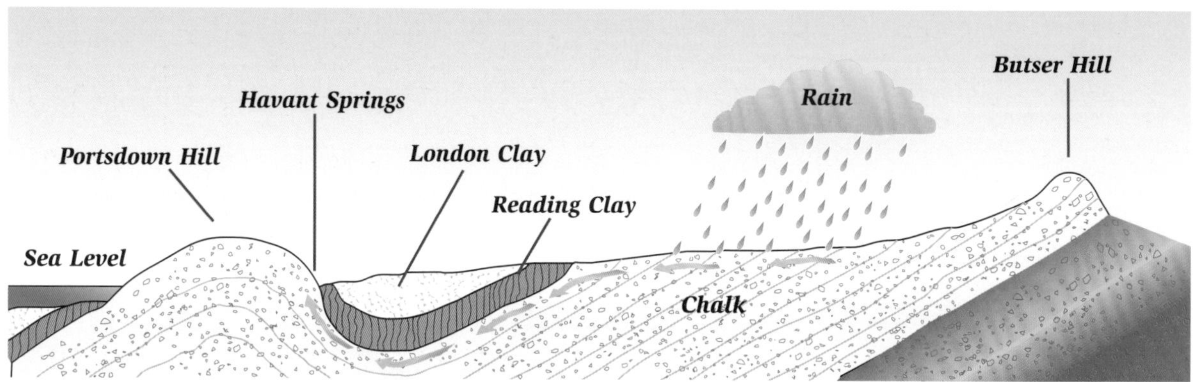

North to south cross-section through geological strata of the South Downs

The South Downs chalk acts like an enormous 'sponge', collecting winter rainfall, which percolates through cracks and fissures on its underground journey from the Downs to the sea. Much of that water flows directly to the sea or appears as perennial springs in rivers, such as the Meon, Hamble or Itchen, whilst many temporary springs rise in the winter and spring to form 'winterbournes' in the upper catchments. Groundwater levels in the chalk aquifer fluctuate during the course of the year; wet weather in the winter causes them to rise but, during summer time, rain quickly evaporates or is absorbed by vegetation, causing groundwater levels to fall. The change in groundwater levels of the South Downs during the course of the year is closely monitored by the Company at Idsworth Well, near Rowlands Castle. These changing levels give an accurate indication of the state of groundwater resources and a graph showing the variation over the course of a typical two-year period is shown opposite. The long-term average is shown in red, while the two critical years when no winter recharge occurred, ie 1933/34 and 1975/76, are shown in blue and green respectively. The yellow line is the plot for 2000/01, when a record wet winter was experienced.

Throughout its area, Portsmouth Water has a number of boreholes and wells in the chalk, from which it abstracts groundwater. It also obtains water from outside its area at an abstraction point just upstream of the tidal limit of the River Itchen, at Gaters Mill, West End, near Southampton Airport. The Company has no large surface water storage reservoirs.

Since groundwater quality is generally of a high standard, the Company does not require complex treatment at all of its sources; at many, chlorine disinfection is all that is required to ensure that microbiological quality is sufficient to meet drinking water standards. The Company's two largest

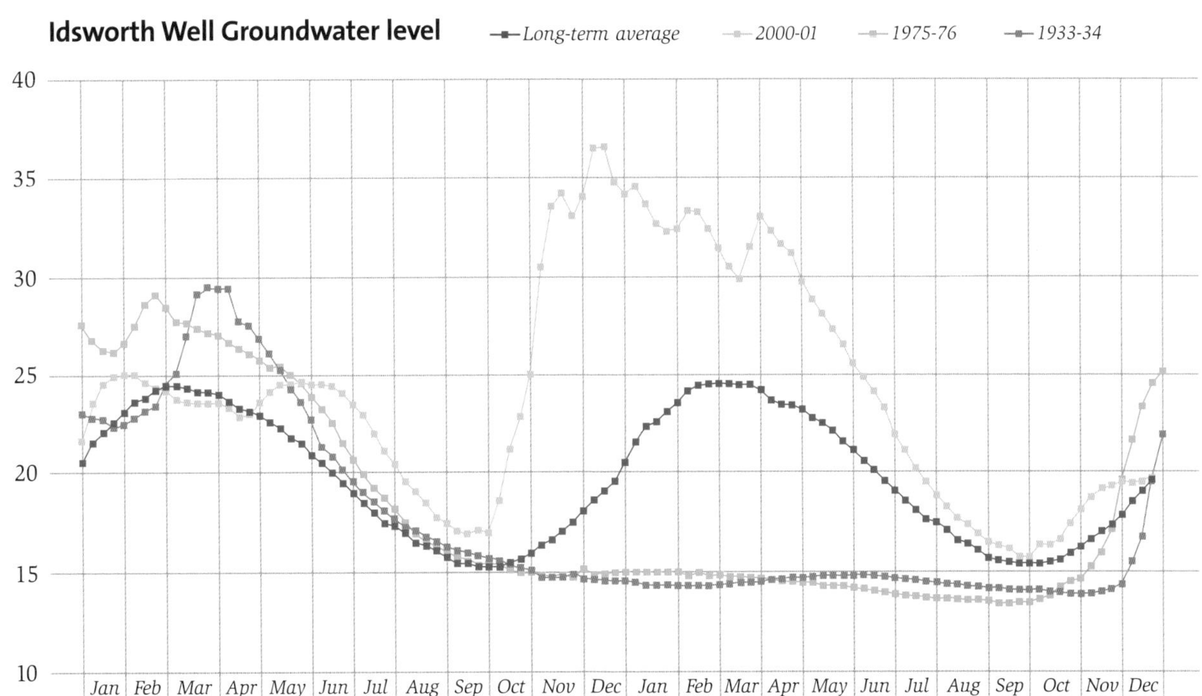

Typical seasonal variation in groundwater levels as recorded at Idsworth Well, Rowlands Castle, over 2 years

sources and several of the borehole and well sites suffer from varying water quality after heavy rainfall. This necessitates much more sophisticated treatment, the development of which is covered in this book, before it can be supplied as drinking water. The 'treated water' from each works is usually pumped to short-term storage in underground service reservoirs, generally situated on hilltops throughout the Company's area. These act as 'distribution warehouses', evening out daily fluctuations in demand, supplying water at a consistent pressure to customers, and providing a reserve of water in case of power, pipeline or treatment failure.

From the service reservoirs, there is a network of over 3,200 kilometres of water mains, laid by the Company and its predecessors over many years, enabling piped supplies to be maintained to households. Connected to those mains are the service pipes, as they are known, which supply each individual property. Around half the Company's employees are engaged in the day-to-day routine of maintaining and repairing the distribution network.

In England and Wales, there are 10 large 'water and sewerage' companies (such as Thames Water and Southern Water) that supply drinking water and treat sewage. Portsmouth Water is one of 13 so-called 'water-only' companies providing drinking water only. The charges and service standards of all these companies are regulated by the Water Services Regulatory Authority (Ofwat); the Drinking Water Inspectorate (DWI) oversees the quality of drinking water supplied and the Environment Agency (EA) controls the abstraction of water and discharge of effluent. The UK probably has one of the most rigorously regulated water markets in the world. Customer service standards are monitored by Ofwat and CCW, the Consumer Council for Water.

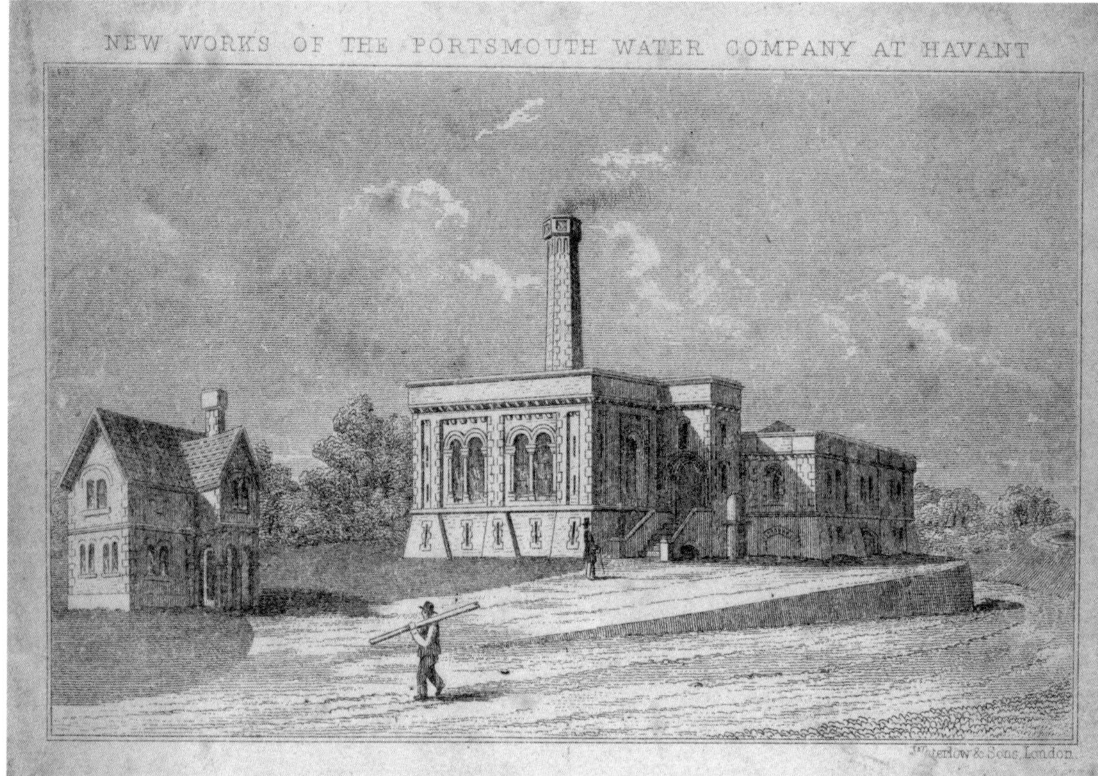

THE above Company being now in a position to give their enlarged and improved supply of Water from the copious and beautiful springs at Brockhampton, through their new works, the Directors request the attention of the Inhabitants to the following points, which are essential for securing the full advantage of this important and costly change :—

1st. All Cisterns, Tanks, Butts, and other receptacles for Water should be very carefully cleansed.

2nd. When such receptacles are outside the dwelling they should be covered so that the water may be effectually protected from the sun and air.

3rd. All Service Pipes should be provided with Ball or Stop-cocks, to prevent waste; waste rendering impossible, or, at all events, weakening the efficient high service the Company are prepared to give throughout the district.

[See the scale of charges and other information on the other side.]

A Company publicity sheet, showing the enlarged Havant Pumping Station of 1878

Portsmouth's Water Supply

Early Years of Public Supplies

The oldest known record of a source of water supply for the inhabitants of Portsmouth dates from 1540 in the reign of Henry VIII, when the town consisted only of what is now known as Old Portsmouth, surrounded by earth ramparts; to the north was open ground and on the west side the beginning of the future Dockyard. The remainder of Portsea Island was entirely rural, with scattered farms and heathland forming the old manors of Stamshaw, Copnor, Fratton and others.

The source concerned was a spring at Four House Green, near Camber Dock, and the water was used to brew beer for Royal Navy ships. To reduce the risk of pollution, in 1562 a penalty of ten shillings was imposed on anyone found to be washing clothes in the spring water channel at Four House Green. In 1646, the Chamberlain of Portsmouth built a stone wall with a gate around the well to prevent children falling in and drowning.

Two more water supply schemes were attempted in the late 17th century, the first by Benjamin Okeshott of Chichester, whose well was situated at White Swan Field, on the east side of Commercial Road. The second scheme was put forward by Richard Barrey of London and George Surracold of Derby but the proposed source of the water is not known. Both schemes were abandoned after a short time.

Some idea of the conditions at the time are outlined in a 1748 pamphlet written about Portsmouth, stating that the inhabitants were badly supplied with water, which was scarce and often saline through infiltration of sea water into the wells. Rainwater had to be stored and was frequently drawn upon.

In 1740, Thomas Smith, Lord of the Manor of Farlington, obtained the first Act of Parliament relating to a Portsmouth water supply, apparently as a reward for reclaiming Farlington Marshes by constructing a sea wall. The Act empowered him to lay water pipes from his estate at Farlington through the streets of Portsmouth as far as The Point and into Portsea. Thomas Smith himself never exercised his powers, because he died in 1741. In 1769, however, the Manor of Farlington was sold with its rights and privileges to Peter Taylor (later MP for Portsmouth). Taylor sank a well in Crookhorn Copse, on the north side of Portsdown Hill, and drove a half-mile long tunnel through the hill to a point above Farlington Church, expecting to find springs in the chalk. Unfortunately hardly a drop of water was found, as any present-day hydrogeologist could have warned him!

At the end of the 18th century, Portsmouth was a growing and thriving community, thanks to the long drawn-out Napoleonic wars. These circumstances led to the steady development of HM Dockyard and the surrounding area of Portsea, which soon outstripped Old Portsmouth in size. According to the first National Census in 1801, the population of Portsmouth was 33,226.

The built-up area was still confined to Portsea, with the beginnings of Landport outside the old fortifications. Southsea was shown on the map only as South Sea Common.

Portsmouth was still without a piped water supply, the inhabitants continuing to rely upon shallow wells and water carts. Towards the end of the 18th century, however, two fundamental engineering developments occurred. The first was the invention by James Watt of his improved steam-driven pumping engine; the second was the large-scale manufacture of cast iron pipes with watertight joints capable of withstanding high pressures. In the early years of the 19th century, these stimulated water supply schemes in Portsmouth and many other parts of the country.

The Rival Portsmouth Companies (1808 - 1840)

On September 21st 1808, a public meeting was held at the old Guildhall in the High Street, to consider two alternative water supply schemes.

The Company of Proprietors of the Portsea Island Waterworks

The first scheme had been planned by William Nicholson, a civil engineer of London, for a water supply to the Borough (Portsmouth and Portsea) and also to the parishes of Wymering, Widley and Farlington, at an estimated cost of £32,000. The source of supply was a well in the White Swan Field, the same well that had been used by Okeshott many years earlier. The well was a large, almost square infiltration basin about 60 feet across, filled by the inflow of groundwater from the underlying gravel and sand. Nearby was an engine house containing two 20 horsepower (HP) beam pumping engines. There was no high-level storage, so the supply would continue only as long as a pump was working. The scheme was enthusiastically adopted by the meeting and, despite limitations on their issue, the shares were all taken up by local people within 24 hours.

Portsmouth, Portsea and Farlington Waterworks Company

The second scheme, promoted by a group of London financiers, was more ambitious, proposing to supply water not only to Portsmouth, but also to Gosport, together with the parishes of Farlington, Bedhampton, Wymering and Widley, and to purchase and amend Thomas Smith's old Act of 1740 mentioned above. This group also decided to proceed, but reduced its original proposals to purchasing the powers of Thomas Smith's Act of 1740. This limited the scheme to supplying Portsmouth and Portsea only and so avoided the need to apply for an amending Act. The London group's proposed source of supply was a series of small springs that emerged from the chalk on Farlington Marshes below high water mark, but protected by Thomas Smith's sea wall. The scheme, as eventually carried out, consisted of two collecting reservoirs about 600 yards apart on the Marshes, with a nearby pumping station containing a 34 HP beam pumping engine delivering water through a 15-inch pumping main to an upper reservoir, known as Drayton Basin, on the southern slope of Portsdown Hill. From this main, a trunk main was laid through Cosham, along the present London Road and Commercial Road to Portsmouth.

Drayton Basin, 1935

Competition Begins

There followed a period of competition between these two companies lasting for more than 30 years. The full name of the local company was 'The Company of Proprietors of the Portsea Island Waterworks', abbreviated here as the Portsea Island Company. The London company had to modify its original name to the 'Portsmouth, Portsea and Farlington Waterworks Company', abbreviated here to the Farlington Company.

Investment in waterworks undertakings was at first a risky venture because, apart from the engineering problems, it was uncertain whether a sufficient number of people would depart from long established habits and be willing to take and pay for a piped supply. Both companies were pioneers in the development of public water supply, which was still in its infancy. Hydrogeology was an unknown science; the laws of hydraulics and heat engines were not fully understood; methods of water treatment had not yet evolved; essential water fittings, such as sluice valves and ball valves, were of crude design. Cast iron pipes had only recently come on to the market. Indeed, the Farlington Company in 1808 advertised for alternative tenders for the supply of 'Iron, Elm or Fir pipes of three to nine inches bore'. Fortunately, cast iron pipes were adopted!

With no railways and limited long-distance transport, the Farlington pumping engine, which was manufactured by Boulton and Watt at their Soho works in Birmingham, was carried in sections by canal to London and then by ship around the coast to Portsmouth. Most of the cast iron pipes were made at Butterley, near Derby, transported in barges by canal and the River Trent to Gainsborough (Lincolnshire), then transferred to ships which carried them to Portsmouth.

Portsea Island Company is the First to Supply

The Portsea Island Company was the first to supply water, having started work on its well and pumping station during the summer of 1809. A pumping test was carried out in August 1810, but the pump was found to be too big for the engine, and after a smaller pump had been installed by the following November, the engine emptied the well in 35 minutes. The well was then deepened, but the sides caved in, undermining the foundations of the engine house, and the pump brought up large quantities of sand in the water.

After another delay while agreement was reached with the local Commissioners for Paving to dig up the streets to lay water mains (despite powers for this being included in the Act), and the Portsea Island Company repaired its well, water was first delivered into Portsmouth on 28th April 1811 and the supply to Portsea began three months later, on 5th August. Although the first piped water supply had come to Portsmouth, it was only intermittent, as pumping took place for a few hours on only two or three days a week.

Farlington Company follows

By March 1811, the rival Farlington Company had completed the two collecting reservoirs and the pumping station on Farlington Marshes. The laying of the trunk main was begun in July 1810, but was delayed by the slow delivery of pipes and again by the need to obtain agreement to lay mains in the streets.

The pumping station building on Farlington Marshes, just prior to demolition in 1928

At last, on 24th September 1811, the inhabitants of Portsmouth flocked out expecting to witness a display of sparkling spring water from Farlington. It was a fiasco. Not only was the water a rusty red, but it had to be quickly turned off, owing to numerous leaking joints along the trunk main. After hasty repairs, pumping was started again on 28th September and, although the water was still rusty red, after a week of continuous pumping, it at last ran clear. The supply to Portsea was started on 6th October.

Although its supply was also intermittent, owing to the non-completion of Drayton Basin, the Farlington Company was able to provide a better service than its rival. However, a constant source of anxiety was the frequent need to repair storm damage to the sea wall protecting the collecting reservoirs from inundation.

Competition Intensifies

During the previous five months before Farlington water became available, the Portsea Island Company, with its local influence, had obtained a large number of consumers, but a period of intense competition now began. Both companies continued to extend their mains, in many cases along the same streets and occasionally even at the same time. The Farlington Company not only attracted consumers rapidly, but also received many requests for transfers from the rival supply. The Portsea Island supply was very irregular; it often stopped for days on end and frequently contained sand. One consumer complained that, when it was used to make tea, the water turned the tea to 'a deep orange colour', making it totally unfit to drink.

To attract and retain consumers, both companies resorted to offering a free connection to their mains and a free supply of water between November 1811 and March 1812. However, they soon found that this extravagant offer was overstretching their resources, and they both had to limit the concession.

A useful source of income for both companies was the supply of water to shipping and they each established 'water houses' for this purpose at The Point in Old Portsmouth. The other principal trade consumers were the breweries, and at first the Portsea Island Company had several of them on its books. It was therefore unfortunate that, just when the Farlington water appeared on the scene, one of the largest brewers, Pike & Co in Old Portsmouth, complained that a whole brew had been spoilt and refused to use Portsea Island water any longer. The Company attempted to escape blame by advertising a reward of 200 guineas (£210) for information leading to the conviction of the person who had thrown offensive matter into the water supplied to the brewery! This action had exactly the opposite effect to what had been intended, because other breweries transferred their custom to the Farlington Company and, three months later, the Portsea Island Company had only one brewery left in supply.

During 1812, the Farlington Company completed the upper reservoir (Drayton Basin) on Portsdown Hill so that, by pumping water into it during two or three days each week, a supply to Portsmouth could then be maintained under constant pressure.

However, the Portsea Island Company was in constant trouble. There was a shortage of water, particularly during the summer months, and there was often sand in the water. To prevent the sand from entering the mains, three settling ponds were constructed. Above all, the Company was badly affected by the keen competition and found it difficult to raise additional capital.

Financial and Operational Difficulties for both Companies

Within the first year of rivalry, rumours of a merger began to circulate, but nothing happened, despite meetings between the two sets of Directors and a failed attempt to present a Bill to Parliament. After the Napoleonic Wars, there was a serious slump in trade following a reduction in Dockyard activity. Both water companies found it harder to obtain new consumers and to collect water rates; there was little point in cutting off services, because water could always be obtained from the public pumps.

The Farlington Company, in particular, felt the pinch owing to a surprising omission in the old Act of 1740. Although the Act gave the Company power to supply water, it contained no specific powers to make charges and the Company could only obtain payment from defaulters by costly court action.

The Directors refused to allow their local manager, William Bellingham, to follow the example of the Portsea Island Company and reduce water charges. Matters were made worse by the flooding of the source and works at Farlington, when the sea wall was breached by exceptionally high tides during several successive winters.

By 1817, the Farlington Company was already experiencing financial problems and, as a result, it reduced its hours of supply. For a number of years, dividends were not paid and, by 1837, it had clearly run into serious financial difficulties.

The slump also caused the affairs of the Portsea Island Company to go from bad to worse. As early as 1814, it had begun to borrow money and an Act of 1827 gave the Company power to raise further capital either in shares or by mortgage. However, in 1828, the mortgage lenders demanded their capital back and, after court action, the Company was sold by auction to two of the mortgagees, Casher and Nance, who had merely hoped to force up the bidding! After failing to re-sell to the Farlington Company, the two were saddled with running the Portsea Island Company until it came to an end in 1840. Its fundamental weakness was that the yield of its water source was simply inadequate.

In March 1840, after four years of negotiations, the two companies were amalgamated into a 'united' company - something of a misnomer, as the Portsea Island Company was absorbed by the Farlington Company, whose name remained unchanged.

On 13th November 1840, during a great storm with exceptionally high tides, the sea broke through the defences at Farlington, flooding many acres of land including the collecting reservoirs, and put the Farlington Works completely out of action for several months. The whole supply suddenly became reliant on the old Portsea Island source where, simultaneously, problems developed with the old boiler that served the pump. By good fortune, a new boiler was already on order and this was hurriedly installed, but not before Portsmouth went entirely without a piped water supply for four days. Fortunately public wells and water carts were still available, because at that time fewer than half the houses were connected to the water mains.

The Rawlinson Report of 1848

Under the Public Health Act 1848, Robert Rawlinson, the Superintending Inspector of the General Board of Health, was appointed to examine the conditions in Portsmouth, which he described as follows:

"Up to 1845 water was laid on to about 4,000 houses, there being in the borough about 10,000 houses; complaints are made both as regards the quality and quantity, more especially the latter. ... The supply is laid on for about two hours daily, except Sunday; often, however for only half an hour. The water, when running from the plugs, has barely sufficient force to flow over the rising of the carriage road. Many of the smaller streets are not supplied at all. Some of the newly erected streets have no pipes laid down... In courts, lanes, and back streets, the poor buy from water carts, and beg and steal of their neighbours, or bring water from a pump at a distance; other courts are supplied by the landlords by means of stand pipes, or by pumps and wells. In many of the new streets small iron pumps are placed in most inconvenient situations at the edge of pavements and some of the wells open in the footwalks, which are dangerous to passengers. Complaints are very common ...The supply is not sufficient for all parts of the town at once, so that different mains are served at different hours.

The difficulty of obtaining water at Southsea has brought into use a private well for flushing the streets, and the well in Elm Grove still supplies many persons with water, which is carried to their houses."

To remedy this state of affairs, Rawlinson suggested that the Company should make use of springs at Havant and Bedhampton, which were well known for their copious yield.

The Report must have made unpleasant reading to the Company at that time, as there were many who had invested significant sums in rescuing it from disaster in the early 1840s. The publicity surrounding the Report led to calls for a new undertaking to be established and, in 1855, Richard William Ford, who later served the Company as Secretary for 40 years, proposed that the local Council purchase the existing Company. The motion was defeated, leading to proposals for the promotion of a new company, which was eventually formed in 1857.

Official reports dealing with other provincial towns showed that the conditions in Portsmouth were by no means exceptional; the rapid growth of the urban population due to the Industrial Revolution had brought many other towns to a similar predicament. The period 1850-60 was therefore one of intense activity in the waterworks world. Undertakings in all parts of the country were being established or reorganised, and Portsmouth found its place in the move towards improvement.

The Borough of Portsmouth Waterworks Company (1857 - 1930)

According to the National Census in 1851, the population of Portsmouth was 72,096, more than double what it had been in 1801.

By 1856, there were about 14,000 inhabited houses. The area to the west of the present Fratton Road, Somers Road, Grove Road and Palmerston Road was rapidly filling up, but only about 4,500 houses had a piped water supply. The older parts of Portsmouth were fairly well provided with water mains, but few had been laid in the newer roads, where the inhabitants still relied on numerous shallow wells or supplies by water cart. A group of new houses in Southsea had a private piped supply from a local well owned by an enterprising architect, Thomas Ellis Owen.

The supply from Farlington depended wholly on a single trunk main six miles long, and mostly of only 10-inch diameter, and the Portsea Island well had become practically useless. Unsurprisingly, this main was unable to supply the whole district at the same time. The turncocks had regular rounds, opening up the mains to the various districts in turn for periods of up to two hours, so that some residents received an early supply, others late in the day. At this time, the average daily supply was about 550,000 gallons.

To remedy this state of affairs, a group of prominent townsmen moved to form a new water company. Their efforts were eventually successful on 13th July 1857, when an Act was passed by Parliament to establish the Borough of Portsmouth Waterworks Company, with a capital of £80,000. The area of supply was Portsea Island, excluding Hilsea and Great Salterns.

The Havant and Bedhampton Springs

In March 1859, it was decided to develop the Havant and Bedhampton Springs as the principal source of supply, as recommended by Robert Rawlinson in 1850. This proved to be a momentous step, because these remarkable springs were to provide almost the whole supply for a steadily growing Portsmouth and a future large country district for more than 90 years.

The springs break out on a roughly east to west line, about half a mile long and up to a mile or so from the north shore of Langstone Harbour. They are fed by the percolation of rainfall into a large area of the chalk forming the South Downs to the north, the underground water being brought to the surface again by the favourable geological conditions. Today there are 29 springs under the control of Portsmouth Water, the average daily yield being more than 100 million litres. This yield is unusually regular since, even in the worst drought periods, it has never fallen below 53 million litres per day.

The overflows from these springs form three separate streams running into the Harbour, which had for a great many years been used for working six water mills, an upper and lower mill on each stream. The springs and the mills with their water rights were acquired by the Company in stages, as demand grew. The Havant Springs, the middle group on the Brockhampton Stream, were the first to be used in the period 1860-74; the Bedhampton Springs, the western and most important group on the Bedhampton Stream, in the period 1878-1908; and the Havant Mill Springs, the eastern and smallest group on the Havant Stream, in 1941.

To make use of these springs, a new pumping station was erected in Brockhampton Road, Havant.

Wyatt's Spring, Bedhampton, 1934

Collecting basins were constructed nearby to store water from the springs. At first, the pumping station contained two beam pumping engines, each with a daily capacity of 2¼ million gallons. A 20-inch pumping main was laid along the main road to the old Drayton Basin at Farlington and a 20-inch trunk main was laid from Farlington to Landport. Havant Pumping Station was opened on 28th May 1860, and the much improved supply was publicised during the following summer by fountain displays on Sundays at four different points in Portsmouth.

Improvements to the Public Supply

The general pressure was later increased by the construction in 1869 of two reservoirs (Nos. 1 & 2) at Farlington, higher up on the slope of Portsdown Hill, each holding about 2.7 million gallons. In order to reduce the waste of water, Portsmouth was until 1875 supplied from these reservoirs only during the day; during the night hours, the lower Drayton Basin was still used.

The first 25 years was a period of rapidly increasing demand. To supplement the water resources, an additional collecting basin was constructed at Havant in 1874 and, in 1878, four springs at Bedhampton were brought into use by laying a 20-inch main to Havant Pumping Station. In the meantime, the pumping station was enlarged to accommodate two additional beam pumping engines, each with a daily capacity of 2¼ million gallons. Increasing demand from Portsmouth and the Dockyard led to the laying of more trunk mains between 1877 and 1887.

By 1869, about 80% of the population had a piped water supply. The daily supply had grown to about 2½ million gallons, a five fold increase in 10 years, and the pressure was much improved. Although the principal mains were kept fully charged, the branch and service mains were turned on for between 7 and 8 hours during the day.

By 1870, the Town Council had begun to introduce main drainage and consequently asked the Company to provide a constant water supply. Protracted negotiations followed, as there was a need for more efficient household taps and other water fittings to prevent the excessive waste of water that was to be expected with a constant supply. New regulations were finally agreed and, as consumers altered their water fittings, the Company started to introduce a constant supply throughout Portsmouth. Following completion in 1880, the domestic consumption per head was actually lower than it had been under the intermittent supply, principally due to improved water fittings, but also because consumers no longer left their taps open to be sure of a supply when it was turned on!

At first, water for extinguishing fires was obtained by removing tapered wooden fire plugs driven into holes in the top of the mains and then inserting a standpipe attached to the end of a hose. Unless the main was first turned off, the firemen had to act with skill and agility to avoid a drenching. In 1879, fire hydrants, each with its own stop valve, were introduced, and by 1883 all the old fire plugs had been superseded.

Another improvement was the introduction in 1882 of the Deacon system for the detection of waste of water. Under this system, the area of supply was divided into districts, each controlled by a meter recording the flow on a chart. At night-time, when little or no water was being used, the supply to a district was temporarily shut off street by street. A reduction of flow, as recorded by the chart, indicated that leakage was occurring in the isolated street.

Over the ten years from 1876 to 1886, the use of this method in Portsmouth reduced the daily domestic consumption from 29 to 22 gallons per head. This saving gave a total daily reduction in demand of more than one million gallons, and yet every household had an unrestricted supply.

As part of the Deacon system, the supply pipes to individual houses began to be provided with outside stopcocks, which could be used not only for detecting waste, but also to shut off the supply for household repairs without interrupting the supply to the whole street.

Supplies outside the Borough

The first supply outside Portsmouth was provided to the Portsdown Hill forts. With a risk of invasion by the French, these had been constructed in 1862 along the crest of Portsdown Hill, as part of the outer ring of defences against a land attack on Portsmouth. They saw no hostile action and became known as 'Palmerston's Follies', after the Prime Minister of the day. To supply the forts, the springs and old pumping station on Farlington Marshes were brought back into use in 1871. Water was pumped to a reservoir at Fort Southwick, the highest point on Portsdown Hill, from which mains led to reservoirs at the other forts.

By 1883, the area of supply had been extended to Wymering, Cosham, Hilsea, Widley, Farlington, Bedhampton, Havant, Warblington, Emsworth, and Waterloo (later Waterlooville). The latter place was supplied from a new reservoir (later named George Reservoir No. 1 after the nearby George Inn) holding 155,000 gallons and constructed on the crest of Portsdown Hill, close to the London Road. A trunk main was laid to Purbrook and Waterloo. Initially, the reservoir was supplied from the Farlington Marshes springs via the pumping main serving the forts. This was the first supply to the country district on the north side of Portsdown Hill.

The Development of a new Head Office

In November 1860, after the Havant & Bedhampton Works had become the sole source of supply, the old Portsea Island Works in Brunswick Road and Middle Street were sold. In 1883, this property was repurchased by the Company for use as stores, workshops and stables. It was then decided to build a new Head Office nearby in Commercial Road. The architect was George Rake of Portsmouth and the new office, built in the style of contemporary French municipal buildings, was opened in May 1884.

The Company Head Office, Commercial Road, Portsmouth

Supply Improvements at the End of the 19th Century

By 1887, the population supplied had more than doubled from what it was when the Company was established; it was by then approximately 165,000 and the total average daily supply had risen to about 5¼ million gallons. By this time, nearly every house was connected to the mains under constant high pressure, and there was greater use of water for trade purposes. Although the population had doubled, overall demand had increased nearly tenfold and was still growing.

Thus, in 1889, a second main pumping station was built at Bedhampton, where the largest springs were located. The daily capacity of Bedhampton Pumping Station was increased in stages from 4½ million gallons in 1889 to 10½ million gallons in 1902, and it became the primary means of supply for the next 15 years. The Havant Pumping Station became a stand-by station to supplement supply during periods of high demand.

Hilsea Tunnel shaft section, as featured in a brochure of the manufacturers, Whessoe Foundry Co Ltd, Darlington

In anticipation of the development of the eastern half of Portsea Island and to improve the pressure in Southsea, a trunk main was laid from Hilsea via Copnor and Milton and along Highland Road and Albert Road; this was completed in 1901. In that year, the Admiralty applied for a substantially increased supply of water, and a 20-inch main was laid from Farlington to HM Dockyard for its exclusive use. This would have been laid at a normal depth under Hilsea Creek, but the Admiralty had plans to deepen the Creek to enable small naval vessels to pass between Portsmouth and Langstone Harbours. A tunnel was therefore constructed under the Creek at Hilsea in 1903/04, through which the whole of the water supply from the mainland to Portsea Island was carried. The tunnel is 600 feet long and the top is about 36 feet below sea level; when built, it contained four trunk mains, one of which was the 20-inch Dockyard main. Ultimately the Admiralty's deepening scheme never took place, but the tunnel remains in service today, albeit with renewed mains laid through it.

In 1905, a new pumping station, the first in the Company to use oil-fired engines, was opened at Farlington to take over the high level supply to Purbrook, Waterlooville and also the Portsdown forts. At the same time the capacity of George Reservoir No. 1 was increased to 200,000 gallons, and George Reservoir No. 2, holding 300,000 gallons, was constructed nearby. This high level supply was extended to the Drayton Estate, the first building development on the upper slopes of Portsdown Hill, and to Durrants and Redhill, near Rowlands Castle. The old Farlington Pumping Station on the Marshes, built nearly 100 years previously, finally went out of use and was demolished in 1928.

Improvements in Water Quality at the beginning of the 20th Century

For the first fifty years or so after the Havant and Bedhampton Springs were brought into use, water was supplied to Portsmouth without any form of treatment. Normally the supply was crystal clear, but on occasions, after heavy rainfall during the winter months, the spring water became temporarily cloudy, sometimes being described as looking like weak coffee.

Laying the 60-inch overflow pipe from the Hermitage Stream, 1898

At first this cloudiness, or turbidity, was thought to be due to local surface water gaining access to the springs after heavy rainfall. Moreover, the Havant Springs were situated close to an inhabited area where cesspits were still in use. When the danger was recognised, a clay puddle trench was built around the area containing the springs to act as a watertight barrier, preventing the inflow of undersoil pollutants. This work was completed in 1886, but water quality did not improve!

Later, when the Bedhampton Springs came into general use, a similar problem was thought to be related to overflows from the adjacent Hermitage Stream. Despite the laying of a 60-inch overflow pipe and the construction of an open diversion channel, the problem remained unresolved. A Local Government Board Inquiry remained critical of the water quality, despite assurances from the Portsmouth Sanitary Committee.

The true cause of the turbidity at the springs was eventually found to be the existence of natural swallow holes in the chalk strata stretching from Rowlands Castle to Lovedean, more than two miles to the north. It was realised that, after heavy winter rainfall, large volumes of turbid water were flowing from the clay surface into these holes, mixing with the chalk water and appearing within 24 hours or so at the springs.

A Parliamentary Bill

Slow sand filters under construction, Farlington, 1906

Concerns about the proximity of cesspits to the springs and the occasional discolouration of the water supply led to strong representations by the Town Council for the introduction of filtration. Eventually, in 1905, the Company promoted a Bill, not only for this purpose, but also for the development of an additional source by sinking a large well in the Ems valley, across the county boundary in West Sussex. The extension proposal met with strong opposition from the County Councils in Parliament, and it was struck out of the Bill. The principal item left in the Act, which was passed on 4th August 1906, was the Company's obligation to filter the water from Havant & Bedhampton Springs.

Farlington Filtration Works were completed at the end of 1909 and comprised seven slow sand filter beds, together with two additional service reservoirs (Nos. 3 and 4), each holding 4 million gallons. Both these reservoirs, as well as the existing Farlington Reservoirs Nos. 1 and 2 and the George Reservoirs Nos. 1 and 2, were roofed in, so that in future all water, after filtration, would not see daylight until it arrived at consumers' taps. Filtered water was first supplied on 1st January 1910, a milestone in the history of the supply. Later, to cope with the increasing demand, an additional filter bed (No. 8) and service reservoir (No. 5) were completed in 1924.

Farlington slow sand filters, 1927

In 1913 the area of supply was extended to include Portchester.

The Impact of the First World War (1914 - 18)

Following the declaration of war on Germany on 4th August 1914, the most important precaution taken by the Company was to guard against the main pumping stations being destroyed. A set of three portable steam-driven pumping engines and four portable boilers was obtained and hidden in a bastion of the Hilsea Lines. At the Bedhampton Works, suitable foundations and buried connections to the pumping mains were provided, so that in an emergency the portable plant could be quickly assembled. By this means, it was expected to provide an emergency supply of about one third of the normal quantity.

Herbert Ashley, Engineer to the Company, 1902-1926. He oversaw the major improvements at Farlington, Havant and Bedhampton

As a precaution against the Farlington filter beds and main reservoirs being put out of action, connections were made between the pumping mains and the gravitation mains, so that the Farlington Works could be bypassed and water pumped direct from Havant and Bedhampton to Portsmouth. In addition, the old Drayton Basin, which had been disused for many years, was cleaned out and kept full of water as an emergency reserve.

Fortunately none of these precautions had to be used.

A new Havant Pumping Station

By 1923, the average daily supply had increased to about 9 million gallons to a total population of about 266,000. After the war, the large Worthington engine at Bedhampton Pumping Station, which had been in almost continuous use day and night since 1902, had to be overhauled and its reliability became questionable. If it were to fail, the supply would depend upon the old Havant beam engines.

The old Havant Pumping Station, built in 1860

A new Havant Pumping Station was therefore built and came into use in April 1927. It contained three triple-expansion vertical pumping engines, each with a daily capacity of 6 million gallons, and became the primary means of supply. The building is still in use today.

The new Havant Pumping Station, 1927

Bedhampton Pumping Station was then relegated to a stand-by means of supply for many years. It was kept available for emergency use during the Second World War, but owing to the construction of Bedhampton No. 2 Pumping Station, described later, it was seldom used; it pumped water for the last time in 1947 and the machinery was eventually dismantled in 1955.

A Hidden Reserve of Coal

A critical situation arose during the National Coal Strike of 1926, which resulted in the complete cessation of coal deliveries for about five months. Fortunately, following previous strikes in 1911 and 1912, the disused mill pond of the Upper Bedhampton Mill had been adapted for use as an underwater coal store. It was filled with 700 tons of coal and flooded with water, preventing spontaneous combustion and also making the store inconspicuous.

During the 1926 strike, this hidden reserve proved invaluable. In anticipation of the strike, coal stocks had been built up to nearly 26 weeks' normal requirements, about half of which was in the coal pond. At the end of the strike, stocks had dwindled to only 2 to 3 weeks' requirements before deliveries were restarted, so the reserve enabled the whole emergency period to be covered, and at pre-strike prices!

Havant Pumping Station boiler house, 1927

Chlorination

The original standard method of assessing the quality of water was chemical analysis. In the early part of the 20th century, however, the science of bacteriology made rapid strides and bacteriological methods, which are more sensitive than chemical methods, were introduced as additional tests for detecting contamination of water supplies.

In 1925, a series of bacteriological tests of the Portsmouth supply showed that the filtered water did not always pass the more stringent standards, probably because the rate of filtration was too high. This implied that there was a need to construct additional filters at Farlington at a substantial cost.

However, by this time, a better and much cheaper alternative had become available. The treatment of water by chlorination, which had previously been regarded solely as an emergency measure during typhoid outbreaks, was coming into general use as a routine method of water treatment. Experiments had shown that a minute dose of chlorine was enough to destroy harmful bacteria that might be present. After trials, permanent plant was installed in 1926 at the Havant and Bedhampton Pumping Stations to inject chlorine before water entered the Farlington filter beds.

The first few years of chlorination were not without problems. Initially, consumers complained of an earthy taste in the water. This was due to the action of chlorinated water on the weed growth that

Sandwashing at Farlington, 1935

appeared in the filter beds in summer, and was solved by temporarily increasing the chlorine dose during warm weather. Another problem was the occasional contamination of the filter beds themselves, caused by the droppings and regurgitations of congregating seagulls. The simple and cheap remedy of stretching a network of wires about 8 feet apart over the filter beds was completely successful in deterring the gulls. The problems from the swallow holes recurred in a different form in 1932, when a musty taste occurred. It proved to be the result of tar from local roads in Rowlands Castle being washed into the swallow holes during heavy rain and combining with chlorine.

The introduction of chlorination enabled the rate of filtration to be increased by at least 25 per cent without detriment to the supply. The increased capacity was expected to be sufficient to filter the maximum supply ever likely to be obtained from the Havant and Bedhampton springs.

Farlington Pumping Station - Electrification

The Farlington Pumping Station performed the dual function of supplying water to the George Reservoirs for the area to the north, as well as to Fort Southwick and the other forts on Portsdown Hill.

After the First World War, much building development took place in the high-level district, with the result that the original oil-driven pumping plant installed in 1905 had become of insufficient capacity and out of date. In 1926, a small auxiliary pumping station containing an electrically-driven centrifugal pump was brought into use, this being the Company's first use of electricity for pumping purposes.

Flooding from burst main at Hilsea, November 20th 1929

Portsbridge Booster Station

In the early 1920s, extensive building development and increased demand for water in the northern part of Portsmouth led to complaints of poor mains pressure in the southern half of Portsmouth (including Southsea).

One solution would have been to lay an additional trunk main from the Farlington reservoirs into Portsea Island, but the advent of electrically-driven pumps offered a much cheaper option, namely to boost the pressure in the existing mains during periods of peak demand, usually during the morning hours. Portsbridge Booster Station was erected for this purpose and came into use in August 1929, with two electrically-driven centrifugal pumps of 8 and 12 million gallons per day capacity. They were started and stopped automatically by pressure sensors.

Portsmouth Water Company (1930 - 1955)

Albion truck

Although Portsmouth was promoted to the status of a city in 1926, the Company's original name could not be changed without statutory authority. The Company was renamed the Portsmouth Water Company in 1930, when further extensions were sought.

Owing to the continued increase in the demand for water, a Bill was promoted in 1929, with the main purpose of obtaining powers to develop a well in the Ems valley in West Sussex and to extend the area of supply on both sides of the Hampshire-Sussex county boundary. Although the site selected for the proposed well was not the same one proposed in 1905/06, strenuous opposition from West Sussex County Council resulted in these powers being deleted once more.

The Act was passed on 4th June 1930, the principal surviving provisions being the extension of supplies into the rural area north of Portsmouth and the purchase of the Catherington and Idsworth Estate undertakings.

Extension of Supplies into the 'Country District'

The area of supply was then extended to include Southwick, Hambledon, Catherington, Blendworth, Idsworth, Chalton and Clanfield. The extensions took some time to be connected and piped water was brought to the villages on the following dates:

North Catherington, Idsworth, Denmead	1931
Clanfield	1932
Hambledon	1933
Finchdean	1934
Chalton	1936
Worlds End	1938

[20 & 21 Geo. 5.] *Portsmouth Water Act*, 1930. [Ch. lxvii.]

CHAPTER lxvii.

An Act to change the name of the Borough of Portsmouth Waterworks Company to extend their limits for the supply of water to consolidate and convert their ordinary capital to authorise them to raise additional capital and for other purposes. [4th June 1930.] A.D. 1930.

WHEREAS the Borough of Portsmouth Waterworks Company (in this Act referred to as "the Company") were incorporated by the Borough of Portsmouth Waterworks Act 1857 and by the Borough of Portsmouth Waterworks Acts and Orders 1857 to 1921 are authorised to construct certain waterworks and to supply water within limits which comprise the city of Portsmouth and an area adjoining thereto in the county of Southampton:

And whereas it is expedient that the limits for the supply of water by the Company should be extended as by this Act provided:

And whereas it is expedient that the Company should be empowered to acquire the existing waterworks at Catherington and Idsworth in this Act mentioned:

And whereas a statement of the share and loan capital of the Company is set forth in the schedule to this Act:

And whereas it is expedient that the existing ordinary capital of the Company should be consolidated and converted as provided by this Act and that the Company should be authorised to raise further capital:

[*Price* 1*s*. 6*d*. *Net*.] A 1

Catherington Water Undertaking

The origin of the piped water supply in the Catherington district goes back to 1904, when the Company first provided a bulk supply at its boundary in London Road to the Hart Plain Syndicate, for houses in Cowplain. In 1925, the Syndicate's water mains were acquired by Catherington Rural District Council, the Company continuing the bulk supply. In 1928, an extended water supply came into use, consisting of a lower reservoir at Cowplain, fed by gravity from the Company's George Reservoirs. A nearby pumping station in Pump Lane delivered water from Cowplain Reservoir to the upper Catherington Reservoir, which at first supplied Catherington, Horndean and part of Blendworth. The Company took over the Council's undertaking in March 1931, the purchase price being £16,000.

Idsworth Estate Water Undertaking

The Idsworth private water undertaking at Rowlands Castle was opened in 1898; the works were in Links Lane and consisted of a well and adits in the chalk, a pumping station containing oil-driven well pumps in duplicate and a water tower. The undertaking supplied about 80 houses.

After the transfer, the tank of Idsworth water tower was kept full by gravity from the George Reservoirs on Portsdown Hill, the well and pumping station being only occasionally used during periods of high demand.

Rowlands Castle water tower and pumping station

Inside Rowlands Castle pumping station, showing oil engine

(both photographs courtesy Dando Drilling International Ltd)

Subsequently, the Idsworth well ceased to be used for water supply, but instead it performed a valuable role in recording the water level in the underlying chalk aquifer supplying Havant & Bedhampton Springs. A continuous long-term record of water levels in the well has been maintained since 1932. Today the well is equipped with an automatic level recorder that continuously transmits the water level by telemetry to the Havant Operations Centre.

Flooding from the Hampshire Lavant, Woodberry Lane, Rowlands Castle, during a period of high groundwater in January 1936

Benefits for Consumers

In 1930, various benefits for the Company's consumers were introduced:

(1) Tappings of the mains for new services could be made 'under pressure', so that existing consumers were no longer inconvenienced by the water being turned off for this purpose;
(2) The rewashering of taps free of charge was introduced and consumers were encouraged to give notice when this work was required; and
(3) House owners, who also owned the service pipes from the mains, were relieved of their liability to repair these pipes under the street, the cost being borne instead by the Company.

The Great Drought of 1933/34

A shortage of rainfall between April 1933 and November 1934 meant that underground water resources were not replenished by the usual winter rainfall. Shortages of supply were experienced in many parts of the country, but the yield of Havant & Bedhampton Springs, although much below their seasonal average, remained sufficient to avoid the need for restrictions. The experience, however, was a warning that the Company's water resources would need supplementing in the near future and, as a first step, the neighbouring Havant Mill Springs were acquired in 1934/35. These springs were first used during the Second World War when, after the heavy 'blitzes' of 1941, the extra water proved invaluable.

Preparations for the Second World War (1939-45)

The first inkling of the need for war precautions was given locally at a confidential conference convened by the Lord Mayor of Portsmouth on 3rd July 1934, more than five years before war eventually broke out. The conference covered the need for future contingencies, in particular against air attack by high explosive, incendiary and gas bombs. As a consequence, the Company decided to carry out various works for the protection of the public water supply.

New 36-inch trunk main being floated into position at Portscreek, 1939

The largest single project was the laying of a 36-inch trunk main from the Farlington service reservoirs to Portsea Island, to provide an alternative supply to reduce the vulnerability to bombing.

Bedhampton No.2 Pumping Station

Next in importance was the construction of Bedhampton No. 2 Pumping Station, which was designed to be of sufficient capacity to deliver a full alternative supply to either of the existing Havant or Bedhampton Pumping Stations. The building was heavily constructed to withstand wartime attack and contained three pumps with a total daily capacity of 18 million gallons. It remains a stand-by pumping station, albeit with more modern diesel-driven pumps.

As a general precaution, cross-connections were laid between a large number of water mains at strategic points to allow water to be diverted around damaged localities. Interconnections were also made between the Company's mains and those of neighbouring undertakings. In addition, extensive protective works were carried out at all pumping stations.

One interesting phenomenon occurred in the last months of peace, when Portsmouth beat Wolverhampton Wanderers 4-1 in the 1939 FA Cup Final. With radio commentary on the match being closely followed in the city, the indicators on the Farlington outlet flowmeters fell to very low readings while the game was in progress; however, they nearly went off the charts as people made cups of tea after the final whistle!

The pumps inside Bedhampton No.2 Pumping Station

The Impact of the War itself

Shortly after the outbreak of war, the Company's works at Havant, Bedhampton and Farlington were placed under military guard, primarily against possible sabotage. Similar precautions were taken a few years later during an upsurge of IRA activity.

The first bomb fell on Portsmouth on 11th July 1940, although the period of intense enemy activity was largely confined to the first four months of 1941, when most of the extensive damage was experienced.

From a water supply perspective, by far the most serious of the raids occurred on the night of 10th/11th January 1941, when 63 mains were fractured in southern Portsmouth. The extensive loss of water through broken mains and service pipes and the heavy demand by the Fire Service caused the average daily demand to rise from 13 to 23 million gallons for two days.

During the critical period, the capacity of Farlington Filtration Works was exceeded. Valves were opened to allow the treatment works and service reservoirs to be by-passed and water to be pumped directly from Havant into the city. As a safeguard, the normal chlorine dose was temporarily increased by 50 per cent.

Filling an emergency supply tank at Long's Brewery, Southsea

Large areas of southern Portsmouth were temporarily without water, but the supply was gradually restored during the following five days. Emergency supplies were provided by means of water carts or standpipes on the hydrants. The many emergency cross connections proved extremely useful in maintaining supplies to many places, as without them the interruptions would have been still more serious.

On the night of the intensive bombing of 10th/11th January 1941, Lawrence 'Lew' Stent, who was a coach painter for the Company at Havant, cycled into the main shopping centre in Portsmouth to carry out his fire-watching shift. The raid was still in progress, the only light being from the burning buildings, searchlights and bursts of gunfire. Stent had to push his bike along the streets because of debris and broken glass from the shop windows. He came across the body of a woman clad in a fur coat, with her legs buckled under her, lying on the pavement covered in glass and dust. He dropped his bike, grabbed her arm to free and lift her but, to his horror, the woman's arm came away in his hands. Totally shocked, and before he could recover his wits, Stent was grabbed from behind by two special constables, arrested, taken to the local police station and accused of looting. The 'body' proved to be a tailor's dummy, and the police took some convincing of his motives before releasing him!

Lew Stent (left) and Fred Creswell, 1935

During two successive intensive raids on 9th/10th and 10th/11th March 1941, the water supply was much less affected than in the previous January, even though a similar number of mains (58) were broken. These mains were nearly all of small size, so only limited areas were temporarily without water.

During the remainder of the war, air raids occurred only spasmodically and on a small scale. Altogether 212 mains were broken and 9,730 supplies were interrupted.

Owing to the widespread damage to water mains and the possibility of mains contamination in bomb craters, medical officers requested that further precautions should be taken to minimise health risks. As a consequence, chloramination (ie the dosing of chloramines – a mixture of chlorine and ammonia - in place of chlorine) of the distribution system was introduced and proved very successful.

Alfred Burgess (born 1904), who joined the Company from Brighton Corporation as Engineering Assistant in 1932, recalls having to wheel his bike carefully around the many bomb craters in the streets of Portsmouth. He was responsible for allocating fire-watch duties to staff for the Commercial Road office and depot, and remembers one occasion when fire bombs landed on the roof of the stores. The fire was dealt with and afterwards David Halton Thomson, the Engineer, kept a half-burnt firebomb case on his desk as a memento.

Ken Bailey (born 1927) worked at the Company for 11 years, having joined as an Apprentice Fitter in 1942. His uncle Alf was in charge of Farlington Works at the time, a post that had also been held by Ken's grandfather George in the 1890s.

Ken Bailey remembers the ingenuity of his colleague Bill Guy, who developed a cutter driven by compressed air (rather than manually with a ratchet) to drill holes in cast iron or steel water mains. On one occasion, Bill Guy and Ken Bailey witnessed the defusing of an unexploded bomb near Bedhampton No. 2 Pumping Station, a process that involved a cumbersome means of drilling a hole in the bomb case, through which a lance could be inserted to steam out the explosive. Guy turned his mind to adapting his air-driven cutter for use in bomb disposal. His adaptation included a low voltage lead on the cutter connected to a small torch bulb; this would flash as the cutter began to break through and could thus be stopped at a safe distance from the explosive.

Ken Bailey, 2006

Having first tested it on a mains pipe, the device was demonstrated successfully on empty bomb and mine cases in a chalk pit off Portsdown Hill Road at Bedhampton (now occupied by a superstore and bowling alley). Representatives from the Mine Department, HMS Vernon and the Bomb Disposal Squad were present and Ken Bailey operated the compressor.

Bill Guy received an award of several hundred pounds for his device, which was adapted and used widely for certain types of bomb disposal. On a later occasion, the equipment was used to defuse an unexploded bomb that had smashed through the roof of one of the service reservoirs at Farlington.

Invasion Precautions

After the fall of France in May 1940, the risk of invasion had to be taken seriously. From the water supply standpoint, the most serious threat was an attack on, or enemy occupation of, the main sources of supply at Havant and Bedhampton.

If these sources became unavailable, reliance would have to be placed on the very limited water resources within the city. As a result, a Local Wells Scheme was prepared by Alfred Burgess (Engineering Assistant at the Company, and later Engineer & Manager of Chichester Corporation Water Department), who examined 47 sources, many of which proved to be of doubtful quality and small in yield. Ultimately it was decided to make 21 of them available for emergency use and, in every case, the owners gave willing consent and co-operation.

Whilst enemy forces entering the works at Havant and Bedhampton could easily wreck the main pumping stations, they could not, however, prevent the springs from yielding water. To meet this contingency, the Bedhampton Emergency Pumping Scheme was developed. Four semi-portable, oil-driven pumping units, each with a daily capacity of two million gallons, were acquired and stored at separate distant points and, at the Bedhampton Works, concrete foundations and connections were prepared for rapid installation in an emergency. Arrangements were also made with the Fire Service for the supply of up to six heavy duty fire engines, each with a daily pumping capacity of about 1 million gallons, together with the necessary manpower. For their use, 24 fire hose connections were made to the principal pumping main, all of which were hidden underground, but could be quickly uncovered if required. Exercises were carried out to demonstrate that the scheme was fully practicable.

Powers for a New Source at Worlds End

While the war was still in progress, it was decided to promote a Bill in Parliament for powers to develop an additional source of supply as well as for other purposes, the intention being to put the work in hand as soon as possible after the cessation of hostilities. After the rejection by Parliament of two previous applications (in 1906 and 1929) for a new source in the Ems valley, an alternative site in Hampshire was selected, at Worlds End in the Hambledon valley.

The Bill received little opposition and became an Act on 22nd July 1941, the principal features being:

(1) Power to carry out the Worlds End Scheme after the war;
(2) Power to utilise the Havant Mill Springs for public water supply;
(3) Safeguarding existing sources by requiring any proposed new source within a two-mile radius of Worlds End and Bedhampton to have the Company's prior consent; and
(4) Only the Company, and not consumers, to have the right to break up streets for the laying and repairing of service pipes.

Preparations for the D-Day Invasion

As the risk of invasion of Britain receded, so the preparations for the invasion of France gradually developed. It was fully expected that the Allied invasion, when it came, would provoke a violent enemy reaction, so most of the precautions taken to meet the air raid contingencies were retained. Prior to D-Day (6th June 1944), a large number of military transit camps for invasion forces were set up in the woods and copses in the outlying districts north of Portsmouth, for which temporary water supplies were installed.

Portsmouth Water Company Home Guard Platoon, 1944 (photo courtesy of Chris Whatley)

When D-Day eventually arrived, the anticipated extra demand for water proved much smaller than was forecast. To general astonishment, retaliatory enemy air raids were completely absent, apart from a few flying bombs, the last of which fell on Portsmouth on 15th July 1944.

Ken Bailey recalls how, every week, he had to make routine visits to pumping plant out in the country district of the Company's supply area. As he travelled around in the weeks before D-Day, it was noticeable how many troops were moving into the area, and in the woods he spotted tanks, guns and amphibious lorries, partly hidden from view. He and his colleagues had been told that the Official Secrets Act applied and they could not breathe a word about what they had seen. They did not, of course, know at the time that all this was part of the patient preparations for the invasion of France.

He vividly remembers Monday 5th June 1944, the eve of D-Day, when he went with his Foreman, Dick Fowles, to carry out a job in the country district. As they climbed Portsdown Hill in their van, they saw the amazing spectacle of the whole stretch of the Solent between Portsmouth and the Isle of Wight covered in ships, large and small, and masses of barrage balloons stretching as far as the eye could see. Lined up along the top of the hill were hundreds of anti-aircraft guns, above which appeared to be a continuous screen of fighter aircraft.

That evening, he left work intending to go to night school in the centre of Portsmouth, but was confronted in every street by convoys of army lorries loaded with troops. Many bomb damaged areas had been cleared and levelled. On them were mobile toilets, mobile kitchens and NAAFI lorries serving food, and the city was swarming with military police. In the end, he was unable to reach night school because of the congestion and headed home.

Staff at Havant, left to right; Charlie Ford, Bob Martin, Bill Barry, Dick Fowles and Reg Treagust

Post War Legacies

Of the various improvements to water supply arising out of the Second World War, three particular changes were of lasting benefit:

- Bedhampton No. 2 Pumping Station, as well as becoming a stand-by to the Havant Station, proved to be a convenient and economical means of providing extra water during periods of high demand.

- The introduction of chloramination during the war as an emergency measure was continued as an additional safeguard to the purity of the supply. This consisted of treating the outgoing water at the Farlington Service Reservoirs with minute doses of chloramines. Its use was finally discontinued in 1964, when the disinfection process at Farlington reverted to chlorination.

- The 36-inch gravitation main from Farlington via Drayton Marshes to Hilsea permanently improved the general pressure in Portsea Island, so much so that Portsbridge Booster Station, only completed ten years earlier, was in effect superseded and only retained as a stand-by.

Havant Pumping Station - Conversion to Oil Firing

Despite the availability of the coal store at Havant, it was decided to convert the coal-fired boilers at the Havant Station to oil-firing, owing to the shortage of coal in the immediate post-war years. The conversion was completed in August 1947 and was the final break from the use of coal for normal pumping purposes. Thus, from 1947, all normal pumping was carried out by oil or electricity.

Ken Bailey recalled how, as a young apprentice, he had been overawed by the three enormous steam engines at Havant. The routine was for two of these to be working at any one time, with the third as a stand-by. To start an engine, there was a 'steam donkey' engine that was locked into the main unit by huge 'dogs' on the inside of the flywheel. The operator then had to drop in a key to lock the 'steam donkey' into the main engine, and when the latter started, the 'steam donkey' was disengaged.

Havant Pumping Station steam engines, with Frank Parvin (left) and Dick Fowles, 1930s

Portsdown Hill Development

During the period between the two World Wars, nearly the whole of Portsea Island had become a built-up area. On the mainland, substantial development had already taken place along the southern slopes of Portsdown Hill.

After the Second World War, Portsmouth Corporation embarked upon an extensive housing scheme at Wymering and Paulsgrove, most of which would have to be supplied from the high-level George Reservoirs, which in turn would place a much heavier demand upon the Farlington Pumping Station. To meet this prospective demand, in 1946/47 two additional large electrically-driven pumping units were installed and additional mains were laid.

Two Critical Summers

After the war, the Company's water resources were put to a severe test. Owing to the previous dry winter, the yield of Havant & Bedhampton Springs was well below the seasonal average during the summer of 1948. Following a second dry winter, many other water undertakings were obliged to introduce restrictions during the summer of 1949. The crisis was met in Portsmouth by warning of possible restrictions and arranging to pump water from the springs at a steady rate throughout the 24 hours, to maximise the daily yield. By a narrow margin, the Company's record of never having restricted supplies on account of a shortage of water resources was maintained.

In both summers, the situation had undoubtedly been saved by the acquisition of the Havant Mill Springs after the drought of 1933/34.

Worlds End Pumping Station Development

Owing to severe Government restrictions on capital expenditure, consent to proceed with the new source at Worlds End was not obtained until the end of 1949. The first contract was let early in the following year.

Laying 24-inch steel pumping main from Worlds End to George Reservoir, December 1952

Two deep boreholes were drilled through the clays of the Hampshire Basin into the underlying chalk. Water was delivered by electrically - driven submersible pumps through a four-mile long, 24-inch pumping main to a new reservoir holding two million gallons, adjacent to the two existing George Reservoirs. New mains were also laid to connect with the existing trunk mains from Farlington to Portsea Island. The commanding position of the reservoir on Portsdown Hill enabled Worlds End water to be delivered either southwards to the City or northwards to the outlying districts.

Tests showed that the source had a daily yield of more than four million gallons, thereby increasing the Company's reliable water resources by nearly 30 per cent. The scheme was completed and brought into use in June 1953. For the first time in over 90 years, the Company was able to make use of an alternative to Havant & Bedhampton Springs.

The new George Reservoir being constructed, 1951

Supplies to Hayling Island

In 1950, Hayling Island was added to the area of supply, although the transfer did not result in any increase in total consumption, as for many years the Company had provided a bulk supply to the Island.

The original supply dated from 1895, when the South Hayling Water Company Ltd obtained an Act to supply the southern half of the Island, the source being a well in the chalk with a pumping station and water tower at Stoke; in 1898 the supply was extended to the whole of the Island.

Hayling water tower and pumping station (photograph courtesy Dando Drilling International Ltd)

In 1922, the undertaking had been offered to the Borough of Portsmouth Waterworks Company, but the proposal was declined. It was, however, acquired by Havant Rural District Council, which asked for a bulk supply from the Portsmouth mains. As Hayling Island was becoming a favourite residential area and popular holiday resort, the yield of the Hayling well was unable to meet the increasing demand for water, particularly during the summer months. It was also being overpumped, the water becoming brackish due to salt water being drawn in from the nearby harbours. Terms were eventually agreed, but conditions had become so desperate that, in October 1927, a temporary supply was made available through a 3-inch main. The permanent scheme was completed in July 1928, when the Hayling well was finally taken out of use and the whole supply was provided by the Company.

In November 1948, the Council opened negotiations for the purchase of the undertaking. The Company agreed to pay off the Council's outstanding loans, amounting to £16,596, and the transfer by Order took place on 1st April 1950.

In 1928, when the bulk supply began, the average daily consumption was about 70,000 gallons; by 1950, this had risen to nearly 300,000 gallons and additional holiday demands during summer months caused a serious loss of pressure in South Hayling. To improve the situation, in 1952 an additional 15-inch main was laid from Bedhampton to Langstone and an automatically controlled booster unit was installed at the disused Stoke Pumping Station. In the same year, the old water tower at this station, which had been a local landmark for many years, was demolished.

The Leigh Park Development

After the war, Portsmouth Corporation began to develop Leigh Park as a housing estate. This was done to accommodate the greater part of the population 'overspill' that resulted from the reconstruction of the many war-damaged areas in Portsmouth. The scheme was essentially a new town of 45,000 inhabitants, with its own industries, shopping centre and amenities. Fortunately, the new estate could be provided with a water supply from the Company's Farlington Reservoirs to the low-level zone and from the newly constructed George Reservoir to the high-level areas.

Life at the Commercial Road office in Portsmouth

A Perspective from George Slater

The late George Slater, who later served the Company as Chief Engineer, Director and Chairman, provided an evocative insight into working life at the Commercial Road office after the Second World War:

"I joined Portsmouth Water Company on the 20th August 1950, after receiving a rather damp appointment letter informing me that my salary would be between £675 and £750, with annual increments of £25.

I mention that the appointment letter was damp because, as I subsequently discovered, every letter that left the office was placed in a leather-bound book between damp cloths after it had been signed, so that an exact replica of the letter was left in the book. The letter of appointment informed me that the office hours were 9 am to 5.30 pm, with one and a half hours for lunch.

On arrival at about quarter to nine on the first day, I found nobody in the office except the caretaker, Mrs Harbour. When I introduced myself to her, her reply was "Oh well, there won't be anybody else here for another hour" and indeed neither was there. I very quickly found that I wasn't expected in the office until about 9.30 am, and lunch time extended from about quarter to one until 3 pm.

The main yard and office at Hyde Park Road, prior to reconstruction

The office was organised very clearly into two 'sides' with Reg Hall as the Engineer and Frank King as the Secretary. The two sides had very little to do with one another as far as the operation of the Company was concerned. The Engineer's staff consisted of an Assistant Engineer, Len Simpson, and myself as Engineering Assistant. The Engineer's front office was occupied by three male clerks, who not only operated the telephone exchange but also took dictation from the Engineers.

The Drawing Office was occupied by the Chief Draughtsman, Horace Benney, and Jack Bennett, who did odd jobs. The Secretary's side was staffed by three collectors, who sat at their counter and each dealt with a section of the Company's area of supply. There was a bell with a notice 'Landlords and Hayling please ring', and when it was rung, Jack Shaw would appear from the back office and deal with the customer. Charlie Light was the Secretary's Chief Clerk and Eric Guymer his Registrar.

Behind the offices was the yard, with a three-storey building on its west side, with ground floor garages and a Yard Foreman's office and the two upper storeys occupied by the Stores. There was also, in that block, a Carpenter's Shop and a Blacksmith's Shop. On the east side of the yard, there was a Yard Office occupied by the Distribution Superintendent, Arthur Pexton, and a Mess Room which was occupied, out of working hours, by a watchman and a driver. It appeared to me that the Company was run by three Superintendents, Arthur Pexton in the Yard Office in charge of mainlaying; Bob Stirk, Superintending Inspector, who looked after the service layers, who at that time were all plumbers; and at Havant, Fred Carter. Bob Stirk was over age and had been given a year's extension by the Directors to oversee the integration of the Hayling Island distribution system into the Company's organisation.

There were only three ladies employed in the Company's offices, Joan Hester, the Secretary's private secretary, and two ladies in the addressograph room. The addressograph was a system of metallic plates on which were recorded the names and addresses of our customers and the water rate that was due. The business of changing the water rate was a major operation, since each new water rate had to be calculated manually and transferred to the addressograph plates. Temporary ladies were brought into the office when this operation was necessary. There was no ladies' lavatory in the building, but the ladies were allowed to use the Directors' toilet, except once a month on Board Days, when they were required to cross Hyde Park Road to the Bus Station Café for such purposes!"

Norman Hudson's Recollections

Norman Hudson joined Portsmouth Water Company in 1947, aged 16, straight from school. He remembers the Engineer, David Halton Thomson, and Reg Hall, Deputy Engineer, who interviewed him. "DHT was one of the old school and even had a chauffeur-driven car to take him to and from the office. People would stand to attention when he arrived. Everyone went to his office, including the Company Secretary, not the other way round. He would press a button and you jumped to it! But DHT was a gentleman and was well respected by everyone who came into contact with him. Reg Hall was a different character – rather 'hen-pecked' – but he was a very nice man. He came to our wedding and gave us two tea-trays as a gift.

There were very much two 'sides', the engineers and accountants, at Commercial Road – the engineers could only reach the accountants by going through a normally bolted door in the front office!"

When Norman started work in 1947, mainlayers still went out with handcarts. They had only two lorries - a Dennis and a pipe lorry - and one or two vans. There was an Engineer's car, a BSA with a fluid flywheel gearbox, and a Drawing Office car, a Morris 8 shared by Drawing Office staff.

The Engineer's office, Commercial Road

Norman's first job was as Drawing Office Junior and he took day-release and night classes to complete his matriculation. His father-in-law, Ralph Barrett, was in charge of the Drawing Office, then Horace Benney joined when Ralph retired. The Drawing Office was long and narrow, with two drawing boards under the windows looking out on to Commercial Road and two others opposite, used by Norman and his colleague Jack Bennett.

Merger with the Gosport Waterworks Company

In 1944, the Coalition Government issued an important White Paper entitled *A National Water Policy*, in which emphasis was laid on the desirability of amalgamating the many separate water undertakings throughout the country into larger units. The previous pages show that this evolutionary process was already at work; over the years, the Portsmouth Company had absorbed the Idsworth Estate Waterworks (1930), those of the Catherington Rural District Council (1931) and the Hayling Island supply of the Havant and Waterloo Urban District Council (1950).

A momentous step was initiated in 1953, when initial contact between the Directors of the Portsmouth and Gosport Companies indicated that both parties were favourable to an amalgamation. The terms were agreed on 28th April 1954 and later approved by the shareholders. Finally a Ministerial Order, which came into force on 1st April 1955, created the Portsmouth and Gosport Water Company, which became the sole water supplier for almost the whole of south-east Hampshire.

The story of this and other mergers is covered in subsequent chapters.

The Water Supply to Gosport

Originally the town of Gosport was the built-up and fortified part of the parish of Alverstoke on the west shore of Portsmouth Harbour facing Old Portsmouth. In 1894, the parish became the Gosport and Alverstoke Urban District and, in 1922, it was promoted to the status of the Borough of Gosport.

Its fortunes have been closely linked with those of Portsmouth, because they have both depended for their main livelihood upon HM Dockyard and its many subsidiary establishments in the district. Gosport is, in effect, the western division of the Port of Portsmouth. Although they are neighbours, the wide expanse of the harbour between them caused their respective water supplies to be developed quite independently of each other.

Early History

It appears that, for a short time, Gosport had a piped water supply more than a hundred years before Portsmouth. Dr L F W White, in his booklet, *The Story of Gosport* (1947), wrote:

"As far back as 1698, an enterprising Londoner named Thomas Lewis obtained an Act of Parliament for the erection of a waterworks at Forton, just outside the boundary of the town, but the Company got into financial difficulties, and only 240 houses ever received their supply, through hollowed-out elm tree pipes.....

Evidence of this supply in the then Middle Street (now High Street) was provided by wooden pipes that were once dug up from time to time along this road.

Old elm water pipe uncovered in High Street, Gosport, December 1936

The next known reference to an early public water supply is found in The Times of 28th March 1816. It contains an advertisement giving notice of a "Special General Assembly of the Proprietors of the Gosport and Forton Water Works.... to consider the propriety of proceeding to effect an immediate sale and disposition of all the property and effects belonging to the Company ...."

Little else is known of this company. It was not in existence in 1808 because, in that year, the promoters of the old Portsmouth and Farlington Company intended to include Gosport in its area of supply - a proposal that was soon dropped. On the other hand, there is in the records of Portsmouth Water Company a letter dated November 1811, referring to a pump "exactly the same as made for the Gosport Water Works". The inference appears to be that this company had a short life, from about 1809 to 1816. The works were a well and pumping station at Forton, which were later purchased by the Government for the supply of the nearby marine barracks.

Apart from these two brief enterprises, both started by London promoters, the inhabitants of Gosport had to rely upon shallow wells and water carts in much the same way as in Portsmouth. Dr White also stated:

"Even in 1850, over 7,700 gallons a day came from three main wells, and 36 great carts, each carrying a ton of water, plied through the streets selling water at one farthing per bucket (about one tenth of a modern penny, which is more than it would cost today!) *It was poor in quality and intermittent in supply, although the vendors collected about £1,700 a year."*

According to the National Census of 1851, the population of the parish of Alverstoke was 16,908, of which 7,414 were in Gosport and 2,432 in the services and other establishments.

Gosport, Forton and Anglesey Water Consumers' Company Ltd

The next step to introduce a piped water supply was a local enterprise; it was inaugurated at a meeting held at the India Arms Hotel, Gosport, on 21st August 1856, with Benjamin Hobbs Senior of Forton in the chair. It was resolved to form a company to be called the "Gosport, Forton and Anglesey Pure Water Consumers' Company", with a capital stock of £25,000 in £10 shares. (The word "Pure" was afterwards dropped). The resolutions were supported by the signatures of 33 leading inhabitants.

At a subsequent meeting, Arthur Wright and William Rogers, both grocers, David Compigné, a solicitor, Henry Dashwood, a timber merchant, Thomas Walton, a naval outfitter, and the Rev. Edward Burney, a school proprietor, were appointed provisional Directors. Joseph Starkey of London joined the Board at a later date.

Horatio Compigné, a partner of David Compigné, became the Secretary. Apparently no Chairman was appointed, each Director taking the chair in turn. An office was opened at the Town Hall and Market House on Gosport Hard where, on 6th September 1856, a public meeting was held and subscriptions for shares were invited.

The directors engaged James Pilbrow, a civil engineer from London, to prepare plans and specifications for a complete water supply scheme. His proposed source was a well with a borehole in the bottom, to be sunk in the water-bearing strata, known as the Bracklesham Beds and Bagshot Sands, at Bury Cross, about a mile west of the town, together with a pumping station, water tower and about eight miles of distribution mains.

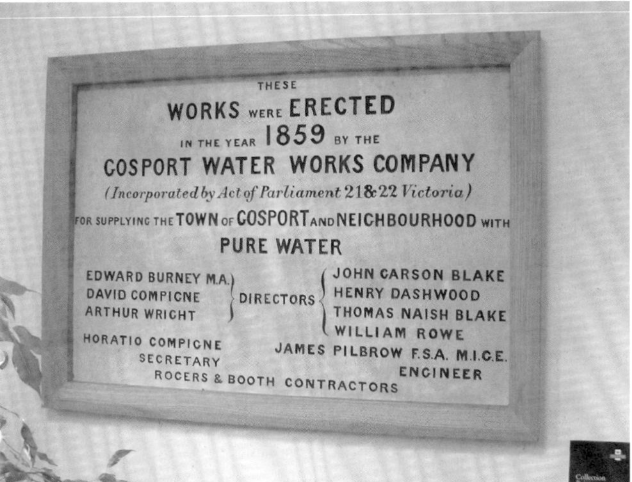

The Bury Cross foundation stone, now located at Maindell Treatment Works, Fareham

On the basis of this scheme, a prospectus was issued in December 1856, inviting subscriptions towards an initial capital of £25,000. It stated that a contractor named Murray was prepared to undertake the complete works for the sum of £23,000 and that, if he was awarded the contract, he was willing to subscribe a quarter of the capital.

Pilbrow, however, on hearing of Murray's offer, informed the Directors that his own estimate for the complete scheme was only £14,331 and advised that the work should be let in six separate contracts. Murray's tender was therefore declined and consequently his offer of financial assistance was lost. In the meantime, applications for shares were coming in so slowly that the intention to go to Parliament immediately had to be abandoned.

In January 1857, an amended prospectus based on a capital of £17,000 was issued. In order to give local investors visual evidence that a scheme was definitely in progress, it was decided to obtain tenders for sinking the well and borehole at Bury Cross. The contract was let in the following May to Messrs Rogers & Booth.

In view of increased support for the enterprise, it was later decided to apply for the intended Act in the Parliamentary Session 1857/58.

Gosport Waterworks Company

The Act was passed on 11th May 1858, under which the provisional company became a statutory water undertaking named the Gosport Waterworks Company with a capital of £17,000 in £10 shares and with the power to borrow up to £4,000. The area of supply was "the whole of the Parish of Alverstoke, in the County of Hants, in which the town of Gosport is situate", and the power to construct the Bury Cross Works was confirmed.

The first Directors nominated by the Act were the seven named earlier, of whom the Rev. Edward Burney became the first Chairman; he remained in office for 30 years. He was part-proprietor, with his brother Henry, of the Gosport Royal Academy, a large boarding school chiefly for naval and military pupils. Horatio Compigné, solicitor, was confirmed as the first Secretary and held that position for 29 years.

The Head Office of the Company remained at the Market House until 1890, when it was transferred to 1 High Street. It later moved to Thornfield House, 4 High Street, in 1910, and subsequently, in 1955, became the Gosport Office of the newly-formed Portsmouth and Gosport Waterworks Company.

Bury Cross Works

The Bury Cross Works were completed in 1860 and water was first supplied on 26th September of that year. The daily yield of the well proved to be about 300,000 gallons, which was ample for some years after. The capacity of the original water tower, however, was found to be much too small, so a second larger water tower, holding about 72,000 gallons, was completed in 1866.

During the next 25 years, various works on the same site were carried out to meet the increasing demand. By 1892, five wells and seven boreholes had been sunk. The fifth well was, in effect, a large underground storage tank, 40 feet in diameter and 100 feet deep. In 1874, additional pumping plant was installed in the existing engine house and, in 1883/84, a second pumping station was constructed over one of the other wells.

Bury Cross Works

Despite all these expensive works, the total daily yield only increased from 300,000 to 320,000 gallons per day. Consequently, from about 1877 onwards, the supply was normally turned off during the night in order to conserve water.

It is significant that all these wells had been sunk in the same geological formation as the well on Portsea Island belonging to one of the old Portsmouth companies. They had likewise been unable to obtain an adequate large-scale supply from such a source.

The Bury Cross wells were in due course superseded by other sources. They finally went out of use in 1907 although, during both World Wars, they were held in reserve as an emergency source of supply.

Foxbury Works under construction, 1890s

Foxbury Works

After the continued failure to obtain more water from Bury Cross, the Company decided to develop new works at Foxbury Point, about three miles north of Gosport and half a mile from the west shore of Portsmouth Harbour; an Order authorising the scheme was obtained in 1897. The source was a well sunk into the chalk through overlying clay beds, from the bottom of which adits were driven to tap the water in the chalk fissures. The surface works consisted of a pumping station with two pumps, each having a daily capacity of about one million gallons, together with a large water tower holding 230,000 gallons; in addition, a 15-inch trunk main, reducing to 12-inch, was laid into Gosport.

The sinking of the well itself was completed in May 1896 and, in view of the extreme shortage of water in Gosport, temporary pumping plant was provided to afford a preliminary extra supply; water from the new source was first pumped on 23rd August 1896. The adits at the foot of the well and the pumping station were completed during the following winter and spring. When tested, the well was shown to have a daily yield of about 11 million gallons. The water tower was not finished until August 1900 when, for the first time in many years, Gosport received a constant supply under good pressure.

This was to prove only a temporary blessing. Month after month, the water became increasingly brackish; it was soon apparent that the normal chalk water in the well was being contaminated by the infiltration of salt water from the harbour. These conditions and the excessive water hardness naturally provoked widespread complaints, reinforced by letters to the press and public protest meetings. The water was alleged to have both taste and smell, and the "Foxbury perfume" became a by-word!

Unsuccessful attempts were made to cut off the fissures yielding the worst quality water and to obtain better water by means of borings; eventually, in 1903, it was decided that a new source should be developed elsewhere and the well was abandoned. Altogether, the scheme had cost about £30,000, which had to be written off. Only the pumping plant, which could be removed to another site, and the water tower, which remained available to maintain water pressure, were saved.

Soberton well and adits under construction, 1906

Soberton Works

To provide an alternative to the Foxbury well, the Borough of Portsmouth Waterworks Company was approached in 1903 about the possibility of a bulk supply from the Farlington reservoirs to Foxbury water tower. However, this proposal was ultimately discarded in favour of a new well and pumping station near Soberton, in the Meon valley, about 11 miles north of Gosport. An Act for this purpose was obtained in 1904.

The well was sunk into the chalk with an adit at the bottom, and the two pumping units for the new station were transferred from Foxbury. A 16-inch pumping main, about two miles long, was laid to a high-level service reservoir, holding 2.1 million gallons, at Gravel Hill, Shedfield, from which a 15-inch trunk main was laid through Fareham to join the existing 15-inch main previously laid from Foxbury into Gosport.

The daily yield of the well was about 1¼ million gallons and the station was brought into use on 24th May 1907. Thus Gosport at last received a constant supply of good quality water. The Bury Cross and Foxbury wells were taken out of use and the Soberton Works, with various subsequent extensions, remained the sole source of supply for the next 34 years.

Shedfield Reservoir under construction, 14th June 1907

The main effect of the First World War (1914-18) was a rapid growth in demand from the local Government

Adit extension in progress at Soberton during the First World War

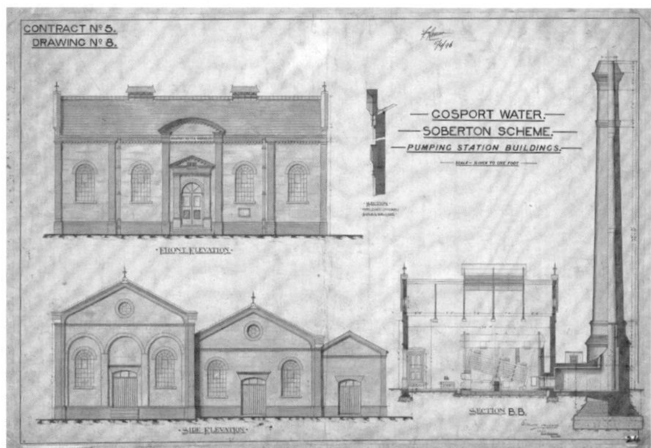

Construction drawing of Soberton Works

establishments. In order to meet this demand, the yield of the well was increased in 1914/15 by extending the adits. In 1918/19, the capacity of the station was improved by a modification of the existing machinery and the installation of a Worthington pumping engine, for which the building was enlarged.

After the war, for a long period the average daily supply remained nearly constant at about 1⅓ million gallons; to provide an alternative means of supply, a second 15-inch trunk main was laid from Shedfield Reservoir to Gosport in 1933.

Lee-on-the-Solent Water Undertaking

Under the Act of 1904, powers had been obtained to acquire the undertaking of the Lee-on-the-Solent Waterworks Company Ltd, but the actual transfer did not take place until 1915. The purchase price was £5,280.

Lee-on-the-Solent was first developed as a private building estate within the Gosport Company's area of supply, but with its own waterworks, which had been constructed by the local company in 1890. The works were in the High Street at the corner of Cambridge Road. The source was a shallow well, the water being pumped by oil-driven plant into a nearby water tower.

Water was first supplied in 1897 and, by the time of the transfer in 1915, about 32 miles of mains had been laid, the average daily supply being about 30,000 gallons to 200 properties. The local waterworks subsequently went out of use, the mains being connected to the Gosport distribution system.

The Second World War (1939-45)

From 1935 onwards, the forebodings of another war caused a further substantial increase in water supplies to Government establishments, and a large development programme was put in hand. In 1937/38, a second pumping well was sunk at Soberton and the headings were further extended, whereby the daily yield was increased up to about two million gallons; the station building was again enlarged to accommodate a Uniflow pumping engine and, in 1939, a second 16-inch pumping main was laid from Soberton to Shedfield Reservoir. In 1940, Shedfield No. 2 Reservoir, with a capacity of 3½ million gallons, was completed; at Soberton, one of the old steam-driven pumps, originally transferred from Foxbury, was removed and replaced by electrically-driven plant with a daily capacity of three million gallons. This was the first use of electricity for normal pumping purposes, the remaining steam-driven plant serving as stand-by.

The Second World War placed an unprecedented strain on the Company's water resources. By the end of the war, the average daily supply had increased from under 1½ million gallons to more than 3½ million gallons. Most of this increase had come from the many Government establishments in the area. Other supplies also increased substantially and, in addition, much more water had to be supplied on account of wastage caused by air raid damage to mains and service pipes, and by the lack of labour to deal with normal repairs.

It became clear that, with the further extension of the adits at Soberton Works in 1938, the probable maximum reliable daily yield of about two million gallons from that source had been reached; moreover, it would be unwise, in the event of war, to rely wholly upon a single means of supply. As a consequence, an Act was obtained in 1940 to develop a new independent source at Hoe, about one mile south-east of Bishop's Waltham.

The initial works were carried out during 1940/41. They consisted of a deep well with adits in the chalk, the water being pumped by two electrically-driven units with a daily capacity of one and two million gallons respectively, housed in a temporary blast-proof building. A 15-inch pumping main, about two miles long, was laid to the Shedfield Reservoirs. After the war, the smaller unit was replaced by another of two million gallons capacity, together with a stand-by oil-driven power unit, and a permanent building was erected. The daily yield of the well proved to be at least 1½ million gallons.

Pump motors at Soberton

In addition to the Hoe Works, various other war precautions were taken. The Foxbury water tower was kept full, while an electrically-driven pump was installed at the Bury Cross underground tank and an oil-driven pump at the Lee-on-the-Solent well. The private wells at the Gosport Gas Works and at the Inverness Laundry were fitted up to provide a limited supply and a fleet of mobile drinking water tanks was acquired. Emergency connections were also made between the Company's mains and those of its neighbours - Southampton Corporation and Fareham Urban District Council.

Gosport, along with Portsmouth, experienced widespread damage to water mains during many air raids. The worst experience occurred on the night of 10th/11th January 1941. During the following three days, the loss of water due to broken mains and service pipes and extra water used for firefighting was so large as to cause the two Shedfield Reservoirs, which together held about six million gallons, to be nearly emptied. By good fortune, the essential parts of the new Hoe Works and pumping main were on the point of completion; an emergency effort to make the final connection brought the station into immediate use, thus avoiding any curtailment of the supply. Throughout the war, all the Company's principal works escaped damage.

Bishop's Waltham Water Undertaking

The piped water supply to Bishop's Waltham has a varied history. It began in 1894 with the formation of the Bishop's Waltham Waterworks Company Ltd, the principal promoter of which was Charles Liddell Simpson, a civil engineer of London. The works consisted of a shallow well in the chalk and a pumping station, both situated in a disused chalkpit at Northbrook, about half a mile north of the town. There was also a service reservoir at Vernon Hill, a little further away, holding about 183,000 gallons. The reservoir was abandoned in 1954, soon after the completion of Street End No. 1 Reservoir. Later, in 1965, the site was sold and the reservoir was ingeniously converted into a private house.

Demolition of original Northbrook Pumping Station, 1956

In 1914, the South Hants Waterworks Company acquired the undertaking, but this company in turn was purchased in 1921 by the Southampton Corporation. Under the Gosport Act of 1940, the Bishop's Waltham supply was transferred to the Gosport Waterworks Company in 1941, the purchase price being £11,170.

As the original pumping plant had become obsolete, a connection was made in 1942 so that most of Bishop's Waltham could be supplied from the Shedfield Reservoirs. An existing small borehole at the Northbrook Works was brought into use, from which water was pumped by means of electrically-driven plant to Vernon Hill Service Reservoir to supply the higher parts of the locality. Further developments at Northbrook are described later.

Rural Supplies

Up to 1904, the Company's area of supply was confined to the then Gosport and Alverstoke Urban District, about six square miles.

The first extension took place under its Act of 1904, by which were added the adjoining parish of Crofton, together with a separate area comprising the parishes of Wickham, Shedfield and Swanmore. These parishes were supplied from the first Shedfield Reservoir.

A second extension was authorised by an Act of 1940, which added the parishes of Boarhunt, Bishop's Waltham and part of Durley. With the exception of the higher parts of Bishop's Waltham (supplied from Vernon Hill Reservoir), they were supplied from the two Shedfield Reservoirs.

A third extension was made under an Order of 1951, which added most of the remaining Meon valley parishes, namely Corhampton, Droxford, Exton, Soberton, Warnford and West Meon, together with the parish of Upham, to the north of Bishop's Waltham.

At that time, the only existing piped supply in these parishes was at West Meon. Here, in 1939, the Droxford Rural District Council had introduced a supply to the village from a small borehole in the chalk at Vinnell's Lane, with an electrically operated pumping station and reservoir. Under the Order, this was transferred to the Company.

Southwick had its own private supply, which is still in use today.

Post-War Developments

Austin A40 pick-up van issued to Soberton Works, May 1951

One of the effects of the very rapid increase in demand during the war was to cause an excessive drop in the daytime pressure of the supply in Gosport; it had also been necessary, on occasions during drought periods, to impose restrictions on the use of water. At first it was thought that this situation would correct itself after the war with a marked decrease in the demand from Government establishments and industry. In fact, these supplies reduced only slightly and a substantial increase was expected from large housing schemes being developed by the Gosport and Fareham Councils. Thus the Company decided on an extensive programme of new works, which was carried out in the period 1953-56.

To safeguard the supply, a second electrically-driven pumping set, with a daily capacity of three million gallons, was installed at Soberton, together with a diesel-driven power unit as stand-by. Consequently, the steam-driven pumping plant retained for stand-by purposes was finally superseded, having last pumped water into supply in 1952. The second old engine, (transferred from

Foxbury in 1907) and the Worthington engine were removed in 1953, followed by the Uniflow engine in 1957. Thus the use of steam raised by coal-fired boilers as the source of power at the Soberton Works came to an end.

Hoads Hill Water Tower, 1955

To improve and regulate the pressure in the Gosport area, an intermediate two million-gallon service reservoir and a water tower were constructed at Hoads Hill, about a mile south of Wickham. The reservoir and tower were built on the line of the trunk mains from the Shedfield Reservoirs. An additional trunk main was laid into Gosport. The scheme was designed by Rofe and Raffety, and their Resident Engineer, John King, later joined the Company in 1962, eventually becoming Chief Engineer from 1986 to 1992, followed by 10 years as a non-executive Director.

A new borehole was sunk at the Northbrook Works and proved to have a daily yield of about one million gallons. As this quantity was much in excess of local requirements, it was decided to use it for the main supply by laying a 15-inch pumping main to the Hoe Works, from where water could be delivered directly to the Shedfield Reservoirs. Since the local conditions seemed favourable for producing even more water, a second borehole was sunk, which proved to have a daily yield of 1½ million gallons. The Northbrook Works thus became a valuable addition to the Company's water resources.

The provision of a mains water supply to the parishes added by the Order of 1951 required further infrastructure, as many parts were too high to be served from the existing Shedfield Reservoirs. For the supply to Upham, a service reservoir holding 200,000 gallons was constructed at Street End on Stephen's Castle Down, about two miles north of Bishop's Waltham, with water initially being boosted to it from Vernon Hill Reservoir. For the supply to the Meon valley parishes, a service reservoir holding 200,000 gallons was constructed at Fir Down, about a mile north-west of Droxford, water being pumped to this reservoir from the Soberton Works.

Street End No.1 Reservoir under construction

In 1956/57, the existing supply to West Meon from the nearby independent works was safeguarded by the provision of a second borehole and pumping plant.

Amalgamation with Portsmouth Water Company

As we have seen, over the years the Gosport Company had acquired the Lee-on-the-Solent Waterworks Company (1915), the Bishop's Waltham Waterworks of the Southampton Corporation (1941) and the West Meon Waterworks of the Droxford Rural District Council (1951).

West Meon borehole no.2 being test pumped, April 1956

However, by the 1950s, the Government was pressing the multitude of local water undertakings to consider merging with their neighbours, in order to improve the efficiency of operations and development of water resources to meet growing demand.

This initiative had its first local impact in 1953, when a preliminary exchange of views between the Directors of the Portsmouth and Gosport Companies indicated that both parties were favourable to an amalgamation. Terms were embodied in an agreement dated 28th April 1954, which was later approved by the shareholders. The transaction was finally confirmed by a Ministerial Order, which came into force on 1st April 1955, thus creating the Portsmouth and Gosport Water Company, which became the sole water supplier for almost the whole of south-east Hampshire.

Inside the Maindell adits, 1954

Fareham's Water Supply

The original Fareham water supply undertaking, which developed in the middle of the 19th century, was a small concern supplying the central areas of Fareham, now referred to as the Eastern Wards. The neighbouring areas were supplied by the Southampton, Gosport and Portsmouth water undertakings until the Portsmouth and Gosport Water Company took over the Fareham undertaking in 1959.

The Works at Maindell was the only source of supply throughout the Fareham undertaking's period of independence.

Fareham Local Board of Health 1860-1934

Following the Public Health Act 1848, an inquiry into the sewerage, drainage, supply of water and sanitary condition of the inhabitants of Fareham was held by Robert Rawlinson, Superintending Inspector to the General Board of Health. As a result of this inquiry, the Fareham Local Board of Health constructed a sewerage system, together with a public water supply. The same Rawlinson was responsible for the inquiry at Portsmouth, which eventually led to the formation of the Portsmouth Company in 1857.

The Development of Maindell and the Wallington Reservoir

The new source at Maindell was constructed in a disused chalk quarry at North Wallington. Below ground, it comprised a single well with adits driven sideways from the well into the chalk to intercept the natural flow of water through the fissures. Above ground, a brick building was constructed, containing steam engines which drove the pumps. These steam engines started work on 6th September 1860 and, in the same month, the yield from the source was assessed at 130,000 gallons per day. The pumps could deliver a maximum output of 10,000 gallons per hour (gph).

At the same time, a brick reservoir of 100,000 gallons capacity was constructed nearby at Fort Wallington, on the hill above the chalkpit at Maindell. In those early years, approximately four miles of water mains were laid from the Wallington Reservoir to and around the town.

The new supply must have been very popular for, just 10 months after the pumps first came into use, the Board employed T Tilley, of Enfield, Middlesex, to sink another well into the chalk. In 1862, the Board instructed its Clerk to have circulars distributed "cautioning persons against wasting water" – and this was in February, not the middle of summer! The new water supply had obviously been taken up with enthusiasm by the people of Fareham, because there were two incidents, in March 1862 and May 1863, when the reservoir was emptied of water. The cause appears to have been the engine driver going off duty without realising, or having the means to know, that the reservoir was nearly empty. Telemetry systems that are commonplace today were not available in the 1860s!

In August 1865, a tender was accepted from Messrs Butterfield, offering to drive a further adit from the well at Maindell at 2s 6d per cubic yard. By September, 160 yards had been excavated at the well and it was agreed to proceed until £25 had been spent on the excavation. Soon afterwards, the Board was informed that the new adit at the well was complete and that "a great advantage would be gained by the increased supply of water". Yet from that same month, because of the very substantial waste of water at night, the supply at Wallington Hill was turned off every evening at 10 pm, except on Saturdays (off at 11 pm), and turned back on at 6 am. This was tolerated for almost a year, until a letter from doctors in Fareham persuaded the Board to keep the water supply turned on for 24 hours per day. Even then, in January 1867, the water had to be turned off again at night during very cold weather.

During the dry weather of July 1867, the Board distributed handbills requesting care in the use of water, to avoid having to shorten the hours of supply. A set of critical spare parts was purchased for the pumps a few months later.

Demands for Constant Supplies

Despite the Board's initiatives, in February 1870 a petition was received from a number of residents about the desirability of having a constant supply of water and drawing attention to the inadequate pressure at certain hours. The Board considered the petition, but took no action.

At that time, the overall capacity of the underground wells and adits was 79,000 gallons. In July 1873, the Surveyor suggested enlarging the storage volume by extending the adits. The work was carried out by Messrs Butterfield, again at a rate of 2s 6d per cubic yard.

The supply must have been turned off overnight for, in 1874, the Board decided to make the supply continuous throughout the day from Monday 9th November. However, water scarcity in the summer of 1876 led to the supply being turned off between 6 pm and 8 pm on working days and 5 pm and 8 pm on Sundays.

Requests from other Areas and the need for further Improvements

By now the residents of Fareham town had enjoyed the benefits of an admittedly rather irregular water supply for some 16 years. In August 1877, the first request was received for a supply to the higher area north of the town in and around Funtley. It came from the School Board and was supported by a number of inhabitants from Funtley, drawing attention to the defective private supply of water which existed. However, the Committee of the Board of Health decided it "could not entertain a supply to Funtley".

The probable reason, apart from the cost, was the continuing difficulty in meeting demand from existing customers in Fareham. In August 1880, the Surveyor complained that the pumps at Maindell were working for up to 14½ hours per day. It was therefore decided that any supply of water for trade purposes would be discontinued wherever a meter was not kept in proper repair by the owner. Inspections for defective fittings in premises were also stepped up, resulting in some success in reducing waste of water.

Records suggest that intermittent supplies continued into the 1880s, but it was a switch to continuous supplies in November 1887 which soon confirmed that major improvements were needed. Waste of water had risen substantially within a month, and the Board decided to look at the cost of duplicate pumps, examine the whole question of payment for non-domestic water and fix a scale of charges.

In 1889, new pumps and gearing were installed by Thomas Horn of Millbank, Westminster, and the new pump house was built by Fulfords.

Supplies to the Uplands and Funtley Districts

With the supply situation stabilised by the provision of new pumps at Maindell, the Board of Health might have expected a period of relative inactivity as far as new works were concerned. This was not to be for, in January 1890, a petition was received from residents in Old Turnpike Road, North Hill and Kiln Road, asking for a better and more efficient supply to the Uplands district of Fareham, which at the time relied on private wells. Thomas Horn, the supplier of the new pumps at Maindell, was consulted and he devised a scheme of estimated cost £900 for a public supply to Uplands. He proposed using the existing steam engines at Maindell to drive additional sets of small pumps, which were to be installed in the wells, along with a new rising main supplying water from Maindell to a new 4,000 gallon storage tank at Uplands. This tank was to be built on the north side of Kiln Road, just west of its junction with Park Lane.

In July 1890, a loan for £1,500 for the Uplands scheme was sought from the Local Government Board. Meanwhile, in September 1890, it was reported that the Funtley brickyard and cottage were wholly without water and that children at the Funtley Board School were causing a nuisance by asking for water at adjacent properties, because there was none at the School. The School was informed that a new supply could not be approved until the new Uplands scheme was completed.

In December 1890, the contracts for the Uplands scheme were awarded to Henry Clark (pipes, hydrants, storage tank and fittings), James Gamblin (tank house) and Thomas Horn & Son (provision and fixing of pumps), and work went ahead.

Finally in August 1891, G G Darby laid on a water supply to Funtley Board School at a cost of £350; the work involved laying a main from Kiln Road to the School and beyond, as far as the railway.

Some indication of the initially dubious quality of the new water supply to Funtley can be gained from an instruction to the Board's Clerk in November 1892. He was asked to write to all owners who had not yet done so to connect to the new main in Funtley, but as the water was still "unpleasant through the solution in which the pipes were dipped", no water rate would be collected until April 1893! For some months, there was resistance to this request from a number of householders, who presumably had private wells which they felt were perfectly satisfactory, and they appeared unwilling to pay the Board for a mains supply.

Requests from Catisfield and Titchfield

Both the Uplands and Funtley districts were on the higher ground north of Fareham town. Their success in obtaining the firm promise of a mains water supply did not go unnoticed by the Fareham Union Rural Sanitary Authority, which wrote to the Board asking if it could supply drinking water as far as Catisfield Hill. It was told that pressure from the present reservoir (i.e. at Fort Wallington) was insufficient. The Sanitary Authority was not told that the new tank at Uplands would have sufficient pressure, but probably insufficient capacity!

In January 1892, the Fareham Local Board of Health met a committee of the Fareham Union Rural Sanitary Authority about the possibility of a water supply from Fareham to Titchfield, but no scheme was implemented. Titchfield was destined to receive a mains water supply from Southampton Corporation Waterworks, but not until 1922/23.

Changes in Staff and further Improvements at Maindell

In April 1890, Mr Roseveare, the Surveyor to the Board for more than 20 years, resigned owing to ill health and died just six months later. A new post, with the quaint title of Surveyor and Inspector of Nuisances, was advertised and 75 applications were received. Walter Butler was appointed to the post from 24th June 1890. His salary was £130 per year for the first year and £150 per year thereafter, with a house being provided by the Board, which in return required £100 security from Mr Butler!

The increased demand being placed on the Maindell source caused the Board to consider a new well and further extensions to the adits in July 1893. Work duly went ahead, but the contractor, Mr J P Hall, found a substantial fissure flow and was unable to keep the water drained from the workings. He was discharged from his contract once he had connected the new well and headings to the existing well system.

A further demand on the system loomed in 1894, when the Fareham Union Workhouse in London Road (now St Christopher's Hospital, Wickham Road) was connected to the high-level Uplands tank zone, it being at too high an elevation to be supplied from the Wallington Reservoir. The additional demand meant that it was necessary to increase the capacity of the Uplands tank.

Fareham Urban District Council 1934-1959

On 31st December 1894, the first meeting was held of the new Fareham Urban District Council (UDC), which (under the Local Government Act 1894) had replaced the Fareham Local Board of Health. The Council's offices were at Westbury Manor, Fareham. The UDC continued in existence until the reorganisation of local government in April 1974, since when Fareham Borough Council has been the district local authority.

Despite continuing problems with maintaining supplies, there were extensions of the water mains system westwards at Funtley and eastwards to East Cams in 1895 and 1896.

With the aim of extending the public supply as far as Catisfield, the UDC decided in August 1897 to carry out further extensions to the adits at Maindell and this went ahead, being completed within eight weeks. The UDC was keen to have control over the chalkpit and the adjacent tips to prevent the possibility of any contamination reaching the wells. In 1900, following a request to the War Department who owned the site, the UDC was granted a formal tenancy.

A Supply for Catisfield at last

In October 1899, the inhabitants of Catisfield petitioned for a water supply, but this was rejected by the UDC. However, in July 1902, it did go as far as preparing a scheme for the extension of the network to Catisfield. The scheme required the laying of 2½ miles of new mains and the construction of a high level tank at Red Barn (north of Fareham), as well as new boilers and additional engines, pumps and buildings at Maindell. The annual repayment cost on the loan was estimated at £250 - £300, while the extra annual water rate receipts would be £34!

Faced with this disparity, the UDC decided to ask residents if they were prepared to assist in the capital outlay involved. The response was, to say the least, unenthusiastic; 13 replies were received, of which seven said they wanted a supply and only one was prepared to make a contribution! The UDC decided that there was no case for extending the supply to Catisfield.

Undeterred, the residents of Catisfield employed a local solicitor to present a petition to the Local Government Board for an inquiry into water supply to Catisfield. Eventually the UDC's Surveyor reviewed his estimates and, when he reported in February 1903 that the Catisfield supply would cost no more than £4,000, it was decided to proceed.

In July 1904, contracts were awarded to Playfair & Toole for the concrete tank at Red Barn, to Jenkins & Sons for the new mains and to Davey, Paxman & Co for the engine, boiler and pumps.

The Early 1900s

Around this time, there was something of a disagreement with the Gosport Waterworks Company, which was promoting a Bill to supply Gosport by laying mains through Fareham from Shedfield Reservoir. The UDC failed to persuade the Gosport Company to amend the routes of the new mains and so it lodged an official petition against the Gosport Water Bill. This objection was unsuccessful but, two years later, after the new mains had been laid, the UDC got its revenge. It served a formal notice on the Gosport Company, requiring it to make good all the road surfaces affected by poor trench reinstatement!

In October 1904, it was reported that the UDC's Water Committee had inspected "apparatus for tapping a water main without the necessity of turning off the water" and decided it would "prove a great convenience" - as it still does in the 21st century!

The First World War

The following years up to the outbreak of the First World War were devoted to extending the water mains network, as the Fareham supply expanded to include Shore Road, Gosport Road, Earles Farm Estate and the Hartlands Estate. In 1914, 2,500 feet of 3-inch mains were laid to serve new houses being built in Gudge Heath Lane.

The years of the First World War saw little activity on water supply improvements, with the country's resources being devoted largely to winning the war. There are one or two more unusual entries in the records for this period; for instance, in May 1915, the UDC accepted a War Office proposal that payment for water for horses stabled at Down End Farm should be on the basis of 20 gallons/horse/day instead of being measured by meter!

Improvements in the 1920s

In August 1921, the UDC resolved to suspend the practice of laying service pipes in lead and decided instead that service pipes beyond stop taps should be of 'galvanised iron steam tubing'.

By 1924, it was becoming clear that increased demand for water would require more improvements to the supply system and, in February 1925, the UDC's Surveyor, Walter Butler, reported on a new scheme that would cost £11,280. The main components were:

An additional reservoir of 330,000 gallons capacity was to be built next to the existing one of 100,000 gallons capacity at Fort Wallington. The two reservoirs would provide "over a normal day's supply" to a new ***Low Level supply area***. The new reservoir was to be constructed of what was then called 'ferro-concrete' (known today as reinforced concrete).

The 1904 Red Barn Reservoir (20,000 gallons) was also too small and an additional ferro-concrete tank similar to the existing one was constructed, with a capacity of 60,000 gallons. The two would provide a ***High Level supply area*** of suitable capacity for the future development of Catisfield, Highlands Road and Gudge Heath Lane.

Additional mains were proposed from the Wallington Reservoirs to Wallington Hill to enable a satisfactory pressure to be provided, and a new pumping main was to be laid between Maindell Pumping Station and Uplands Tank.

By then the existing engines at Maindell had to work to their full capacity on occasions, leaving no stand-by capacity for a breakdown. Thus new electrically-powered pumping equipment was proposed to replace some of the steam-driven plant. An electric pump was installed to supply the new reservoir at Wallington and an electric booster pump to supply Red Barn Tanks.

In July 1925, the contract for laying the water mains and construction of the two concrete reservoirs was awarded to John Hunt Ltd and, in October, the contract for the new electrical pumps was awarded to Stone & Co, of Deptford. By August 1926, the new pumps, reservoir and tank had been completed and successfully tested.

Red Barn Tanks

Staff Changes

In April 1927, the Surveyor, Mr Butler, wrote to say that, after nearly 37 years' service, he could no longer carry out the full duties of water supply, highways, sewerage and other local services. The Council appointed him to the new post of Waterworks Engineer & Manager, with Harry Privett being appointed Surveyor to perform the remaining duties. Within two years, Butler had retired and Privett had taken over Butler's duties in addition to his own, albeit with more assistance.

In December 1928, it was agreed that men at the waterworks should be medically examined each year to make sure that they did not have any disease that might be transmitted to the water at the source.

Later Improvements to the Supply System

By 1928, still more strain was being placed on the UDC's source at Maindell. In September, a report was received from Mr H C Head of Winchester on the water supply of the district. He was subsequently appointed Engineer to design and supervise further improvement works. Soon afterwards, the UDC purchased the Maindell chalkpit from the War Office, as well as the land and garden attached to the waterworks cottage and the Wallington allotments.

In August 1929, the UDC's application for a loan of £2,500 for driving new adits at Maindell was approved, but the Ministry of Health also asked that steps be taken to determine if there was any waste of water by means of a waste water detector in the mains. Five months later, the contractor, A G Osenton, was excavating the new well and adit at Maindell. On completion of the work, tests showed that the yield of Maindell had increased to 632,000 gallons per day.

In 1930, substantial work took place to enlarge the mains from the Wallington Reservoir to Gosport Road, in Mill Road and Southampton Road. In 1932, water mains were laid to supply the new Down End Estate to the east of Wallington.

The Drought of 1934 and the continuing Rise in Consumption

In summer 1934, there was a serious water shortage owing to the drought. It was decided to issue a notice prohibiting the use of water for garden purposes, fountains and washing of cars, restrictions that were to remain in place until February 1935. The Council's consultants, Messrs Taylor & Wallin, were asked to prepare a report on the present Maindell Works and any necessary extensions, taking account of likely future development in the area of supply. The cost of their recommended improvement works was estimated at £16,200.

The need for an extension to the capacity of the supply was brought home in November 1935, when consumption for the month was 13.6 million gallons, an increase of 2.1 million gallons on November of the previous year. The pumps to the High Level area were working 18 hours per day, and the Surveyor, Harry Privett, feared that they would not cope with demand in the following summer. The new Co-operative Laundry in Gudge Heath Lane had, on its own, consumed 46,000 gallons on one particular day. At certain times of the day, more water was being consumed than could be pumped. By the end of the year, the daily average consumption of 383,000 gallons had risen by almost 15% to 440,000 gallons.

By May 1936, notices were being issued asking all consumers to avoid waste of water, with separate letters being sent to all large consumers. It was also decided that no additional supplies for garden watering were to be granted in the High Level area.

Further Improvements at Maindell and the Construction of Portsdown Reservoir

In July 1936, the Ministry of Health approved the Taylor and Wallin proposals, which comprised more extension work at Maindell Pumping Station and a new 500,000 gallon reservoir on War Office land on Portsdown Hill, to the west of Fort Nelson. Two months later, contracts for the well, adits and waste water drain were let to J Croad of Gosport. The contract for the alterations and additions to the building at Maindell was awarded to J Hunt Ltd.

By May 1937, the adit had been driven for 430 feet of the eventual 610 feet and the yield had increased to 27,700 gph over six hours. In view of these results, the UDC decided to increase the capacity of the High Level pumps from 18,000 to 30,000 gph. In addition, a further adit was driven in a northerly direction, parallel with Wallington Road.

In order to keep the water at a low enough level for the miners to work safely, high-rate pumping to waste was used to de-water the adits. Consequently, there were difficulties in maintaining supplies to Fareham, because groundwater levels were sometimes too low for the existing supply pumps to work properly.

However, the new adits were finally connected to the existing wells on the night of the 12th August 1937 and proved to be an outstanding success. The total yield was now found to be 76,000 gph, or 1.8 million gallons per day. Thus the new works had increased the output of the adits by a factor of three.

Following these improvements, the plant at Maindell consisted of:

a) Two High Level Sulzer 7-stage pumps, each of 30,000 gph capacity, pumping against a pressure of 305 ft and of 60.5 HP.

b) A Low Level Sulzer 3-stage pump of 51,000 gph capacity, pumping against a pressure of 135 ft and of 46.5 HP.

c) A new diesel oil-driven engine, with a dynamo for stand-by in case of grid failure, as well as the capability to transfer 50 kilowatts to the electricity grid.

d) The Stone turbine pump installed in 1926, of 44,000 gph capacity, pumping against a pressure of 143 ft.

e) Chlorinating and ammoniating plant.

These works marked the end of an era at Maindell, as the existing steam-driven beam engines and Cornish boiler were dismantled and replaced with electrically-driven pumps.

The total length of underground adits was now approximately 500 yards, with seven wells, the deepest being 60 ft 1 inch deep. The adits varied in size from 17 ft high by 3 ft wide to 5 ft high by 6 ft wide.

Maindell Pumping Station

In 1938, the Ministry of Health issued a circular asking water undertakers to ensure that water they supplied was at all times wholesome. As a result, a chlorination scheme was approved, with separate systems for the High and Low Level areas.

In May 1938, J Croad commenced work on the Portsdown Reservoir and arrangements were made to lay the new 12-inch pumping main from Maindell to the reservoir through War Office land.

The now disused Portsdown Reservoir

The Impact of the Second World War

With the situation in Europe deteriorating, water undertakers began to agree mutual self-help measures for use during a possible war. In October 1938, the Council approved a connection between its main and that of Portsmouth Water Company at Portchester, on the parish boundary.

With the outbreak of war, a number of precautions came into effect. In July 1940, the Ministry of Health wrote to urge the guarding of vital points of water supply and, in May 1941, the pumping mains at the reservoirs were cross-connected to the delivery mains, allowing the reservoirs to be isolated and by-passed if they were damaged by enemy action. In 1942, the old buildings beneath the Uplands tanks at Kiln Road were converted to air raid shelters, and a connection was also made between the High and Low Level systems at Wallington. This gave an increased pressure to premises on Portchester Road and would improve any emergency supply to Portsmouth Water Company's main at Portchester. In December 1942, the UDC cross-connected its mains to those of Gosport Waterworks Company, and a connection was also made to the private mains at Knowle Hospital, where there was a separate borehole supply.

By 1945, it was clear that consumption of water had risen substantially over the six wartime years. The Surveyor reported that average daily consumption had risen from 536,000 gallons per day in 1939 to 833,000 gallons per day in 1944. Whilst a rise of 179,000 gallons per day could be accounted for, the remaining 118,000 gallons each day were believed to have arisen from the washing facilities provided by the inhabitants for some of the many thousands of troops in the area in 1944. The Water Inspector was concentrating on testing all sluice valves and hydrants to find out if there was any serious leakage, but the Surveyor thought that the only effective solution would be to install a system of waste detecting meters. In addition, he felt that there were a number of unmeasured commercial premises, such as cafés, fishmongers, ladies' hairdressers and nursing homes, which should instead be metered. However, it was decided to defer this compulsory metering until the implications of the forthcoming Water Act 1945 were known in full.

Post-war Leakage Reduction and the Water Act 1945

Total consumption now averaged 900,000 gallons per day. In June 1945, measurements showed that in the Low Level area, a night flow of 12,000 gph was leaving the reservoir and most of this was leakage; there was also an unmeasured amount of leakage past the sluice valve separating the Low Level area from the High Level area. It was eventually decided to cut off the supply between midnight and 4 am from 2nd - 14th July 1945 in certain parts of the town - a reminder of the manner in which supplies had to be managed prior to the 1880s.

At the end of summer 1945, the whole of the mains in the town were sounded at night and some leaks were found. However, increased consumption in the High Level area was attributed to the very large number of people still occupying the Prisoner of War and Labour Camp at East Cams.

By September 1945, the new Water Act had passed through the House of Commons and, once the Minister had granted the necessary Order in 1946, commercial premises could be compulsorily metered. The Water Act 1945 standardised certain aspects of water industry practice that remain in place today, such as:

- All new service pipes from the boundary of premises to the main had to be laid by the Undertaker and the cost could be recovered from the person requiring the supply.

- Repairs to service pipes were to be carried out by the Undertaker at its expense.

- The Undertaker was to fix a stopcock on every new service pipe and could do so on existing service pipes.

- The Undertaker was to connect and disconnect all meters.

- The Undertaker could require the provision of a separate service pipe for each house.

It was not until 1948 that the UDC's efforts in metering commercial properties and detecting leaks brought some reduction in the amount of water supplied. The average daily consumption for 1948 was 845,000 gallons, compared to 902,000 gallons in 1947. Even then, the fall in consumption was accounted for largely by the vacation of the Prisoner of War and Labour Camp at East Cams.

During dry weather in June 1949, 1,087,000 gallons were pumped, the highest ever recorded in one day, and this prompted further calls for voluntary restrictions and increased waste detection. The problem was clearly widespread, because in January 1950 came the publication of a Ministry of Health report into the causes of the increase in consumption of water across the whole country.

The Surveyor, Harry Privett, suggested that much water was wasted by running hot taps until the cold water had cleared and that, in his view, there had been a slackening in the pace of improvements to domestic water systems. Therefore, it was decided that plumbing work in the UDC area should only be carried out by authorised plumbers and a list of these was prepared and issued.

Efforts throughout 1950 in checking for waste and defective private water fittings helped to bring average daily consumption in that year down to 782,000 gallons, a reduction of over 80,000 gallons per day on 1949. The reduction was also due to the wetter weather that year and the lower consumption that resulted from Southern Co-operative Laundries Ltd in Gudge Heath Lane using its own borehole from May 1950.

The 1950s - Amalgamation looms as Development puts more pressure on Supplies

In April 1951, the Ministry of Local Government & Planning sent the UDC a summary of a recent survey of water supplies in the Hampshire area. It asked the UDC to consult with other water undertakers about the practicability of mergers or amalgamations. Fareham UDC formed part of the Ministry's South-East Hampshire Area, comprising Portsmouth, Gosport, Fareham, Havant & Waterloo and Droxford. No positive moves towards any amalgamation were made at that stage, although the Portsmouth and Gosport companies were to merge in 1955.

Further Housing and Commercial Development - and the need for still more Improvements!

In the early 1950s, new housing on the Uplands and Heathfield Estates reversed the falling trend in demand, as did a request in 1952 from Schweppes to increase the existing supply of 2,000 gph to its factory in Broadcut, Wallington (the site being occupied by Sainsbury's in 2007), to at least 3,500 gph.

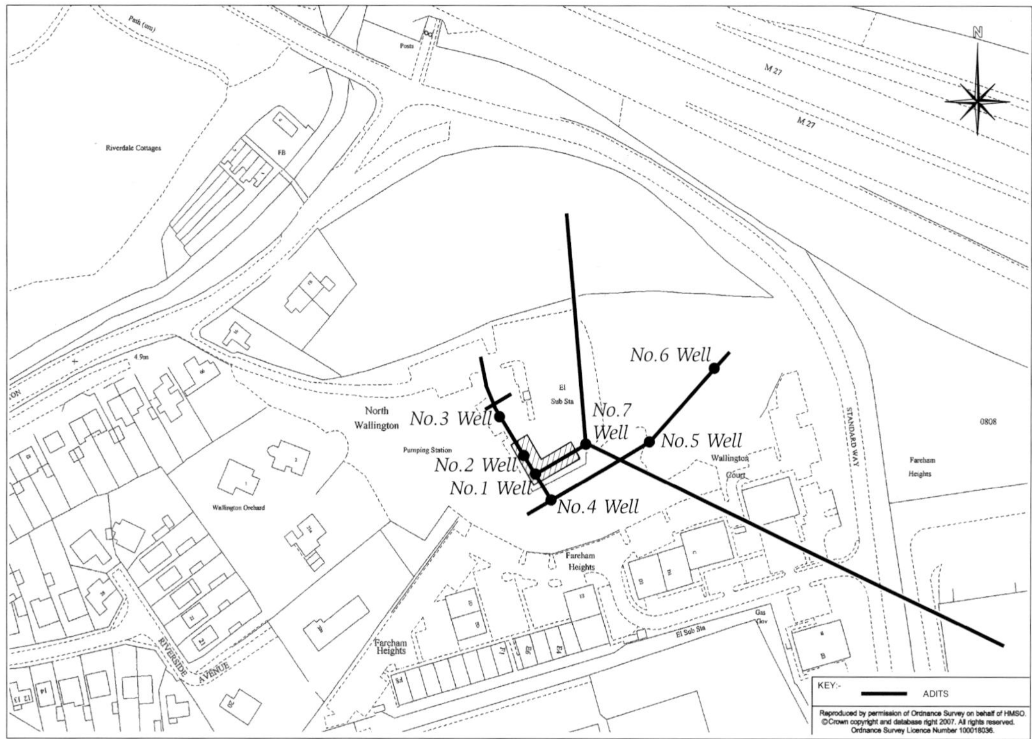

Plan of wells and adits at Maindell

In 1953, housing development continued apace in Fareham on sites at the Blackbrook and Heathfield estates, Highlands Road, Hoeford Close and Highfield Avenue. It was abundantly clear that yet more extensions to the whole supply and distribution system would be needed. Consultants Herbert Lapworth Partners devised a scheme comprising:

a) A 15-inch borehole 420 ft deep in the base of well no. 7 at Maindell. This borehole was intended to tap an additional supply to augment the yield from the wells and adits.

b) A new 12-inch main between Maindell Pumping Station and Portsdown Reservoir.

c) A 12-inch main (reducing to 9-inch) from the new 12-inch pumping main, westwards through Fareham to connect with existing mains in Highlands Road, near Catisfield, to improve distribution pressures.

d) Two new submersible pumps in the new borehole in No. 7 well, serving the High and Low Levels.

By the autumn, the Heathfield development was under way; Schweppes was requesting an increase in its supply to 8,000 gph and Knowle Hospital an increase in its supply to 2,000 gph - yet more upward pressure on demand.

In February 1957, the Ministry consented to the installation of further machinery at Maindell and the laying of distribution mains, at a total cost of £49,850. The Minister recommended that tenders be invited as soon as possible, owing to the serious lowering of water pressure caused by the increased amount of house building in recent years.

The 1950s pump motors at Maindell

Approval was given by the Ministry on the understanding that arrangements were made at Maindell:

a) To prevent the water level being lowered to more than 20 ft below sea level, as proposed by Herbert Lapworth Partners.

b) For the regular determination of the chloride ion content as a means of checking for saline infiltration from the sea.

c) To consider a regular system for the detection and remedy of waste and the installation of one or more waste meters, while informing the Minister of progress "since effectiveness in the control of waste was a necessary factor to be considered by him in approving any further proposals for improving the Undertaking."

Owing to the dry weather from May 1957 onwards, consumption increased to the point where many consumers, especially in the western district most remote from the waterworks, were without sufficient water or pressure from time to time. As a result of press notices, touring the district with loudspeakers and writing to people seen to be using hoses without permission, consumption dropped and it was not necessary to ration consumers, turn off the supply or forbid the use of garden hoses. However, there was a record number of applications for garden hose permits, providing additional income which would otherwise have been lost!

Meanwhile, the improvement works recommended by Herbert Lapworth began at Maindell. The contract for a submersible pump in the new borehole was let to the Harland Engineering Co Ltd, of Alloa. In December 1958, the Low Level pumping unit was complete and the High Level unit was fitted early in the new year. New 12-inch and 9-inch mains to and from Portsdown Reservoir were put into service on 8th December 1958, resulting in a considerable increase in the pressure of water to the Catisfield and Hill Park areas.

In April 1959, the two new submersible pumps at Maindell were started up for testing and flushing out. The pumps finally came into service just in time to help deal with the water shortages arising during the 1959 drought. At the same time, the practice of chloramination, introduced in 1937, was discontinued and replaced by chlorination. During the summer months of 1959, both new submersible pumps were running almost continuously. In the evenings, when gardens were being watered, demand actually exceeded pumping capacity, but was met by drawing down the service reservoirs. In July 1959, a record quantity of water, 43.7 million gallons, was pumped in the month, equivalent to more than 1.4 million gallons per day. It was necessary to pump most evenings to keep the reservoirs as full as possible. However, the recent new works enabled the undertaking to maintain uninterrupted supplies at good pressure, albeit through long hours of pumping.

Life in the Fareham UDC water undertaking in the 1950s

In June 1953, Harry Privett, the Engineer & Surveyor, retired after 26 years in the post. He was succeeded by his deputy, Keith Trask, who had his old boss looking over his shoulder once again when Harry Privett was elected as a Councillor and appointed to the Public Undertakings Committee a year later!

After an interview with Keith Trask, the late Roy Etherington joined Fareham UDC water undertaking in May 1957 as an Assistant Water Inspector (after amalgamation he worked for the Portsmouth Company until he retired in 1994). He recalled the strange and amusing things that happened during his everyday duties. “I remember calling at a house to repair a ball valve, only to find that the elderly lady resident wasn’t worried too much about the repair, but her old mother had just fallen out of bed and could I put her back in bed please!”

Norman Trivett, who was Water Inspector from 1957, remembers one occasion when he and Roy Etherington were despatched to isolate a main at Wallington Reservoir in order for a connection to be made. “We had no radios in those days and we had to get around the town on bikes. So it wasn’t until several hours later that we found out we had closed the wrong valve at Wallington and the whole of the Fareham Low Level Zone was without water! We quickly returned to the site to open up the valve and restore supplies. The next day, we were sent back again, this time to uncover the correct valves, which were hidden under a mass of undergrowth!” Norman Trivett went on to become Distribution Manager for Portsmouth and Havant, retiring in 1990.

Amalgamation with the Portsmouth and Gosport Water Company

In June 1955, the question of water undertaking consolidation once again came to the fore. At Portsmouth and Gosport Water Company’s (PGWC) suggestion, Fareham UDC held a meeting with it to discuss a possible amalgamation. The meeting was inconclusive and the UDC subsequently wrote to Portsmouth, saying that it did not feel that an amalgamation would be in the public interest at present.

In October 1955, PGWC wrote asking if the UDC was now prepared to give further consideration to amalgamating the two undertakings. Negotiations then plodded slowly onwards and, in March 1957, PGWC requested an exchange of financial and engineering information. The Ministry began to take an increased interest in the proposed amalgamation between the Portsmouth and Fareham undertakings and wrote in April 1957 asking the UDC for the history of the negotiations and its reasons for objecting.

In November 1957, a letter was received from PGWC setting out the general principles that were usually followed for the re-grouping of undertakings. By June 1958, the Treasurer had supplied PGWC with all the financial information requested and the Fareham Engineer & Surveyor had met PGWC's Engineer to discuss the engineering aspects. Finally, in January 1959, PGWC tabled its detailed offer for the UDC undertaking, the terms being:

- The UDC was to remain responsible for all outstanding loan charges.
- PGWC would take into employment six of the current staff.
- PGWC would pay the agreed value of any stores held at transfer.
- PGWC would pay a cash sum equal to the debt of the UDC undertaking at 31st March 1959, plus £27,500.
- For the first five years, domestic water rates were to be 50% in excess of Portsmouth charges, for the next five years 25% in excess, and thereafter the same.
- PGWC would repay all capital expenditure, beyond the loan debt at 31st March 1957, incurred by the UDC with the Company's consent, up to the date of transfer.

The UDC decided to accept these terms and the amalgamation with PGWC came into effect on 1st October 1959.

STATUTORY INSTRUMENTS

1959 No. 1594

WATER, ENGLAND AND WALES

The Portsmouth and Gosport Water Order, 1959

Made - - - - *11th September,* 1959
Coming into Operation *1st October,* 1959

The Minister of Housing and Local Government in exercise of his powers under subsection (1) of section 9, and sections 23 and 33 of the Water Act, 1945(a), and of all other powers enabling him in that behalf, hereby orders as follows:—

PART I

PRELIMINARY

Citation and commencement.

1.—(1) This order may be cited as the Portsmouth and Gosport Water Order, 1959, and shall come into operation on the 1st day of October, 1959.

(2) The Portsmouth and Gosport Water Acts and Orders 1857 to 1955 and this order may be cited together as the Portsmouth and Gosport Water Acts and Orders, 1857 to 1959.

Division of Order into Parts.

2. This order is divided into Parts as follows:—
Part I—Preliminary.
Part II—Transfer of undertaking.
Part III—Limits of supply and powers.
Part IV—Additional capital.
Part V—Miscellaneous.

Interpretation.

3. In this order, unless the context otherwise requires—

"the Company" means the Portsmouth and Gosport Water Company;

"the Company's undertaking" means the undertaking of the Company as from time to time authorised;

"the Council" means the urban district council of Fareham;

"the day of transfer" means the first day of October, 1959;

"the existing Acts and Orders" means the Portsmouth and Gosport Water Acts and Orders 1857 to 1955;

"the Fareham undertaking" means the water undertaking of the Council as existing on the day of transfer and described in the First Schedule to this order;

"the added limits" means the area described in the Second Schedule to this order;

"the existing limits" means the limits within which the Company are authorised to supply water under the existing Acts and Orders;

(a) 8 & 9 Geo. 6. c. 42.

[H.L.G. 8042]

The water tower in London Road, Bognor (Lithograph by James Akerman, London)

Water Supplies in Bognor Regis

Until the second half of the 19th century, the population of Bognor Regis and surrounding villages obtained its water from much the same sources as it had done for centuries past – garden wells, village wells or wells on private estates.

However, with the coming of the railway in the 1860s and the concept of day trips or holidays to the seaside, the summer population of the Bognor Regis area increased and the limitations of the local water supplies became quite apparent, both in terms of quantity and the salty taste that resulted from the proximity of some of these wells to the sea.

The Bognor Water Company 1874 - 1929

In order to improve matters, in 1871 and with an initial capital of £6,000, five local people promoted a company to supply water to Bognor, South Bersted and Felpham. They were Rev A Conder of Middleton-on-Sea, Dr Thompson, Mr Lovett, proprietor of the Bognor Observer, Alfred Long, a chemist, and Mr Yarnell, who was a grocer and house agent. A further £4,000 was raised, but the necessary statutory powers were not granted to the Company until 1874, by which time the population of Bognor was around 3,000.

On 3rd July 1874, the first meeting of the Bognor Water Company took place, with Alfred Long in the chair. Its offices were at Aston House, now long gone, in the High Street. A public subscription for shares at £1 each met with some success and soon work was able to start on the Company's first source of supply. Under the supervision of Mr J Grover, a well six feet in diameter was sunk to a depth of 80 feet on a site located in London Road. Owing to unstable ground, the first 30 feet were lined with bolted cast iron segments but, below that, the clays and gravels were firm enough to permit the remainder of the well to be lined with bricks. From the bottom of the well, a borehole was sunk a further 120 ft into the underlying chalk, but after disappointing test pumping results, the borehole was deepened to 330 ft below ground level.

The borehole must have penetrated substantial water-bearing strata when it was deepened, because water suddenly rose to within 20 feet of the surface. More test pumping was carried out over six days with a steam-driven pump and the average quantity abstracted was 150,000 gallons per day, well in excess of what was then needed.

Financial Difficulties

The Board therefore proceeded to let contracts for the construction of a water tower in London Road, designed by local architect Arthur Smith, and the laying of water mains. However the work was bedevilled by the bankruptcy of three contractors employed in the construction and by a shortage of capital. Archie Ford, one of several engineers who had succeeded Mr Grover, wrote to the Company: "Having been concerned as your Engineer for over two years without receiving any payment for my services and expenses, I must request you to send me a cheque for one hundred guineas." The Company's reply was not encouraging: "At the present time there is no money in hand to pay you but, when in due course the works get under way, we will probably be able to pay you."

It was not until 1879 that the Company could celebrate the opening of its works with a public dinner and, even then, its straitened finances meant that its existence remained precarious, for few people actually took up the opportunity to connect their houses to the new water mains. The local Board of Health suggested to the Company that communal tanks should be placed for the public to obtain water, and the first such tank, made of riveted iron sheets, was erected in Waterloo Square. Water was then sold by Company employees at a rate of one old penny per bucket and three old pennies per churn, costing more in 1879 than it does in 2007!

The Company's financial state improved gradually as the number of connections to the mains grew. Fire hydrants were installed around the town and the Company provided metered supplies to commercial users.

The Problems of Saline Intrusion

In 1881, a serious problem came to light. Water from the well had been under suspicion for some time because of a salty taste. A sample of the water was analysed by the laboratory at Oxford University and the results showed a salt content of 102.76 grains per gallon. The cause of the salinity was the lowering of the water table by pumping, to the extent that sea water was infiltrating the aquifer and tainting the supplies.

An urgent search now began for a replacement source. In 1884, a borehole was sunk to a depth of more than 400 feet on a site at South Bersted, but test pumping soon showed that water from this borehole was also prone to saline infiltration.

Lingering financial difficulties were probably behind the Company's decision in 1885 to advertise, without success, rooms for rent within the four storeys of office space beneath the water tower. However, in 1891, a further Act (the Bognor Water Act 1891) received Parliamentary approval and, in effect, dissolved the old company and created a new one of the same name. The new company had capital of £50,000 and its limits of supply were Bognor Regis, South Bersted, Felpham, Boxgrove, Eartham, Aldingbourne, Slindon, Oving, Tangmere, Eastergate, Walberton, North Mundham, Merston, Pagham, Barnham, Middleton-on-Sea and Tortington. Whilst these parishes represented the legal limits of the Company's supply area, some of them would not actually receive mains water for many years. The Bognor Water Act 1891 also authorised the Company to construct a new well and pumping station in a field on the border of Merston and Oving parishes and to connect with the existing mains network on the Bognor to Chichester road.

Unfortunately the site at Merston, along with others at Mundham and Drayton, produced water that was either saline or of insufficient quantity. Consequently, for a while, the people of Bognor had to accept the salty taste of their water.

A Successful Source at last

It was clear that drinking water with a salty taste would not be tolerated indefinitely. The contractor for the 1893 trial boring at Drayton was Messrs Docwra, a name still prominent in water industry contracting in 2007. They appear to have impressed the Bognor Board and its Engineer, Edward Brown, sufficiently to be retained to give an opinion on other potential sites for a water source. Docwra examined one at Elbridge Farm on the Chichester Road and another on land owned by William Collins at Fontwell, on the lower incline of the South Downs. They considered that the Elbridge Farm site was likely to be brackish and therefore recommended that the Board should first investigate the Fontwell site, with a view to purchasing it. They also considered that, for the necessary service reservoir, the Board should buy another plot owned by Mr Collins next to the Balls Hut Inn, just east of the junction of the Arundel Road with Fontwell Avenue. The site chosen for the water source investigations at Fontwell was adjacent to the site of the future racecourse, on the west side of what is now Fontwell Avenue.

In September 1893, work proceeded to sink a well with a borehole in the base, but it produced a very limited amount of water. In a somewhat courageous move, the Company then sunk another well and borehole, only nineteen feet from the first one, this time finding a copious amount of water in the chalk despite being so close to a poorly-yielding borehole. The second well and borehole is still in use today at what is now known as Eastergate Pumping Station.

The sinking of No.1 well and borehole at Fontwell (Eastergate), 1891

Eastergate Pumping Station, c1913

Almost 100 years later in 1992, a closed-circuit television survey by Portsmouth Water of the second borehole showed that all the water enters it from a series of holes in a narrow flinty band in the chalk at a depth of 58 metres (190 feet, just 10 feet above the bottom of the borehole). As there were no other water-bearing fissures in the very solid chalk wall of the borehole, the Company was fortunate to have been so successful just a few metres away from the first borehole, which presumably had no such holes!

So successful was the new borehole that when groundwater levels in the South Downs chalk were high, the borehole became artesian, water rising to ground level under the natural pressure in the aquifer. Whilst the water would normally have been constrained by the clay layers covering the chalk in the Eastergate area, once the clay had been 'punctured' by the borehole, out came the water! The road and nearby farmland were quickly flooded and water soon reached Collins' store at Eastergate Square. The borehole had to be hastily capped off, as construction of the permanent pumping station did not begin until 1894, once the Bognor Water Company had finally purchased the land. It would be reasonable speculation that the name Fontwell might have originated from an early artesian well nearby.

The new reservoir at Balls Hut was constructed at the same time as the Fontwell source; and like any service reservoir, its purpose was to even out peaks and troughs in demand, as well as to minimise pumping and provide stand-by storage in the event of temporary pump failure. Bognor now had a plentiful and fresh-tasting water supply, which would last for many years.

The Lead Plug

The only serious problem remaining after the opening of the Fontwell source was the flooding that occurred when groundwater levels rose in winter. Frank Martin, who succeeded Edward Brown as Engineer to the Bognor Water Company in 1912, devised a solution to the problem. He conceived the idea of a large, tapered lead plug that could be lowered from a gantry into the mouth of the borehole, located 80 feet below on the floor of the well. By raising and lowering the plug, its tapered shape permitted the

The lead plug mould, c1913

yield from the borehole to be varied to suit demand and therefore prevent flooding. This plug was cast on the site and Frank Martin took a number of photographs of it.

At the beginning of winter, the plug would be lowered about 10 inches to throttle the borehole outflow. It would be raised again in the spring, as the flow from underground receded. The square steel supporting shaft had its top end rounded and threaded, and a large nut on it held the plug on its staging. To lower or raise the plug, the nut would be turned by a large spanner. The plug was still in position when Portsmouth Water took over the Bognor undertaking in 1963. In fact it was not removed until 1986, when the old Eastergate Pumping Station buildings were demolished and replaced with a single new building.

The removal of the lead plug at Eastergate, 1986. Left to right: Ian Smith, Tom Reynolds, Pete Bridger and Dave Cross

The lead plug began its life as the saviour of the Eastergate source, but years later was identified as the culprit behind a restricted water yield. Alan Twort, who began his engineering career at Bognor in 1938, recalls that, by that time, demand from Bognor was beginning to outstrip supply. The Engineer at that time, Harold Lea, was considering a new source in Eartham and Alan remembers surveying the site in 1940, at the time the Battle of Britain was starting. However, the Bognor Waterworks undertaking (by then part of Bognor Regis UDC) was saved the substantial expenditure on a new source and pipelines by the canny knowledge of Alfred Wilkinson, who had been appointed Engineer in 1944 in succession to Lea.

Alan Twort remembers clearly what happened in 1945: "The new Engineer, Alfred Wilkinson, had been trained at the pump manufacturers Hathorn Davey, and had come to Bognor because he'd heard there was a prospect of building a new water scheme there. However, he was puzzled by the pumping characteristics of the well. Nobody could explain to him the characteristics of the plug and so he decided to remove it; this was not so easy because it was formed of lead, weighed several tons and was about seven feet long. When it was finally lifted enough to get it out of the borehole to rest on the well bottom, it proved to have such a slight taper that it had created a very narrow annular space between it and the borehole lining. Even when in its 'raised' position, it had severely restricted the flow from the borehole.

Wilkinson then set about testing the borehole again, but with the plug removed, and the result was that the pumping level only fell its usual amount of about 10 feet drawdown when pumping at a much higher rate of more than four million gallons per day - which was the maximum rate achievable by the pumps. The plug was replaced, but in future it was raised to a higher level when pumping, so as not to restrict the borehole output!

Wilkinson wrote a polite letter to Bognor UDC Waterworks Committee to tell them he would be looking for another job because he'd come to Bognor to build some new works, but he'd found they didn't need any! I don't remember whether they gave him a bonus for his efforts - but they should have done. He'd saved them many thousands of pounds!"

The Balls Hut Siphon

In July 1922, Frank Martin reported to the Board that he had doubts about the ability to provide an adequate water supply to the new racecourse at Fontwell, which was being developed. His misgivings were well-founded; in 1923, when the first race meeting was held, it attracted large crowds and pressure problems were soon created by the consequent large demand for water.

At the time, the only storage facility for water pumped from Eastergate was the 1894 service reservoir at Balls Hut. Although the reservoir held 500,000 gallons and its elevation was sufficient to give a good pressure in Bognor, some 100 feet lower, the racecourse experienced poor pressure because it was much closer in elevation to the reservoir. Martin therefore erected a standpipe that reached about 30 feet above the reservoir level and, during race meetings, water for the racecourse was pumped up and over this siphon to provide much improved pressure.

Balls Hut Reservoir and siphon
(Photo courtesy of the late Allan Pierce)

Working Life at Bognor Water Company in the early 20th Century

When he was first appointed Engineer in 1912, Frank Martin was provided with a house in London Road, next to the water tower; his Chief Inspector lived in a cottage nearby. Martin was given a bicycle to visit his 'patch' and in fact it was not until June 1923 that he received a somewhat faster mode of transport, in the form of a bull-nosed Morris car. His Chief Inspector, Mr Ford, had to make do with a motorcycle!

By the mid-1920s, the Fontwell Avenue works had become known as Eastergate Pumping Station. It had been enlarged, new engines had been installed and the demand from an ever-increasing population meant that the source was pumping an average of some 10 million gallons of water per month. By this time, the water tower in London Road was being used principally as offices, but in the summer months the water tank itself was kept topped up in case of unforeseen or high demand. On the second floor, beneath the tank, was a room where the ganger, general hands and the tea boy were based. On the first floor of the water tower, the Inspector and an assistant had an office, while Frank Martin himself had his office on the ground floor, along with his clerk.

The daily working routine demanded that, by 7 am, all workmen should be out on the roads, wheeling their two-man hand trucks to carry out work in any part of the Company's area of supply. The trucks were loaded with sufficient tools and materials for all types of work, which of course was required to be done in all weathers. The jobs carried out varied from the excavation and laying of water mains and service pipes to indoor work, such as the rewashering of household taps. The men were expected to continue working on a job until it was complete; much of the time, they would be out until 6 or 7 pm and would count themselves lucky to be back in Bognor before 5.30 pm. Their average wage was 35 shillings (£1.75) per week. Horses and wagons were used to transport new water pipes after they had been delivered by rail to either Bognor or Barnham Station yards. It was not until the 1930s that hand trucks were completely superseded by motor transport.

Bognor Regis Urban District Council 1929 - 1963

In 1928, Bognor Regis Urban District Council (UDC) sought powers to take over the Company and, in 1929, duly succeeded, the transfer price being £74,653. To his disappointment, Frank Martin was made deputy to the Surveyor. Martin eventually retired from the Bognor UDC on 31st March 1934. His successor as Water Engineer & Manager was Albert Watkins, aged 34, from the Oxford Corporation Waterworks Department. However, Martin was retained in an advisory capacity for one year after his retirement, for a fee of 100 guineas.

In 1934, the water tower in London Road was demolished and, in 1935, a water depot was constructed on land to the rear of allotments in Hawthorn Road.

The Slindon Supply

The Slindon Waterworks Company was taken over by Bognor UDC on 25th March 1931, following an Act of Parliament of 1930 that empowered the UDC to purchase the Slindon Company on mutually agreeable terms. The total cost of the land, water supply assets and the undertaking itself was £7,557. The agreement included the purchase of land on Nore Hill to build another service reservoir for Bognor Regis, as outlined in the next section.

The Slindon Waterworks Company had been established in 1906 by the Leslie family, who lived at Slindon House (now Slindon College). Its registered office was at 16 Dover Street, Piccadilly, London. In the same year, the Company constructed a small borehole source and service reservoir to the north-

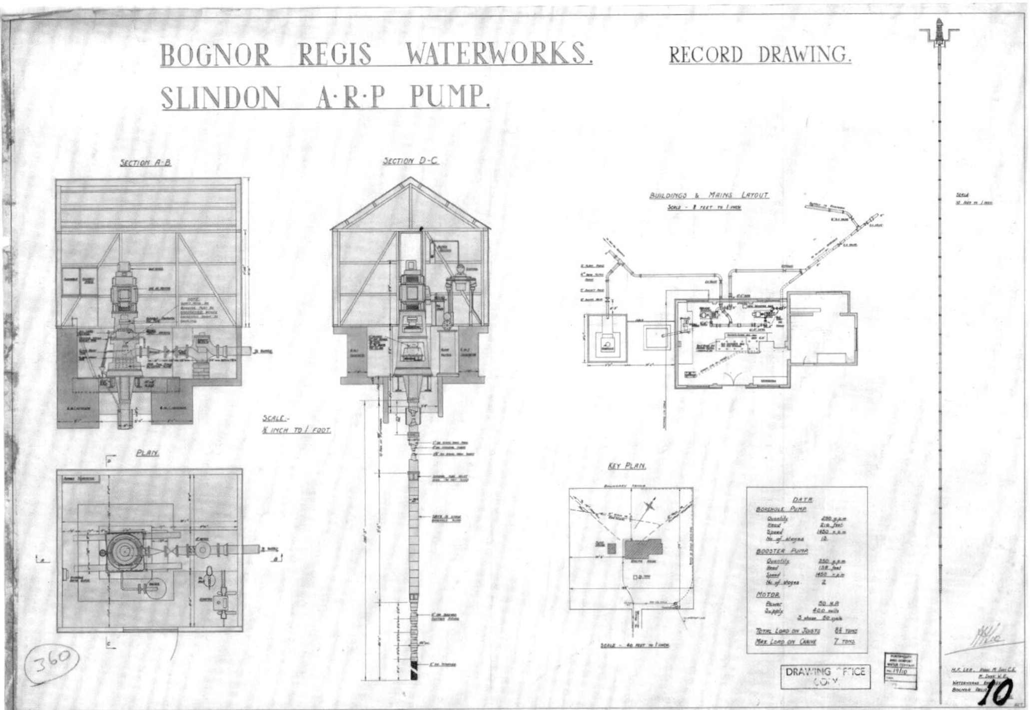

Drawing of new pump installed at Slindon Pumping Station for air raid precautions during the Second World War

west of Slindon village. The borehole was 12 inches in diameter, 400 feet deep and had an estimated yield of 3,000 gallons per hour. It was used to pump water along a 6-inch main to the service reservoir, located just behind The Folly on Nore Hill. This reservoir, holding 125,000 gallons of water, was designed by the consulting engineers Hampton & Sons Ltd, of Pall Mall, London. A separate 6-inch main was laid from the reservoir to supply the village of Slindon.

In the early 1940s, a gas engine was used to drive the pump. The local Waterworks Inspector for the Slindon area would use a blowlamp to heat up 'the bulb' of the engine to something approaching red-hot and then stand on the flywheel to turn the engine, after which it would invariably start easily!

More Improvements to the Supply during the 1930s

In 1932, a new service reservoir holding two million gallons of water was constructed at Nore Hill, one mile north-west of Slindon village, to supply Bognor Regis with water pumped from Eastergate. The Balls Hut Reservoir was taken out of service and, in addition, new 12-inch and 9-inch water mains were laid into Bognor. The Stanton Iron Works manufactured the pipes and Glenfield & Kennedy provided the valves. The works were designed and supervised for the UDC by the consulting engineers T & C Hawksley and the contractor for the reservoir construction was the Cumberland Reinforced Concrete Construction Company. At the Water Committee meeting of 6th December 1932, it was reported that Nore Hill Reservoir had first been filled with water on 24th November and that there were no leaks from it.

Alan Twort remembers his annoyance that Nore Hill Reservoir was built too high for Bognor Regis, so high in fact that a pressure reducing valve had to be installed at Eastergate village to prevent excessive pressures bursting mains and service pipes. This valve was not without its problems; Alan Twort recalls that the Chargehand at Eastergate Pumping Station frequently had to cycle down to Eastergate village to adjust the valve, which had stuck open!

Changes at the Top

After only two years, Albert Watkins left Bognor in 1936 to become Engineer at Chatham & District Water Company. Between 1936 and 1938, the Engineer at Bognor was Robert Burrow who, by all accounts, was not particularly popular. Alan Twort says: "I used to meet him rushing into the toilets at lunchtime to shave and put on a clean collar and tie to attend the Waterworks Committee in the afternoon. There were tales about his eccentricity. Allegedly he once quarrelled with the distribution foreman over which main was which, and they ended up having a bout of fisticuffs. Staff at Eastergate were reputed to have flown the Union Flag when they heard the news that he was leaving the UDC to work in Jersey!"

Harold Lea, Water Engineer, Bognor Regis, 1938-1944 (Photo courtesy of Alan Twort)

In 1938, Harold Lea was appointed as Water Engineer at Bognor, but he left in 1944 to become Water Engineer & Manager at Halifax.

Eastergate Pumping Station in the late 1930s

In late 1938, Alan Twort had transferred from the Treasurer's Department to the Waterworks Department at Bognor. 67 years later he was able to recall in detail the installation at Eastergate. The main engine used was a 6-cylinder Ruston diesel coupled to a direct current (DC) generator, which ran the main DC vertical spindle pump in No. 1 well. In the same well was a Sulzer diesel engine, direct-coupled via 90-degree gearing to a borehole pump. This was used as stand-by. The borehole pumps fed into a cascade aerator (for carbon dioxide removal), from which an electrically-driven, horizontal spindle pump delivered the water through a 'base exchange' water softening plant into a 'rise and fall' main just outside the station. This supplied Bognor, with any surplus water going up to fill Nore Hill Reservoir, mainly at night. The softening plant, installed in 1936 at a cost of £10,750, was the pride and joy of Bognor Regis UDC, which gave it much publicity as being a benefit to all domestic users and visitors to the town.

Following the 1937 typhoid outbreak at Croydon, the Ministry of Health advised water undertakings that chlorination should be practised on all underground supplies potentially liable to pollution. For this purpose, a contact tank had to be built at Eastergate so that superchlorination and dechlorination could be adopted. Alan Twort carried out the design of this tank and used it in support of his successful sitting of the Institution of Civil Engineers' examination.

The water softening plant at Eastergate

Harold Lea installed a third diesel engine in the building housing No. 2 well. It was an opposed six-cylinder Brush diesel engine driving a generator. It was not popular because it was noisy and one had to avoid its exhaust piping, which was at shoulder level with unprotected flanges. It had a speed-increasing gearbox, which Lea judged to be too noisy and called back its manufacturers in an effort to reduce the noise. In addition, the outer shaft driving the generator had such a heavy flywheel that the flexing of the shaft (which was around 6 inches in diameter) cracked the concrete pedestal holding the outer bearing.

Alan Twort remembers: "No mobile cranes were readily available in those days, so when the Brush engine, weighing many tons, was delivered, it had to be off-loaded and transported along the gravel path and round the back of the pumping station, and up on to its foundations manually, using baulks of timber and rollers. It took a whole day, but Harry, the distribution foreman, a splendidly competent chap, managed it without incident.

The cylinder heads seemed to 'jump outwards' visibly at each firing. The Ruston engine serving No. 1 well was less noisy, but it often had to run from 6 am to 11 pm to meet the summer water demand. One of the attendants had to be moved to other work after he went up to the chargehand and maintained that the engines were saying "Jesus Christ, Jesus Christ ..."!"

The No. 2 well was in an annex to the main building that housed No. 1 well and the Ruston and Sulzer engines. In this annex, there was a staging made of joists, supported on four iron columns, forming a platform about 8 feet above No. 2 well. From this staging, a steel shaft hung down into No. 2 well, at the end of which was the lead plug described earlier, which entered the top lining of the 24-inch borehole protruding into the base of the well.

The Second World War

The area around Bognor Regis witnessed much activity during the Battle of Britain. One incident serves to illustrate the resourcefulness of local water undertakings in maintaining supplies in extreme conditions. In summer 1940, a German bomb landed directly on the bridge over the Aldingbourne Rife between South Bersted and Shripney, destroying it. This bridge not only carried the main road, but also the 12-inch and 9-inch water mains supplying much of Bognor. While a restricted supply to the town was available from the Felpham direction, hurried consultations occurred between Harold Lea and his staff.

Eventually a worker, who had once been employed by the Selsey Tramway, suggested that redundant tramway bridge girders that still spanned the canal at Hunston should be moved up to the Rife. The idea was accepted gratefully, clearance was obtained to remove this bridge and a local haulier was engaged for the painstaking task of transporting the girders, hauled by draught horses, over a 24-hour period. At the Rife crossing, meanwhile, concrete pads had been constructed. Using a crane borrowed from the nearby gasworks, the girders were laid over the Rife and the replacement sections of 12-inch and 9-inch mains were erected and strapped to the girders, restoring full supplies.

Post-War Problems

Edward Bacchus succeeded Alfred Wilkinson as Waterworks Engineer & Manager in 1949. He remained in charge of the Bognor Regis UDC Waterworks undertaking until 1961. His successor, Clifford Teale, remained in post until the takeover by PGWC in 1963.

In 1949, the dry summer led the UDC to impose a ban on the use of water for watering gardens or washing cars for three months from July 4th.

The old Eastergate Pumping Station building, just prior to demolition in 1986

On one occasion, in 1950, Bognor Regis experienced an unpleasant taste in its water, rather reminiscent of the problems of taste that had bedevilled the supplies prior to 1894. The 1936 softening plant relied for its process on rock salt from Cheshire and an imported mineral known as Zeolite[1]. By this time, rock salt and Zeolite were becoming more expensive, so the Council tried out a synthetic substitute for the latter. In reaction with chlorine, the substitute compound generated an unpleasant taste like disinfectant. The softening plant was rapidly taken out of service, mains had to be flushed and staff

[1] Zeolites are natural minerals that are very porous, and this property enables them to be used widely in industrial processes, one of which, ion exchange, was used to soften the water at Bognor.

were sent out in vans around the district to advise against drinking the water. By 1960, the softening plant had become unreliable and, after one period of three or four weeks of non-operation of the plant, the chairman of the Waterworks Committee, Mr Reginald Martin, pointed out that in this period there had only been one complaint about the harder water and that had come, not surprisingly, from the local laundry! Soon afterwards the cost of running the softening plant and the need for expensive refurbishment led to the decision to cease softening the supplies.

In 1952, a number of locations for potentially productive additional boreholes were examined in a report submitted to Bognor UDC by Henry Milner, of the Geophysical Laboratories, Wembley. The need for a new source was being considered owing to the still-growing population and the desirability of a stand-by source for Eastergate. The recommended site for further investigation was at the eastern end of Boxgrove village, immediately north of the A27 road. Drilling of this borehole proceeded during the autumn and winter of 1954/55; the depth was 300 feet but, although an apparently promising fissure was struck during the drilling, when test pumping started, the pumps lost suction after only 15 minutes – in other words they had 'run out of water' and the trial borehole was a failure. In the late 1950s, other unsuccessful attempts to find a new source were made at Park Bottom, north-west of Arundel, and again at Boxgrove.

A New Reservoir

A remodelling of the Bognor Regis water supply was carried out in 1957, when a new service reservoir was built at the northern end of Littleheath Road. The contractor was Campbell & McGill of Winchester, whose tender price was £46,035 13s 1d. Water from Eastergate, instead of being pumped to Nore Hill Reservoir, was now diverted to the new Littleheath Reservoir along an 18-inch main laid by A L J Davis (Public Works) Ltd of Chichester. Nore Hill Reservoir was henceforth supplied by booster pumps located at Eastergate and provided water only to the lower part of the local area, with Slindon Reservoir continuing to supply the higher part. The new reservoir at Littleheath was built at a level 85 feet lower than Nore Hill. Thus the pressures in Bognor Regis were reduced to a more practical level, which nonetheless provided an adequate service to the population.

The Final Years of Independence

In October 1956, the residents of Slindon and Eartham had to boil their water before use for several days. The problem was contamination of the Slindon Reservoir, where rainwater passing through the soil covering the roof had seeped into the reservoir itself through a minute crack in the reinforced concrete roof. While repairs and sterilisation took place, the villages were supplied by direct pumping into the distribution mains. There was criticism in the local press that the problem might have been found earlier had the UDC not decided to cease the practice of duplicate water sampling and analysis seven months previously.

By the late 1950s, the austerity of the immediate post-war years had receded and the economy was growing. The Bognor undertaking, like many others, was finding it increasingly difficult to fund the improvements necessary to meet the steeply rising demand for water. At that time there were, in fact, a myriad of water undertakings, some large but many (like Bognor) being small.

A welcome success for the Bognor Regis UDC undertaking came in 1962 with the drilling of a trial 24-inch borehole, 250 feet deep, on a site adjacent to Westergate Woods, half a mile east of Fontwell racecourse. The trial followed an unsuccessful attempt in 1960 to find additional water with two trial boreholes at Eastergate. However, the Westergate borehole proved to have a yield of some 2½ million gallons per day and these results, having exceeded all expectations, led to the drilling of a second 24-inch borehole nearby. The contractor for the scheme was George Stow & Co Ltd. This source was eventually developed as Westergate Pumping Station by Portsmouth Water Company and brought into service in 1968.

The late George Slater remembered the period leading up to the takeover of the Bognor Regis undertaking by Portsmouth. He recalled that, in the late 1940s, the Ministry of Health had dispatched various engineering inspectors around the country to prepare reports on the state of the many water undertakings that existed at that time. For West Sussex, the Inspector proposed that a new Water Board should be established to take over the undertakings of Chichester Corporation, Chichester Rural District Council, Selsey Water Company and Bognor UDC. The new Water Board was to be called the 'Regnum Board'. Nothing happened in this direction until 1963, when the Chairman of the Bognor Regis UDC water undertaking realised that, if the Board was formed, it would take over the debts of the various water undertakings in the Regnum area. He therefore proposed the sale of the undertakings to PGWC. This was effected in 1963, at a cost of £2 million.

Thus it was that, on 1st October 1963, there ended a 92-year period of independence for the Bognor Regis water undertaking.

Chichester Corporation's Water Supply

Apart from wells and a somewhat intermittent supply available from the River Lavant, the first piped water supply to Chichester is believed to have been laid by the Romans. Fragments of earthenware pipes suggest that water was drawn from a source at the Broyle, outside the North Gate, where there was possibly a Roman summer camp.[1]

Much later, in the early 19th century, it was recorded that Chichester had a plentiful water supply, drawn from wells and also from a spring source at the Broyle, from which water was conveyed by pipes to a large underground reservoir in South Street.[2]

Alfred Burgess, then Engineer & Manager of Chichester Corporation Water Department, carried out an investigation into this early water supply from the Broyle in 1952. He identified the sources of supply as two chambers with arched brick roofs, both near what is now the Bishop Otter Campus of Chichester University.

An excavation in College Lane revealed a lead junction pipe where the supplies from the two chambers came together. Further excavations in Oaklands Park and Priory Park traced a lead pipe (later dated to the 17th century) on a straight line between College Lane and the junction of Priory Road with St Martin's Street, a distance of 700 yards. Access to the east chamber (north of the Bishop Otter Campus) was gained by excavating around its projecting arched brick roof to reveal a removable stone slab. The water level was lowered by pumping and the inside of the chamber was inspected by Dr A E Wilson FSA, who concluded that it was not of Roman construction. The walls, built mainly of flint, were founded on heavy timbers.[3]

The Chichester Water Company 1873 - 1897

In the late 19th century, the need for a safe public water supply for Chichester was given greater importance than in some other places by its poor public health record, which was among the worst in the country, especially in relation to typhoid. This was caused by the location of agricultural markets, contaminated wells and a lack of main drainage.[4]

[1] *Memorials of Chichester* by Mackenzie Walcott (1865).
[2] *History of Chichester* by Alexander Hay (1804).
[3] Report by Alfred Burgess to Chichester Corporation Sewerage and Waterworks Committee, 14th November 1952.
[4] *The Story of Chichester* by Dr Philip MacDougall (Sutton Publishing, 2004).

The system of private local wells, combined with a spring supply stored in the South Street reservoir, served the inhabitants and businesses of Chichester until the late 19th century. By this time, larger-scale water supplies were being established around the country to improve public health. In 1873, the Chichester Waterworks Act authorised the formation of the Chichester Water Company, to be responsible for the public water supply in the City of Chichester and the surrounding parishes of Bosham, New Fishbourne, Oving, Rumboldswyke, Mid Lavant and Westhampnett.

The capital of the new company was £20,000, in 2,000 shares of £10 each. The original Directors were William Tenney Bradley, William Duke, Charles Stanley Osborne, William Smith and Charles Anthony Swainson. The Act gave the Company powers to construct:

- A well, shaft, engines, pumps and engine house situated in the parish of Bosham at or near certain springs or pond on the south side of the highway leading from Chichester to Portsmouth.

- Line of pipes from the pumping station through all or some of the parishes listed earlier.

- A service tank or reservoir with valve house and water tower, buildings and accessories adjacent to the access road leading to New Broyle Farm.

The site of the well and springs was in Fishbourne village (then in the parish of Bosham) and this site remains in use today as a water supply source and treatment works.

The Fishbourne Pumping Station foundation stone

In 1874, the Chichester Water Company sank the Fishbourne No. 1 well and completed the East Engine House. The well was 47 feet deep, the first 17 feet being lined with 9-inch brickwork and the remaining 30 feet with wrought iron cylinders. Water was found in large quantities at a depth of 26 feet and the maximum yield was reportedly up to 15,000 gph. At that time, the pumps were driven by steam. A service reservoir and water tower were also constructed near New Broyle Farm, the site, now developed for housing, being north of no.95 Broyle Road.

These developments in water supply were, however, not enough to prevent an outbreak of typhoid in Chichester in 1878, believed to have been caused either by pollution in the River Lavant or by milk contaminated by water from the well at Moore's dairy. The impact was severe because only a small number of properties were connected to the new water supply and the wells that remained in use were at risk of contamination from human faecal matter. Improvements came when main drainage was laid in the City between 1893 and 1895, but nonetheless further outbreaks of typhoid occurred in the years leading up to the end of the century. This was of great concern not only to the residents of Chichester, but also to the Local Government Board, which appointed various inspectors to report on the outbreaks that occurred in 1878, 1896 and 1899. There were 108 deaths in Chichester from typhoid between 1870 and 1898, a rate four times the national average. In 1898, of the 2,570 houses in the city, 1,705 received a piped water supply, but 865 still relied on wells.[5]

[5] From a note by Alfred Burgess, Engineer & Manager, Chichester Corporation Water Department.

The ceremonial laying of the foundation stone at Fishbourne, 1874

Chichester Corporation 1897 - 1963

The high incidence of typhoid was believed to be linked to the very slow rate at which properties were connecting to a mains water supply. This led to Chichester Corporation taking over the supply from Chichester Water Company under the Chichester Corporation Water Act 1897. In addition to the city of Chichester itself and the parishes already supplied, the Corporation became responsible for water supply to 13 parishes, these being Donnington, Appledram, Birdham, Earnley, Hunston, Sidlesham, Selsey, West Itchenor, West Wittering, East Wittering, Funtington, West Dean and Singleton. Of course, it was many years before some of these parishes actually received a public water supply; for instance, West Dean and Singleton did not have a public mains supply until 1954, relying until then on wells and the private supply owned by the West Dean Estate.

Among its various provisions, the 1897 Act required the Corporation to pay the Chichester Water Company the sum of £47,597 1s 8d for its assets, plus interest and contributions. The Corporation accepted the Company's scheme to sink a new well at Fishbourne and enlarge the engine and boiler house.

Development of Fishbourne Pumping Station

Work on improving the Fishbourne source started promptly. In 1898, Fishbourne No. 2 well was sunk and the West Engine House was constructed, being fitted with a Simpson-Robby Compound pump with a capacity of 21,000 gph. This pumping set remained in use until 1923.

The new well was 120 feet deep, the first 16½ feet being lined with brickwork with cement and clay puddle and the next 50 feet with cast iron cylinders. Below that, the well was open to the chalk aquifer. In 1906, the average amount pumped daily was 250,000 gallons and the maximum was 400,000 gallons.

In 1900, a Simpson Triple-Expansion pumping engine (capacity 42,000 gph) was installed in the East Engine House and was connected to the well in the West Engine House. This pumping set was used until 1925 and scrapped in 1929. In 1907, the Fishbourne No. 1 well in the East Engine House was abandoned, but was not filled in until 1929.

In 1907 too, the Selsey Water Act authorised the formation of the Selsey Water Company, which relied upon a bulk supply of water from Chichester Corporation for distribution to Selsey, Sidlesham, Hunston and North Mundham.

Removal of piston from Blackstone engine, 1963. On the left is Tom Bridger

From the 1920s to the mid-1930s, Chichester Corporation Water Department continued to refurbish and expand the pumping capability at Fishbourne. In 1923, a Campbell gas engine and Cochrane 3-ram pump (capacity 45,000 gph) were installed in the West Engine House. This pumping set remained in use only until 1936, being replaced in that year by a 300 HP Blackstone oil engine and Pearn pump (capacity 80,000 gph). The 1923 Cochrane 3-ram pump was backed up by an electrically-driven Mather & Platt turbine pump installed in 1926. In 1930, the East Engine House was fitted with a 200 HP Blackstone oil engine and Worth-Mackenzie pump (capacity 65,000 gph). This saw considerably more service than the Cochrane pump in the West Engine House, finally being scrapped in 1963.

The Pearn pump at Fishbourne

There was a significant improvement in the supply of treated water to the Chichester area in 1927, when a service reservoir of 2 million gallons capacity was built on land next to Chalkpit Lane, to the north of the village of East Lavant. The contractor was Playfair Toole & Co, the designers were Mouchel & Partners and the Engineer was F J Lobley, the Surveyor to Chichester Corporation. The official opening of the new reservoir took place in May 1927, following which the original reservoir and water tower at Broyle Road were taken out of service, as the new reservoir at Lavant was of sufficient elevation to provide an adequate pressure to the whole of Chichester.

Inside the 1927 Lavant Reservoir

The Development of a New Source at Funtington

By the 1930s, it was becoming apparent that an additional source of water would be needed for Chichester as more houses were built and new businesses started up. The idea of developing a source at Funtington was first proposed by the long-serving City Surveyor, F J Lobley. In 1935, the Chichester Corporation Act granted rights to compulsorily purchase land and construct new works at Funtington. The rights were set to expire on certain dates and, as there was insufficient time to achieve these deadlines, a further bill was promoted to extend the time limits. It was eventually authorised by the Chichester Corporation Act 1938.

On 25th March 1938, the Corporation instructed its consultant, Sandford Fawcett, to prepare a specification for a trial borehole and well at Funtington. On 21st June, the contract was let to Le Grand, Sutcliff & Gill. On 13th March 1939, the yield from the trial borehole was reported as being 'ample for many years', as well as having a sufficient margin for a bulk supply to Chichester Rural District Council (RDC).

Further progress at Funtington was somewhat hampered by a second proposal for Chichester Corporation to take a bulk supply from the neighbouring Chichester RDC water undertaking, which had plans to develop a new source at Ellbridge Farm, adjacent to the River Ems at Aldsworth. However, terms for this bulk supply could not be agreed and, on 26th and 27th April 1938, the Ministry of Health held an inquiry into the alternative Ellbridge Farm and Funtington schemes. Following this inquiry, the Minister decided that the RDC's Ellbridge Farm scheme could not be justified and suggested that, instead, the Corporation should develop Funtington and provide a bulk supply to the RDC.

The Corporation could now proceed with the construction of a well, pumping station and pumping main at Funtington. The progress of the scheme was substantially slowed by the outbreak of the Second World War on 3rd September 1939.

Sandford Fawcett proceeded with the design of Funtington and, in September 1939, a contract for the Funtington borehole, shafts and adits, including a duplicate borehole, was let to Richardson, Timmins & Co. By April 1940, the 36-inch borehole had been sunk to a depth of 300 feet and Sandford Fawcett recommended that it should be connected to the 1938 14-inch trial borehole to maximise the yield. By November 1940, the 6-foot diameter winding shaft had been sunk and adits had been driven to the 12-inch and 36-inch boreholes.

Amid widespread fears of an invasion, protective measures had to be adopted for Lavant Reservoir, while the old Broyle Road Reservoir was adapted for use as an air raid shelter. In July 1940, the Corporation bought an emergency stock of mains couplings, standpipes and mains repair equipment. Cross-connections and valves were installed at Fishbourne and the fuel tanks for the pump engines were lowered and protected.

Preparations were also in hand for the laying of a new 15-inch main from Funtington to Lavant Reservoir. In May 1940, a contract for this work was let to C Firbank & Son and completed by November 1941. In normal times, the main would, of course, have been laid much more quickly, but deliveries of pipes were subject to major delays, owing to the high wartime demand for iron and the use of pipe factories for munitions manufacture.

In July 1940, a contract for the pumping house and cottage at Funtington was let to F E Smith of Grays, Essex. The contract was beset with problems - Smith did not begin work until February 1941, and immediately claimed additional payments owing to increases in costs and delays in starting. Although the west cottage at Funtington was completed in December 1941, there was a delay of several months before work started on the pumping station building itself. Eventually, in March 1944, Smith was expelled from the site and the construction of the pumphouse building was finally completed by the Corporation's own labour force on 9th March 1945.

Better progress was made with the underground works and, by 21st January 1941, the well had been lined to a depth of 46ft 8 inches below ground. In September 1942, further underground works were completed, increasing the yield to 2 million gallons per day. In March 1943, Messrs Hathorn Davey were awarded the contract for a 235 HP motor-driven borehole pump and, in the following September, Wallace & Tiernan won a contract for the disinfection equipment.

The official opening of Funtington Pumping Station, September 1946. Standing front, left to right: Alderman Burden, reporter, Alfred Burgess, reporter, Alderman Eastland, Alderman W H G Napper, The Mayor of Chichester (Alderman Herniman), The Chairman of Chichester RDC, Eric Banks (Town Clerk)

The first supplies of water were pumped from Funtington to Lavant Reservoir on 19th October 1945. The total cost of the construction of this, the first stage of development at Funtington, was around £48,000. Very good pumping results were achieved from Funtington in the abnormally hot week commencing 1st April 1946, when 12.9 million gallons were abstracted.

Funtington was officially opened by the Mayor of Chichester in a ceremony held at 3 pm on 12th September 1946. However, the Waterworks Committee's recommendation to spend £50 on a bronze plaque to commemorate the opening was refused by the full Council. The Waterworks Committee Chairman, Alderman W H G Napper,

Funtington Pumping Station, 1970s

offered to pay for it himself, but even then only four councillors voted in favour! The idea of a plaque was abandoned for the time being, but eventually one was erected and, in fact, retained in the new treatment works building when Portsmouth Water refurbished Funtington in 1998.

The Post-War Era

After the Second World War, economic conditions remained dire until well into the 1950s. Nonetheless, for the water industry, these were years when the luxury of a piped water supply was made available for the first time to a great many rural areas, helped by a new system under which councils and developers could requisition water mains under the Water Act 1945. At the same time, additional water resources and infrastructure were needed to meet the increasing demand for water, as the number of properties with a piped supply grew and industrial expansion began to take place.

Post-War Improvements at Fishbourne and Lavant

There were no further major improvements to the Fishbourne and Lavant Reservoir supply system until 1948. In that year, improvements were recommended by Herbert Lapworth Partners at Leggatt's Farm, near Fishbourne, to protect the Fishbourne source from pollution. As a result, a watertight container was installed for drainage from the cowshed, sewers were laid to serve cottages at the Black Boy public house and Leggatt's Farm, ponds at Leggatt's Farm Lane were filled in and a pig farm east of Leggatt's Farm Lane was closed. In 1949, the Corporation made a compulsory purchase of 20.47 hectares of land at Leggatt's Farm as a further precaution.

A strange phenomenon occurred on 15th August 1950, when the Engineer & Manager, Alfred Burgess, noticed an unusual oscillation of the water level on a daily recording chart taken from the Lavant Reservoir. Investigation confirmed that this coincided with an earthquake in Assam, northern India. Similar wave motions were recorded at a reservoir at Margate, Kent, and at two of Portsmouth Water Company's reservoirs on Portsdown Hill.

Fishbourne Pumping Station, May 1965

In December 1953, superchlorination of Fishbourne water was introduced. This involved injecting a higher dose of chlorine into the water and then removing the excess with sulphur dioxide. This process improved the standard of disinfection at the treatment works and is still practised today.

Post-War Extensions at Funtington

The Funtington source clearly had potential to help meet the rising demand after the end of the war and, in November 1947, more test pumping was carried out there. In September 1948, Alfred Burgess recommended that, to help meet rising demand, the following work should be carried out:

- Pressure control in the Witterings and Chichester city to reduce leakage.

- Improved metering of night flow (most of which was, naturally, leakage) in the city.

- Purchase of 'Freez-Seal' equipment to speed up the repair of mains by freezing them locally.

- Driving of more adits in the chalk at Funtington to improve the source yield.

It was not until April 1951 that the Ministry of Health finally approved the further development of Funtington, the maximum yield from the source being limited to 3 million gallons per day. In September 1951, the well-known borehole contractor, George Stow & Co Ltd of Henley-on-Thames, won the contract to sink a 24-inch and a 48-inch diameter borehole and drive 961 feet of adits into the underlying chalk. The two boreholes were then interconnected at a depth of 100 feet by underwater blasting.

Between 5th May and 17th June 1952, 620 feet of adits were driven at Funtington and, to keep groundwater levels low enough for the miners to work underground, water had to be pumped out at a rate of 64,000 gph.

Leading Miner Braithwaite, of George Stow & Co, working in the Funtington adits, 1952

In March 1954, the Corporation decided to apply to the Minister for Housing & Local Government for a loan of £33,709 for further improvements at Funtington:

- Extension of pumphouse.

- Improvements to the existing building.

- Two multi-stage borehole pumps.

- Automatic pump control to eliminate shift working.

- A second attendant's cottage on the east side of the site, along with two garages, one of these being for the existing west cottage.

The loan was approved in April 1956 and, in October, contracts were awarded to A L J Davis (Public Works) Ltd for building works and pipework, and to Sulzer Bros (London) Ltd for pumps. The pumps were commissioned in May 1959. In the dry autumn of that year, as a result of further pumping tests, the reliable yield of Funtington was downgraded to 2.5 million gallons per day.

Improvements to the Supply to East and West Wittering

Despite having the benefits of a good new water source at Funtington to supplement the output from Fishbourne, parts of the Corporation's water mains network were proving inadequate to distribute the additional water to the area. On 17th September 1946, Alfred Burgess reported that the capacity of the Witterings supply was insufficient, primarily because the 6-inch main in Birdham Straight was at full capacity. Storage tanks were not being filled at times of peak demand and this was leading to a number of complaints.

Initial suspicions that the problems might be caused by a major leak on the Witterings supply system proved to be unfounded. After reviewing his demand forecast in November 1946, Alfred Burgess recommended that a water tower of 80,000 gallons capacity should be built at Church Road, East Wittering, to improve pressures during peak demand periods. The estimated cost was £19,385, compared with £25,375 for an alternative scheme involving the laying of larger mains to serve the Witterings.

The Minister approved a loan for the new water tower in principle in September 1949 and a site investigation was completed. However, the Minister delayed the start of work, owing to the volume of capital work already in progress across the country. Meanwhile, it was necessary to impose restrictions on the use of water in the Witterings from 7 am to 7 pm, between June and September 1950.

In June 1950, however, as a result of pressure from the Corporation, the Minister agreed that the tower could proceed after all. By September 1950, a water main had been laid into the site and the piling of foundations by Concrete Piling Ltd was well advanced. In the autumn of 1950, contracts were awarded to Concrete Structures Ltd for the tower construction and to G A Neal & Sons for the approach road and drainage.

Wittering Tower on completion in 1952

The construction of the Wittering Tower finally started on 12th February 1951, having been delayed for 11 weeks by the non-availability of steel reinforcement. During the summer of 1951, restrictions on water use had to be imposed again. The tower was eventually filled with water for testing purposes on 10th March 1952 and finally went into service on 28th May 1952, just in time for the summer peak demand.

Unfortunately, this was not the end of water supply problems for the Witterings, as water demand was growing at an unprecedented rate. Despite the new Wittering Tower, low pressure complaints were received in summer 1953. This time the cause was high pressure losses through the supply main from Fishbourne. A scheme to lay a larger 10-inch diameter main from Cutfield Bridge to Birdham was put forward in September 1953. The pipe manufacturer was unable to deliver pipes until September 1954 and, in the interim, restrictions on water use in Birdham, West Itchenor, West Wittering, East Wittering and Earnley had to be imposed in the summer of 1954. Mainlaying finally started by direct labour in October 1954 and was completed in June 1955.

In October 1955, Alfred Burgess put forward another stage of improvements to the Witterings supply. This was to comprise a duplicate main from Salthill Road to Birdham Road, but Ministry approval was not forthcoming for several years.

An indication of the frustration felt by Witterings residents at the standard of their water supply was revealed in July 1957 in the Chichester Observer. The Observer reported that Mr John Newman, proprietor of the Shore Hotel, East Wittering, was retiring, having written 2,500 letters of complaint in the previous 20 years. Councillors had been his main targets, principally over water supplies to his home. He had written 36 letters to Sir Lancelot Joynson-Hicks MP, 500 to the Chichester Corporation, 40 each to the West Wittering Parish Council and Chichester Rural District Council, and between 200 and 300 to the Chichester Corporation Water Department!

The need to carry out further improvement to the Witterings supply was highlighted in the hot, dry

Laying of 10-inch trunk main at Birdham, 8th October 1954. Wearing the hat is Alfred Burgess, with the Mayor of Chichester, Charles Newall, on the left

summer of 1959, when the Wittering Tower emptied for periods of up to seven hours on nine occasions. The proposed duplicate main was now increased in size to 18 inches between Salthill Road and Appledram Lane and work commenced in early 1960. Famously, it was in June 1960, during the excavation of a trench for this main, that the remains of Fishbourne Roman Palace, one of the most important archaeological sites ever discovered in Britain, were exposed.

As the area's popularity as a summer holiday destination continued to grow, a further stage of the 18-inch duplicate main was recommended between Dell Quay Road and Cutfield Bridge in 1962.

Before this main could be laid, there was a further hosepipe ban, in June 1962, in Birdham, Earnley, the Witterings and Itchenor. This had to be imposed because there was insufficient trunk main capacity to fill the water tower and thus to meet the summertime demand from holidaymakers. The Chichester Observer reported that many hotels and restaurants were without water for long periods and, in fact, the Bracklesham Bay Hotel had to call in the fire brigade to provide water for baths and drinking water for guests.

The Discovery of Fishbourne Roman Palace

In 1998, Alfred Burgess recalled the events that led up to the discovery of the Roman Palace at Fishbourne. In his own words:

"Anyone closely involved with the excavation of the ground will be aware of the possibility of unearthing something of value, perhaps an old coin or other artefact of bygone times. However, the discovery of a Roman building is not an everyday occurrence, especially when the building is given the status of a palace. But this is what happened in May 1960, when the Chichester Corporation Water Department's direct labour gang was excavating a trench through fields north of Fishbourne. The 18-inch water main then being laid between Salthill Road and Appledram was the second stage of a scheme to improve the supply to the Wittering and Selsey areas.

The first stage, between East Ashling and Salthill Road, had been completed the previous year. It was during the carrying out of this first stage that a trench had cut through a Roman midden near Sennicotts. I was amazed one wet Sunday to find a lady and gentleman down in the muddy trench, pinning labels to the walls where they had found items of interest, while their baby in the pushchair above remained calmly reconciled, as though it was an everyday occurrence. After a while the parents broke off from their preoccupation and introduced themselves as Mr and Mrs Rule of Westbourne. We exchanged visiting cards, and theirs remained in my desk until, twelve months later, it provided the telephone number for conveying news of the initial findings at Fishbourne. Mr and Mrs Rule were the first to recognise the importance of the find and were instrumental in enlisting the support of their fellow archaeologists. Twenty years later, Margaret Rule became nationally famous as director of operations when the Tudor warship 'Mary Rose' was raised from the Solent.

It was fortuitous that the excavation of the trench at Fishbourne caused no damage to the most spectacular of the mosaic floors, namely the one depicting a winged cupid at the centre.

Professor Barry Cunliffe, who had directed excavations at the Roman Palace throughout the following decade, described the discovery in his 1971 book as 'typical of the rescue activity which is going on all over the country - but unlike many chance finds, because of close local co-operation, the Fishbourne discovery was properly recorded and eventually followed up.' Chichester Water Department employees were proud to have played their part in this spirit of co-operation."

The exposed remains of Fishbourne Roman Palace, 1963, featuring the 'Cupid on a Dolphin' mosaic. (Photo courtesy of Fishbourne Roman Palace/Sussex Archaeological Society)

Water Supply to West Dean, Singleton, Charlton and East Dean

Immediately after the Second World War, many villages on the South Downs still relied on local wells for their water supply. West Dean, Singleton, Charlton and East Dean were perhaps more fortunate, being served in part by the extensive private supplies of the West Dean and Goodwood estates.

On 17th February 1948, Alfred Burgess reported on a revision to an earlier scheme to supply East Dean, comprising the construction of Charlton Booster, together with the takeover of and alterations to Goodwood Estate's East Dean Reservoir. In addition, he proposed a booster at Yarbrook, just north of Lavant, to pump to West Dean Estate's Highdown Reservoir, a new pumping main from the booster to West Dean and the takeover of and alterations to West Dean Estate's Highdown Reservoir.

On 13th July 1948, he further recommended the acquisition from West Dean Estate (owner Edward James) of the Nursery Well, Canada Reservoir and mains. The agreed price for the Goodwood Estate undertaking at East Dean was £3,490 4s 2d.

It was not until 29th November 1950 that a Public Inquiry opened into the scheme. The Inquiry heard that water supply wells were at risk of pollution from cesspools. Of the 196 houses, 172 took their supplies either from private estate mains or from 216 wells or 29 tanks, while 24 lacked any water supply at all. A sound case had clearly been made, because on 17th April 1951, the Minister of Health made the necessary Orders. G A Neal & Sons were awarded the contract for mainlaying and buildings on the East Dean scheme, while G C Pillinger Ltd, of Sutton, Surrey, won the contract for the booster pumps at Yarbrook and Charlton. However, work was then delayed by the new Ministry of Housing & Local Government, owing to the dire national economic conditions.

Yarbrook Booster Station, 1953

In October 1952, G A Neal & Sons finally commenced work on the scheme. By April 1953, construction of the booster station buildings at Yarbrook and Charlton had started. The booster pumps were delivered in October 1953 and, by the end of December 1953, the booster stations were complete.

On 1st February 1954, the West Dean water undertaking was formally taken over by Chichester Corporation and Yarbrook Booster Station came into operation. One month later, the East Dean Reservoir and pipelines were taken over and Charlton Booster Station began operation.

The Development of a New Source at Lavant

The spur for the development of a new water source at Lavant appears to have been a letter sent to the Corporation in January 1960 by Portsmouth and Gosport Water Company (PGWC) about its intention to seek a new source in the Ems valley, which was outside its limits of supply. The Corporation's Waterworks Committee resolved to recommend objection to that proposal, but at the same meeting they approved a proposal by Alfred Burgess for trial boreholes to be drilled on a site for a possible new source where the Chilgrove and Lavant valleys meet, just north of Mid Lavant.

Problems occurred with the landowner in agreeing access to the Lavant site. In December 1960, the site of the Lavant trial boreholes was moved to the east side of the disused Chichester to Midhurst railway line.

On 20th June 1961, the Corporation accepted George Stow & Co Ltd's tender for the eight trial boreholes, the price being £23,857 12s 0d. The start of work was delayed to allow Bognor Regis UDC some time to investigate its Westergate Woods scheme because, if the four West Sussex water undertakings became part of one body, the development of substantial additional capacity might become unnecessary. However, in January 1962, in the absence of results from Westergate Woods, the Chichester Corporation decided to proceed with the Lavant trial boreholes without further delay. As there was now a strong possibility that PGWC would be buying the West Sussex undertakings, the decision was taken with its approval.

To avoid limiting the potential output, PGWC asked the Corporation to put down 36-inch rather than 24-inch boreholes and offered to pay the extra cost of £4,581 13s 10d. In October 1962, at PGWC's request, the optional third 36-inch borehole (originally to be drilled only if the first two failed) was drilled while the rig was on site.

By November 1962, the first 36-inch borehole at Lavant had been drilled to a depth of 400 feet and, in January 1963, it was acidised and test pumped at 128,000 gph. Work began that same month on borehole no. 2 and, in February, divers were employed to clear cement grout from slots in the lower lining tube on this borehole. Preliminary test pumping on 8th and 9th April showed a yield of 120,000 gph.

By mid-June 1963, the third Lavant borehole had been drilled to a depth of 160 feet. This borehole was fitted with a steel liner to 70 feet depth, the lower 20 feet being slotted. By July 1963, all three boreholes were complete and ready for test pumping during autumn, using a mains electricity supply to operate the pumps.

The new boreholes were destined to be put to productive use under a new owner because, in January 1962, the Water Committee recommended that the City Council should accept PGWC's offer of purchase. In October, approval was given to the application to the Ministry of Housing & Local Government for PGWC to take over the four Sussex undertakings.

In June 1963, it was reported that the Minister had decided to make the Portsmouth and Gosport Water (Regnum Area) Order 1963 substantially as drafted. On 1st October 1963, the Chichester Corporation Water Department was duly transferred, after an existence of 66 years.

Chichester Rural District Council's Water Supply

Water supplies to the rural area west of Chichester were originally the responsibility of Westbourne Rural District Council (RDC) until it ceased to exist on 1st April 1934. From this date, the newly-formed Chichester RDC was the water undertaker until October 1963, when Portsmouth Water Company became responsible.

Westbourne RDC 1899 - 1934

The first reference to public water supply in the records of Westbourne RDC is on 29th August 1899, when a special committee met to select a site for a well and water pump for public use. After due deliberation, a location 'outside the garden wall at the north-west corner of Hill Cottage, Hermitage' was chosen. It seems that this well was actually constructed, but was only ever equipped with a hand pump for use by local people and did not ever serve a wider population. Thus, in January 1903, a deputation from Westbourne RDC met the Borough of Portsmouth Waterworks Company to discuss the possibility of a public water supply being made available to Westbourne, but the outcome is not recorded.

In December 1908, an RDC sub-committee was formed to consider the question of a public water supply. It made two approaches for bulk supplies. The first was to the Borough of Portsmouth Waterworks Company again, this time for terms for a supply at Hampshire Bridge, Westbourne. The second approach was to Chichester Corporation for a supply at the boundary of the two councils. It also sought to investigate using a spring near an old disused mill at Hambrook, and finally to ascertain from the Hayling Water Company how much it had cost to lay its mains, along with the power consumption, running cost and pumping rate of the Hayling engine at Stoke.

In April 1909, the results of the local inquiries were reported as follows:

1) Portsmouth offered a metered supply at 9d per 1000 gallons for a minimum duration of 10 years, thereafter with one year's notice on either side.

2) Chichester Corporation offered a metered supply at 6d per 1000 gallons and also provided an estimate of the cost of laying mains to supply Westbourne and Bosham.

3) Hambrook spring was considered.

4) The information about the Hayling waterworks was tabled.

The RDC now engaged Trentham, Heming & Saunders to prepare details of the three schemes listed above, along with the RDC's own scheme for a supply from Hermitage Well. Already local politics were playing a part because, on 7th May 1909, the Portsmouth scheme was dropped. It was considered that it might prejudice the RDC's chances of successfully contesting any further attempt by the Borough of Portsmouth Waterworks Company to extend its supply area into Sussex, the first attempt having been made unsuccessfully in 1905.

In the same month, Mr W J Chadwick of London wrote offering to design a water supply works, as he had constructed the Hayling waterworks and 'was well acquainted with the hydrogeological conditions along the south coast'. This offer was not taken up, but the Committee then sought the advice of West Sussex County Council. Its Clerk, Mr Merrifield, recommended Baldwin Latham Senior, who had given evidence on behalf of the County Council against Portsmouth's 1905 scheme to extend its area into Sussex.

In 1909, the RDC prepared details of all the houses and rateable values along the main roads in Westbourne, where water mains would be laid. This duty fell to a Council officer whose job title was Inspector of Nuisances!

At this stage, the ideas most favoured were either the bulk supply from Chichester Corporation or the RDC's own Hermitage well scheme, but the Corporation subsequently withdrew its offer of a bulk supply, since the RDC was considering its own scheme. The Corporation stated that it would reconsider its position, should the Hermitage well proposal be abandoned.

On 29th December 1909, Baldwin Latham's report on a water supply scheme at Hermitage was tabled and accepted in principle, except that the Committee thought a reservoir of 100,000 gallons capacity, rather than 50,000 gallons, would be preferable, so as to allow for future development.

On 11th January 1910, the Committee decided to ask other small undertakings about their income, expenditure, loan repayments and degree of financial success. On 10th February, the replies received were considered, as a result of which it was resolved to ask the Borough of Portsmouth Waterworks Company if its offer of a bulk supply to Westbourne at 9d per 1000 gallons would also apply if Bosham was supplied as well.

Later that year, on 22nd August, Mr Saunders of Trentham, Heming & Saunders submitted an amended water supply scheme for Westbourne. It seems that Mr Saunders was appointed as the RDC's Engineer, in preference to Baldwin Latham.

Woodmancote Waterworks

There is a gap in the RDC records until 7th October 1913 when, after all the vacillation of the previous 14 years, the record refers to a special meeting about a borehole at Woodmancote. It is apparent that construction of a water supply scheme had at last begun, because the purpose of the meeting was to consider a telegram from the Engineer, Mr Saunders, stating that the borehole at Woodmancote must be lined for another 170 feet to stop soft chalk falling in. Boring had been stopped, pending the meeting. It was decided to put the extra lining work in hand, with unperforated lining for the first 100 feet followed by perforated lining, which was to be carried into hard chalk. The contractor for the borehole was Duke & Ockenden of Littlehampton[1].

In summer 1914, the Council obtained Local Government Board approval to drill a well and second borehole at Woodmancote. However, in September, one month after the outbreak of the First World War, it was decided to 'postpone further consideration of proceeding with Woodmancote Waterworks until after the Peace was signed'.

Within a year of the end of the First World War, on 24th September 1919, the RDC's Water Committee instructed its Engineer to estimate the costs of proceeding with the old Woodmancote scheme of 1914 and also determine what it would cost to supply Woodmancote only. Fresh tenders for the whole scheme were invited. The Council was recommended to accept tenders for the supply of pipes from the Clay Cross Company, valued at £7,975 17s 3d, and from a Mr Barry for the mainlaying and construction of the reservoir, at a cost of £8,248 16s 9d.

The Westbourne RDC's propensity for delay came to the fore again on 1st January 1920, when a petition was received from Southbourne against the Westbourne water scheme. The opposition presumably arose from those people who preferred to carry on using their private wells, rather than pay the RDC for a mains water supply.

As a result of this petition, the Council referred the scheme back to its water committee and a local referendum of Westbourne electors was held on the water supply scheme on 5th February 1920. The result was declared as follows:

Against	829
For	425
Blank	11
Gone away or dead (!)	61
Not returned	307

The Growth of the Mains Network

The Council then decided to refer the whole matter to the Minister of Health for his advice. The records do not say what this advice was, but finally on 24th April 1920, contracts were let for the works at Woodmancote and must have advanced rapidly, because on 17th July, it was reported that the reservoir would be complete in three weeks' time. At the same time, additional mains along Cemetery Lane and Duffield Lane, Westbourne, were approved. Machinery and pumps at Woodmancote were supplied by Worthington & Simpson. Oil for the engine to drive the pump was delivered to Emsworth railway station and transported to the works. The site of the borehole at Woodmancote is the same site that remains in use in 2007 as a water source and treatment works.

[1] Duke & Ockenden Ltd were borehole contractors and equipment manufacturers based at the Ferry Wharf Works in Littlehampton. They were known locally as 'D and O', a nickname that inevitably became 'Dando'. The firm was founded in 1867 and still exists in Littlehampton today as Dando Drilling International Ltd. The Company now concentrates on the manufacture of drilling rigs and associated equipment.

The ratepayers of Westbourne were charged a special expenses rate to cover the capital and interest for construction of the water scheme, together with a separate water rate to pay for water used, based on the rateable value of domestic premises.

It is worth recording the existence at this time of a small private water supply system that supplied houses on the Southbourne Park Estate. The source of water was a 420-foot deep borehole located half a mile north of Prinsted church. In due course, the supply was taken over by the RDC, but the pumping machinery was sold and the pumphouse was let to a tenant in 1951, soon after the Stoughton water supply scheme came into use.

1921 was a year of continual progress and, in January, a notice was issued to the public stating that applications for connections to the mains could now be made. On 10th June, the RDC's water byelaws were amended to permit the use of lead service pipes instead of 'tin-lined [ie galvanised steel] piping'. The following week, an Engineer's letter stated that the plant at Woodmancote and the mains were satisfactory and connections could be made. It was stipulated that John Harrington, the 'Working Engineer', was to be present when each connection was made. Shortly afterwards, Harrington was given approval to buy 4 to 6 pounds of paint for the pumping station at not more than 1 shilling per pound – and a paintbrush too!

On 20th October 1921, the Medical Officer, Dr Butcher, reported on the wholesomeness of the water supply from private domestic wells in Church Road, Second Avenue, Breach Avenue and Southbourne Avenue (all Southbourne) and Commonside and River Street (both Westbourne). He recommended inspections of all houses in the district and the Inspector of Nuisances was asked to undertake this work, starting with the 'obviously bad' supplies. Generally, people were trying to avoid the expense of connecting and paying for mains water by pleading the wholesomeness of their current arrangements, whether from wells or, in one case, a stream! However, the Council had the legal powers to compel them to connect to mains if the water supply was not judged to be wholesome or sufficient. Many excuses were tried ; Mr Cox, of the Barley Corn Inn at Nutbourne, wrote to complain about the water being cloudy and smelling of tar. After flushing of the main, John Harrington reported that 'the water was now good', but the complaint may well have been justified, because on 4th July 1922, Harrington was instructed to flush the mains more frequently.

Duplication Works

Other problems began to occur. On 12th - 13th June 1924, there was a breakdown of the Worthington-Simpson engine and Duke & Ockenden were called in to help with emergency pumping to the reservoir. Calls for voluntary restraint were needed until the problem was resolved and, to improve security of supplies, it was decided to buy a stock of spares for the engine. Then, in April 1925, Duke & Ockenden advised that the only way to provide more complete security would be to sink a second borehole and equip it with its own pump, but the RDC deferred a decision for the time being.

In September 1925, after advertising for the services of a consulting engineer to prepare a duplication scheme, the Council appointed Mr F N Chapman. By December 1926, Duke & Ockenden had completed the duplication scheme, which included a second borehole and pump, a second engine to drive the pump and a larger 1000-gallon fuel tank. Both the existing and new engines could be used to run either borehole pump and both pumps could be operated together. The old pump could deliver 7,000 gph, the new pump 8,000 gph.

With the supply more assured, the network began to expand more rapidly. In 1928, new mains were laid as far as Hambrook Hill. However, the expansion of the network led to summer demand that sometimes stretched the available water resources. On 26th July 1928, owing to excessive and unauthorised watering of gardens and lawns, it was announced that the water supply would be cut off daily from 6 pm to 9 pm. A penalty of 40 shillings (£2) could be levied for the use of water for other than domestic purposes. Even in the late spring of 1929, 700 handbills were issued, warning consumers against wasting water.

The popularity of the new supply can be judged by the rise in connections from 150 in 1922 to 725 by the middle of 1929.

Insufficient Funds for Further Development

In October 1929, the Borough of Portsmouth Waterworks Company wrote to the Council, stating that it intended to seek powers in Parliament to develop a source in the Ems valley, near Racton, and suggesting that it should take over the Westbourne undertaking from the RDC. David Halton Thomson, the Engineer of Portsmouth, attended a meeting to explain the proposals and was permitted to view the Woodmancote Works, to have copies of the drawings and to have a statement of the financial position. However, in February 1930, after considering its position, the RDC instructed its Clerk to take all necessary steps to oppose Portsmouth's Bill, including the raising of a petition. This, combined with strenuous opposition from West Sussex County Council, was successful in having all the relevant clauses deleted from the Bill.

The County Council was apparently concerned about Portsmouth's narrow failure to take over the Westbourne water undertaking. It perceived the problems to be Westbourne's inability to raise funds for further extensions to its water supply system, as well as the health implications of water drawn from wells adjacent to domestic cesspits and septic tanks. In June 1930, it informed Westbourne RDC that it was appointing the consultants, Willcox & Raikes, to prepare a report on the Westbourne supply.

Having received the consultants' report and prompted by a petition from Forestside residents pressing for a mains supply, the RDC wrote to Stansted Estate (at Rowlands Castle) and Littlegreen Estate (near Compton), asking if they could provide bulk supplies to Forestside and also Castle Lane. Both these estates had substantial private water supplies. Littlegreen's response was that it was impossible to make sufficient water available with its existing plant, although Stansted said that it could provide a supply, subject to satisfactory

Sinking a well at the Stansted Estate, late 19th century
(Photo courtesy of Dando Drilling International Ltd)

conditions. The RDC was also keen to supply water to Chidham and West Thorney, but all these improvements would inevitably need substantial finance beyond its means.

Chichester Rural District Council 1934 - 1963

In 1934, Westbourne RDC ceased to exist and was replaced by a new Chichester RDC which, in 1938, also took over the Westhampnett RDC area on the southern and eastern sides of Chichester. The new body quickly took up the problem of water supplies and, in July 1934, the Surveyor, J K Lawson, reported on a scheme to bring supplies from Woodmancote Pumping Station to Funtington, Racton, Lordington, Walderton, Stoughton and Forestside. Two booster stations would be required, one for Forestside and one for the other four areas. No progress was made with this scheme, although a smaller scheme proposed in October 1934 to install small boreholes and pumps at Halnaker, Boxgrove and Westerton did go ahead. Meanwhile, the Goodwood Estate Company was asked to continue carting water to Boxgrove, to alleviate the frequent water shortages in that village.

In 1937, Chichester RDC proposed a new source in the Ems valley at Ellbridge Farm, near Aldsworth, to be used to supply water to Stoughton and West Marden. These proposals were rejected by the Ministry of Health, after an inquiry in April 1938. Although the Minister was convinced of the need for mains water supplies to be brought to these communities, he considered that the RDC should instead take a bulk supply from Chichester Corporation, after its new Funtington source had been developed.

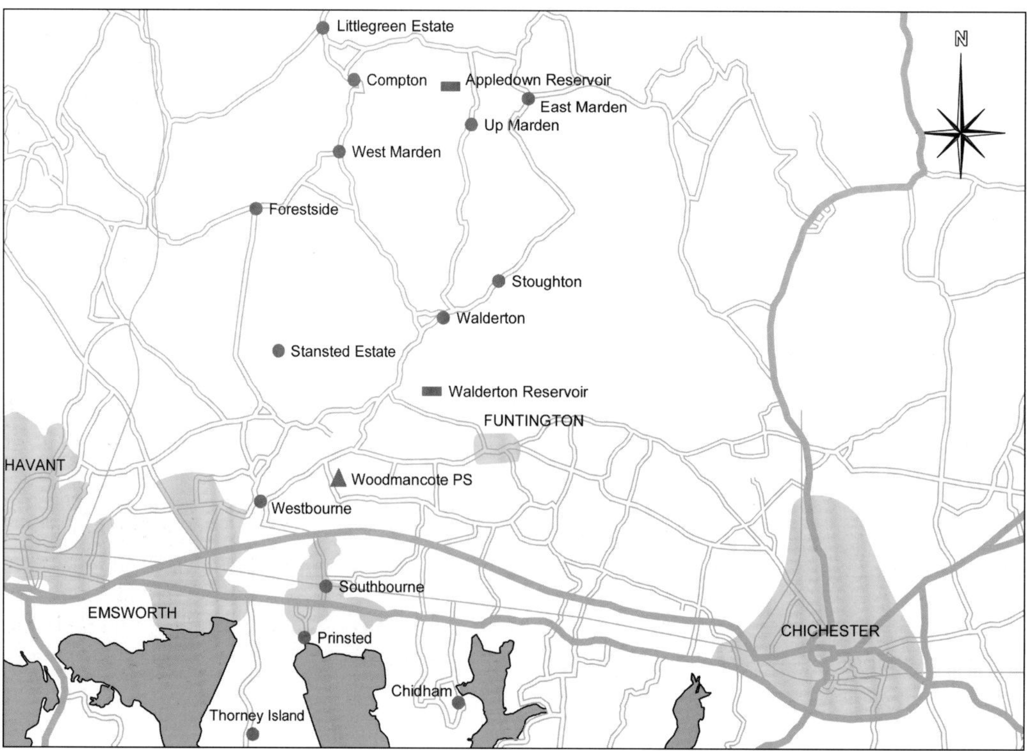

Improvements prior to the Second World War

Negotiations over a bulk supply seem to have come to nothing because, in April 1939, proposals for two new boreholes and pumps for Woodmancote were submitted to the Ministry of Health and approved, the RDC having made it clear that they were the first part of a development scheme to serve Forestside, Walderton, West Marden (including a booster), Compton, the higher parts of Westbourne, Chidham and West Thorney. The scheme also included a new 200,000 gallon service reservoir at Walderton and connecting mains from Woodmancote.

In May, the Ministry said that it was prepared to consent only to the duplicate boreholes at Woodmancote. Having obtained tenders, the Council's consulting engineers, Binnie, Deacon & Gourley, recommended the tender of Le Grand, Sutcliff & Gill, in the sum of £1,789 11s 0d.

By now there was a strong sense of approaching war. In June 1939, the military authorities asked the RDC to supply water to local searchlight stations at Foxbury Lane (Westbourne), Walderton Camp (where water was supplied by cart) and Thorney. At the same time, the Officer Commanding, RAF Thorney Island, was consulted as to whether any part of Woodmancote Pumping Station should be camouflaged.

Meanwhile, work went ahead on the first of the two new boreholes at Woodmancote but, after disappointing test pumping results from the first borehole, work on the second one was suspended. In October 1939, with all energies being directed at wartime problems, the RDC decided to postpone the rest of the scheme, apart from the reservoir at Walderton and the main to it, which were needed to provide additional storage in the event of the failure of mains power supplies. Hopes were, however, dashed in June 1940, when the Ministry of Health refused the request for a loan of £15,460 for these works, suggesting that they could be avoided by the cheaper option of providing an 'oil engine dynamo set' [ie a generator] at Woodmancote to drive the pumps if the mains electricity supply failed.

On a brighter note, the Ministry approved expenditure already incurred on the boreholes and pumps at Woodmancote and also the proposed expenditure to acquire land for the Walderton reservoir. It indicated that a loan for the generator would be forthcoming and so the RDC immediately applied to borrow £8,400.

The Littlegreen Estate

No further work took place until 13th March 1946, when the RDC applied to the Ministry of Health for a loan for the Stoughton scheme, including the purchase of the private water undertaking of the Littlegreen Estate, Compton, valued at £3,600.

Terms for the purchase of the Littlegreen undertaking were agreed with the owners, E Gomme Ltd, in July 1946. It finally came under RDC control on 1st July 1948 and immediately two men were allocated to operate the pumping plants at Compton and East Marden. The RDC was also quick to impose its policies on the former private undertaking and, on 28th July, the Surveyor reported that, to comply with RDC policy, 21 meters had been taken off houses in the former Littlegreen water area and 29 commercial meters had been installed at certain premises.

The Stoughton Scheme

The whole Stoughton scheme was submitted to the Ministry of Health in September 1946, after the RDC's consulting engineers, Binnie, Deacon & Gourley, had developed the proposals further. The loan sought was £36,255. It was not until 15th February 1947 that the Ministry wrote to say that a local inquiry into the Stoughton scheme would be arranged as soon as possible!

The Stoughton Public Inquiry finally took place at the RDC's chambers at Pallant House, Chichester, on 11th November 1947, the Inspector being Mr J Gardner of the Ministry of Health. Dr Eric Ward, the RDC's Medical Officer of Health, spoke in favour of the scheme. The Inquiry heard that the RDC area covered 103,000 acres and that, of the 12,092 houses, 82% currently received a mains water supply.

Mr H J F Gourley, the Consulting Engineer, said that the scheme's cost was now estimated at £55,000 and that it would enable another 298 houses (including 26 in North, East and Up Marden) to have a public supply.

Dr Eric Ward cited the fact that some houses had wells sunk in porous chalk under their gardens, which were also used for disposal of excreta in cesspools that overflowed into the soil. He said that samples of well water had been found to be grossly polluted, even on Council housing sites where efforts had been made to seal the wells at ground level. Forestside was probably the place most in need of a piped supply; wells there had to be sunk to a depth of around 300 feet to obtain water and Dr Ward said, that from personal experience, he knew it took an average of 15 minutes to lower and raise a bucket of water to the surface. This was beyond the capability of some elderly people, who paid up to one shilling (5 pence) for a bucket to be raised. Rainwater supplies were used, but of course these ran out in dry weather. Some farmers brought in water from elsewhere in barrels and Dr Ward said that one local farmer had carted thousands of barrels of water in a three-month period for his livestock.

There were three schools in the area concerned, at Compton, Forestside and Walderton. At Forestside, two bucketfuls of water, drawn from a well 290 feet deep, at a cost of 1s 6d, were used to provide water for cooking meals for 30 children. There was insufficient water for the children to wash their hands and faces before and after a meal, or to have a glass of water with the meal. At Walderton, water for the school canteen was drawn from a well known to be subject to heavy pollution, being only 10 yards from the soakaway from the boys' urinal.

Dr Ward's evidence was unanswerable and, in January 1948, the Minister wrote to confirm that the Stoughton scheme was approved in principle.

In 1949, momentum finally built up for starting the scheme, for which the estimate had risen to £65,000. In February, the contract for the pumping plant at Woodmancote and West Marden was let to G C Pillinger. On 1st June, the tender of S M Tidy (Public Works Contractors) Ltd, of Brighton, was accepted for the mainlaying, the construction of reservoirs at Appledown and Walderton and the booster station at West Marden. Work started on 26th September 1949.

In November 1949, approval was given in principle for a bulk supply to the Stansted Estate reservoir at Lumley Seat, which involved laying a main for about one mile from Lodge Farm.

West Marden Booster Station

In September 1950, the contract for the Stoughton scheme was extended by two months, owing to delays in mainlaying caused by the persistently high groundwater table between Woodmancote and Walderton. Only a month later, a further two-month extension was granted, because of continuing bad weather. Finally, on 8th June 1951, the scheme was completed at a cost of £47,941, a saving of £6,739 on the Ministry's loan.

With the Stoughton scheme coming into operation, some pumping machinery at the Park Estate (Southbourne), Compton, East Marden and Woodmancote had become redundant. The old pumping house on the Park Estate was let to a tenant, but eventually it was decided to retain the plant at East Marden for a further year.

Extensions to Supplies in the District

Meanwhile, mains water supplies were being brought to other parts of the RDC's area. In May 1948, the RDC approved two groups of new mains, the total cost being £35,723.

The first priority was to lay mains in North and South Mundham, Nutbourne, Hunston, Climping, Aldingbourne, Walberton, Oving, Flansham and West Wittering. The second phase involved mains at Fishbourne, West Drayton, Colworth, Merston, Birdham, Sidlesham, Barnham, Ford, Tortington, Binsted, Lagness, Bosham, Funtington and Chidham.

The 1950s onwards

The records show that, by this time, all the RDC's water plant was electrically operated, but with boosting, some of the water had to be pumped three times. The development of the Stoughton scheme had increased daily electricity costs to £2 per 270,000 gallons pumped.

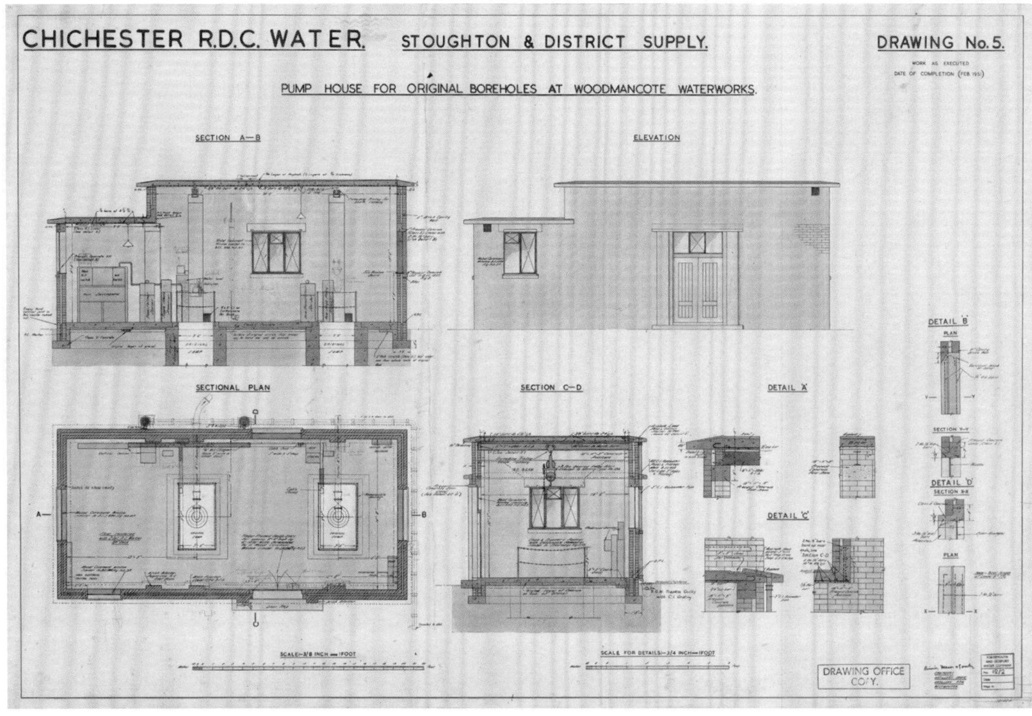
CHICHESTER R.D.C. WATER.
STOUGHTON & DISTRICT SUPPLY.
DRAWING No. 5.
PUMP HOUSE FOR ORIGINAL BOREHOLES AT WOODMANCOTE WATERWORKS.
SECTION A—B
ELEVATION
SECTIONAL PLAN
SECTION C—D
DETAIL 'A'
DETAIL 'B'
DETAIL 'C'
DETAIL 'D'
DRAWING OFFICE COPY.

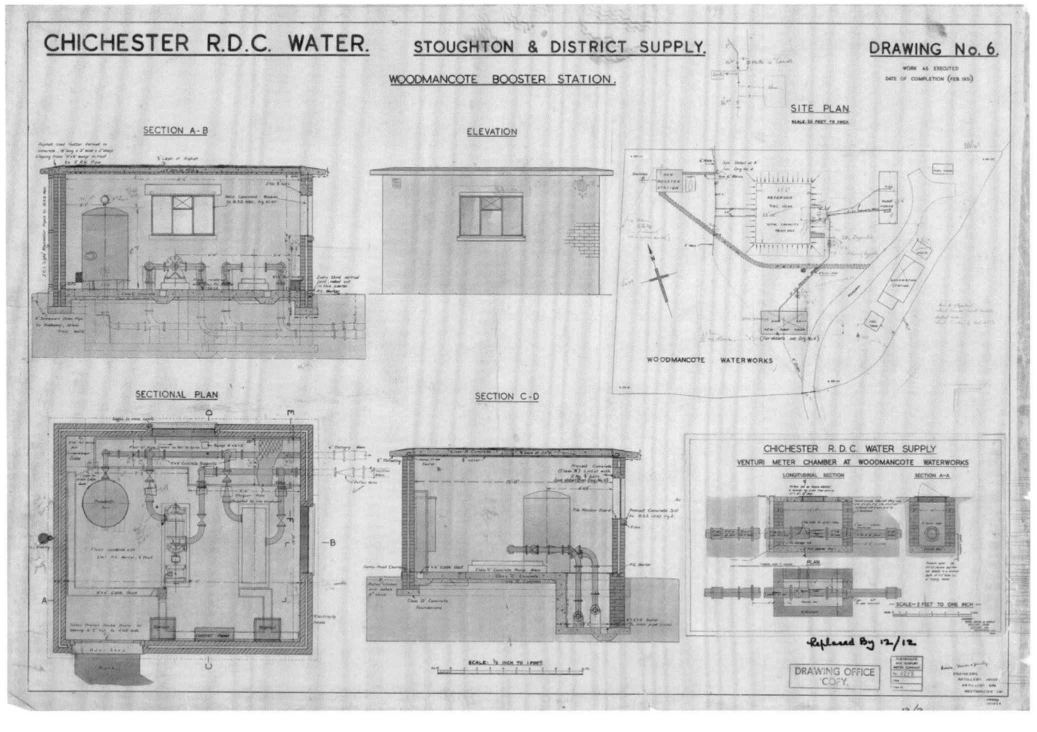
CHICHESTER R.D.C. WATER.
STOUGHTON & DISTRICT SUPPLY.
DRAWING No. 6.
WOODMANCOTE BOOSTER STATION.
SITE PLAN
SECTION A-B
ELEVATION
SECTIONAL PLAN
SECTION C-D
WOODMANCOTE WATERWORKS
CHICHESTER R.D.C. WATER SUPPLY
VENTURI METER CHAMBER AT WOODMANCOTE WATERWORKS
DRAWING OFFICE COPY.

In December 1954, the RDC completed the laying of a larger main to RAF Thorney Island, to guarantee a supply of 150,000 gallons per year to the base.

By April 1955, the residents of Up Marden were complaining about their frequently inadequate supply of water. The hamlet, comprising 10 houses and four farms, was served by a 1-inch galvanised pipe from Appledown Reservoir, one mile away. The RDC replaced the 1-inch pipe with a 3-inch main over a 1,200 yard length.

In September 1955, the owners of a small private waterworks, serving 124 houses in Gordon Terrace and Thorney Road, Southbourne, asked if the RDC was prepared to take over the supply. The request was initially refused, but the owners then applied to sink another borehole to improve the supply. Whether this was subterfuge or a genuine application is unclear, but the prospect of another borehole close to Woodmancote (with potential to reduce the output) persuaded the RDC to take over the supply on 1st April 1959.

Prospects were looking up for the RDC water undertaking and, on 9th March 1956, it was reported in the Chichester Observer that the undertaking had shown a financial surplus for the first time ever! Water demand was, however, rising rapidly in the 1950s and, in July 1956, inadequate water pressures were reported at Chidham. The Engineer & Surveyor, J K Lawson, reminded his Committee that a larger main along the A27, between Southbourne and 'The Barleycorn' public house at Chidham, was the long-term answer to the problem. With insufficient funds, the RDC decided on the short-term measure of supplying Chidham from Walderton Reservoir via a pressure reducing valve.

Rising demand was, in fact, the reason for the RDC imposing a hosepipe ban on the residents of the parishes of Chidham, Compton, Marden, Stoughton, Westbourne and West Thorney (ie its whole area of supply) in June 1957.

In December 1960, problems of sufficiency and wholesomeness were reported with the borehole belonging to Messrs A B Bray & Son, which supplied both the local farms and houses in East Marden. A scheme was prepared for serving all of East Marden from RDC mains and the work was carried out by Bridgwater Bros (Public Works Contractors) Ltd in May 1962.

In summer 1962, the water supply situation became critical with the highest ever demand being recorded. Indeed the demand on Walderton Reservoir was only just matched by running the duty and stand-by Woodmancote boosters together. Appledown Reservoir was emptied, even though both the West Marden booster pumps were operating.

Woodmancote, 2007

By July, although the Woodmancote borehole pump was only running for 17 hours per day, the duty and stand-by boosters had run together for 160 hours, or 95% of the time. A stand-by booster had been 'borrowed' from Portsmouth and Gosport Water

Company (PGWC) in case of emergency. At West Marden, the two boosters had run for a total of 125 hours in one week yet, even then, Appledown Reservoir had emptied on occasions.

Cyril 'Jim' Treagust, the RDC Inspector, who was eventually transferred to PGWC, had a novel way of carrying out his duties. John Reed and Des Rutter both remember that Jim had equipped his wife with a bike and a set of valve keys. This meant that, if any call came in while Jim was already out on duty, she could deal with the problem herself! On one occasion, there was a request for a mains turn-off from a local builder, who asked: "Can you send the lady turncock - I prefer her to the man!"

Amalgamation

At an RDC Public Services Committee meeting on 12th October 1956, a 'momentous' Circular, no. 52/56, from the Ministry of Housing & Local Government was tabled, promoting the regrouping of water undertakers to make most effective use of the country's resources. The circular recognised that undertakers had met needs admirably in the past, but might find that their resources were no longer equal to the tasks set by the growing demand for water from domestic, industrial and agricultural consumers. The circular suggested that amalgamations, takeovers or the setting up of joint boards might achieve the regrouping.

This set in train the long-drawn out process that was to end with the take-over of the Chichester RDC undertaking by PGWC. From the outset, the RDC appeared to be in favour and, over the following months, tried several times to persuade its neighbours to meet to discuss the way forward. Eventually, on 11th April 1958, a joint committee of the so-called 'Regnum' undertakings (of Chichester RDC, Chichester Corporation, Bognor Regis UDC and Selsey Water Company) was proposed. The RDC approved the Regnum Board proposal in October 1958, but it seems that the Chichester Corporation continued to drag its feet.

In July and August 1961, a local inquiry was held into PGWC's Ems valley scheme, the objectors to which included the RDC and West Sussex County Council. The scheme involved the sinking of boreholes near Walderton, a similar scheme to those thrown out by Parliament in 1906 and 1929. However, this time in February 1962, it received Government approval, although the amount to be abstracted was restricted to 2 million gallons per day.

On 13th July 1963, it was reported to the Public Services Committee that the Minister had made the Order for the transfer of the RDC undertaking to PGWC, with effect from 1st October 1963.

Selsey Water Company

Prior to 1907, water supplies in the Selsey area had been obtained from local springs and wells. Indeed, older maps of the area show wells located alongside roads and tracks.

The Selsey Water Act 1907

The Selsey Water Act, passed in 1907, authorised the formation of the Selsey Water Company to take a bulk supply of water from Chichester Corporation.

The original Directors of the Company were Francis Hill Tod (City of London), Alfred Stansfield (Islington), Henry William Ingram (Southfields, Surrey), Luther Clayton (Sidlesham), Edwin Richard Painter (City of London), William Bentham Martin (Outer Temple, London) and Edward Oxenford Preston (City of London). These gentlemen were also Directors of the Petersfield & Selsey Gas Company and presumably identified the commercial benefit of bringing mains water to an area whose relative remoteness meant that it would otherwise have waited for some time for the benefit. As a result, for many years the Water Company was operated in conjunction with the Gas Company in Selsey, with one local manager for the two undertakings. The Company's initial capital was £15,000 in 1,500 shares of £10 each.

The Supply Area

The supply area consisted of the three parishes (Selsey, Sidlesham and Hunston) in the Corporation's statutory area of supply and the parish of North Mundham in the Bognor Water Company's area of supply.

Although not recorded, there must have been considerable debate between those setting up the new company and the Bognor and Chichester undertakings. The Act stated that the Selsey Company could only supply North Mundham by the written agreement of Bognor Water Company. The Selsey Company could not take a bulk supply from anyone other than Chichester Corporation, nor sink any well or construct works, other than distribution works, unless the Corporation consented. Consent could not be unreasonably withheld for a temporary alternative supply if a bulk supply from the Corporation was not available.

Terms and Conditions

The bulk supply point was in Stockbridge Road, Chichester, at or near the point where the city boundary crossed the road. The Corporation was required to lay a 5-inch diameter main from Southgate along Stockbridge Road to the supply point. The Act stated that the amount supplied in bulk on any day could not exceed 50% more than the annual average daily amount supplied in the year ending on the previous quarter day.

Even the charges were stipulated; the maximum charge for metered non-domestic consumers was two shillings (10 pence) per thousand gallons and, for public purposes (such as street cleaning, watering of parks etc), 1 shilling per thousand gallons.

Selsey Water Company was required under the Act to install 15 fire hydrants in Selsey and nine in each of the other parishes at its own expense. Any fire hydrants in excess of this number were to be paid for by Westhampnett RDC (predecessors to Chichester RDC).

To prevent a Petition of Objection that had been lodged in the House of Lords by Chichester Corporation, a Schedule to the Act was also compiled. Presumably as a result of negotiations with the Corporation, it was quite specific. Some of the more significant provisions of this Schedule were:

- A water tower or reservoir was to be constructed, with a maximum water level of 85 feet above Ordnance Datum[1].

- Water was to be conveyed by the Selsey Company through a 5-inch diameter main to the water tower or reservoir and without undue pressure loss.

- The Selsey Company was to provide a bulk meter at its own expense, with the right to install a reflux valve.

- The water supplied by Chichester Corporation was to be pure and wholesome, as defined in section 35 of the Waterworks Clauses Act 1847.

- The Selsey Company had to pay for the water supplied, at a rate of 6d per 1000 gallons up to an average of 100,000 gallons per day over a quarter. Above this, the price for the excess amount was to be agreed, or decided by arbitration.

- If the revenue received by the Selsey Company from consumers was insufficient to pay the Corporation, charges had to rise.

- The bulk supply meter was to be read and tested jointly.

- In times of drought, the Selsey Company was required to take reasonable steps to prevent waste of water, if requested to do so by the Corporation.

- Sufficiency of supply was to be completed within three years of the Act becoming law. If this was not achieved, then the local authority that included any parish without a sufficient supply could make a supply available if it wished.

[1] 'Ordnance Datum' is the mean sea level at Newlyn, Cornwall, which is the Ordnance Survey's reference level.

The Official Opening

Good progress appears to have been made, because the new water mains associated with the proposal were officially opened by Alderman J O Holt, who had two roles, being the Chairman of Selsey Water Company and also the Mayor of Chichester. The opening took place at 1.30 pm on Saturday 19th December 1908 and afterwards there was a celebratory lunch at the Station Hotel, Selsey.

The opening was followed by a fire hose display from a fire hydrant, performed by A J Cutler and Lieutenant J O Holt (son of the Chairman), who had also been Clerk of Works for the water main laying.

Selsey Water Tower, 1977

December was hardly the time of year for such a display and the Chichester Observer of 23rd December 1908 published an evocative description of the weather during the opening ceremony:

"Water, water everywhere. Roads ankle deep in mud and water, rain falling in a miserable drizzle and a breeze coming from a mist-enveloped sea that sent a chill to the very marrow."

The main laid from Chichester to Selsey comprised 7½ miles of 5-inch cast-iron mains, the pipes being supplied by the Stanton Iron Works of Nottingham. The contractor for the main was Williams & Carnall, their foreman being a Mr Hampton, and site supervision for the Selsey Water Company was carried out by J O Holt Junior. The works were carried out under the overall supervision of the Company's Engineer, Mr G H Perryn. A section of the Chichester Canal had to be drained to enable the main to be laid under it.

A reinforced concrete water tower of 50,000 gallons capacity was constructed in Selsey in 1915 by F Moehl Ltd of London, at a cost of £532. The top water level was 82 feet above Ordnance Datum and the highest point supplied at the time was 30 feet above Ordnance Datum. The tower was located in Cross Road, later renamed School Lane. The site is located opposite the present-day library and is now used by the local scouts. After many years of disuse, the tower was finally demolished in 1984.

Demolition of Selsey Water Tower, 1984
(Photo courtesy of Peter Ogden)

New Connections and the Development of Selsey

Surviving records of the Selsey Water Company are very scanty, but they show that the early years were quite successful. The initial rate at which consumers connected their properties to the mains is recorded in press reports of the time. From a total of 94 properties connected in 1909, it quickly rose to 394 by 1913.

By 1914, Company profits grew sufficiently for the first dividend of 2% to be paid and, by 1925, the annual profit had risen from £289 in 1914 to £568.

Rising Discontent in the 1920s

Selsey's development as a holiday resort was sufficiently rapid in the 1920s to require water rates to be raised substantially to pay for new mains, but not without widespread complaints from residents. The Company soon became unpopular because of its escalating charges and a decline in the standard of the water supply as demand increased.

Prior to 1926, Selsey Water Company had purchased water in bulk from Chichester Corporation at a price of 6d per thousand gallons and sold it to consumers at two shillings per thousand gallons. In 1925, Chichester Corporation sought to double the bulk supply price to one shilling per thousand gallons, but this was reduced to 9d per thousand gallons, after objections from Selsey Parish Council. The Water Company then sought approval from the Ministry of Health for an increase in the charge to consumers from two shillings to 2s 9d per thousand gallons. In other words, as well as passing the 3d bulk supply increase on to consumers, the Company wished to add a further 6d too!

Strong objections were made by Selsey Parish Council to the Minister, as a result of which a Public Inquiry was held at the Marine Hotel, Selsey, on 3rd March 1926. Following the Inquiry, the Minister issued the Selsey Water Order 1926, which initially allowed the charge to consumers to rise by 25% to 2s 6d per thousand gallons. However, after being notified by the Company of a correction to the preliminary accounts submitted to the Inquiry, the Minister revised the increase to 33⅓%, ie the rate increased to 2s 8d. Unsurprisingly, further vociferous protests were raised by Selsey Parish Council, but to no avail. The episode was punctuated by a pointed exchange of letters in a local newspaper between Edward Heron-Allen, Chairman of Selsey Water Company, and Samuel Day, Chairman of Selsey Parish Council.

In February 1928, the Company proposed to introduce new water byelaws, under which it was the only body permitted to connect properties to the mains. The Parish Council objected to the byelaws, principally because of the high charge that would be payable. However, the Minister pointed out that the proposed byelaws all conformed closely to the new model byelaws that he had already approved.

In July 1928, the Parish Council wrote again to the Minister, this time detailing complaints from several Selsey householders about the inadequacy of the water supply, the consequent risk of 'bursting boilers' and concern that residents were 'unable to carry out the simple rules of sanitation'. The Company responded, saying that it was planning to duplicate the main from Stockbridge Road, Chichester, to Street End, Sidlesham. Meanwhile, as consumption per consumer was now much higher than previously, the Company had decided to prohibit the use of water for gardens and other non-domestic purposes that summer.

In the following dry summer of 1929, there was a further ban on garden watering, along with prohibition on washing cars, horses, yards and outbuildings. In the same year, an increase in rateable values in Selsey led to further rises in water charges.

The 1930 Act

A new Selsey Water Act in 1930 aimed to improve the local supply. Section 4 of the Act required the Company to provide storage equal to the annual daily supply in the previous calendar year, and lay pipes so as to deliver the maximum daily supply into storage with an annual average pressure of 140 feet at the Stockbridge Road meter.

Selsey Water Company staff outing, 1932. Clem Rose is second from the left, and on the right is Alfie Barrett (Photo courtesy of Hazel Ousley)

Selsey Water Company Staff

For almost its entire existence, the Selsey Water Company was run as part of the operations of the Petersfield & Selsey Gas Company. In 1930, the Company's office was at 163 High Street, the premises now being occupied by Den's Fish Bar. In later years, its office was located at 26 Hillfield Road, Selsey. The relatively small scale of the combined gas and water operations allowed both to be run by one manager. Walter Clement Rose (well known locally as 'Clem') served both companies from 1926 to 1957, when the gas operations were taken over by Southern Gas Board. He was appointed as the local Manager in 1930.

Selsey High Street, 1930s. The Selsey Water Co office was in the building with the gable end facing the camera (Photo courtesy of Tom Creedy)

There were other long-standing associations with this small enterprise. Edward Heron-Allen (1861 - 1943), a well-known Selsey resident, served as a Director of the

Company from 1911 to 1942 and, for most of that period, he was Chairman. Heron-Allen was a true polymath; a solicitor by profession, he was also a zoologist, Fellow of the Royal Society, Persian scholar and cheirosopher (palm reader). He wrote a classic work on violin making and many science fiction novels, some under a pseudonym.

Selsey mainlaying gang, 1930s - left to right: Alfie Barrett, Jim Lee, Walt Hoare, Fred Cole, Jock McGarry and Jack Lee (Photo courtesy of Gillian Cole)

From 1909 until the takeover by Portsmouth Water Company in 1963, the role of Secretary of Selsey Water Company was filled by different partners of Painter, Mayne & Walker, a firm of chartered accountants based at 103 Cannon Street, London EC4. Similarly, the Company's auditors for many years were Shrove and Strover, of Moorgate, London.

Mr F J Hazeldine of South Godstone served the Company as a Director from 1921 and was Managing Director from 1934 until his death in 1945. Mr A E Whitcher of Haywards Heath joined the Board in 1939 and, by the time of his death in 1963, he had completed almost 25 years of service. For 17 of those years, he had been either Managing Director or General Manager.

Hazel Ousley (born 1926) is the daughter of Walter Clement Rose (1902 – 1961), who worked for the Selsey Water Company from 1926 until 1957. He was the local Manager from 1930 and was known universally as 'Clem'. As the Selsey Water Company was owned by the Petersfield & Selsey Gas Company, Clem Rose performed the dual role of manager of both the gas and water operations.

Hazel Ousley says that her father came originally from Petersfield and trained as a gas fitter. On transferring from Petersfield to Selsey, he extended his skills to plumbing and water engineering. Clem arrived at a time when the early success of Selsey Water Company was fading, with growing complaints about increases in charges and lack of water pressure.

Hazel recalls that the poor water pressure appeared to be an ever-present problem. Whenever pressure was low, Clem would wince if he saw the fire brigade out practising with their hoses, because they were of course making the problem worse!

As a young girl, Hazel lived with her family at 163 High Street, Selsey (now Den's Fish Bar), where there was a single Gas and Water Company office on the ground floor. Hazel's family occupied a ground floor room and the whole of the first floor. "But," she says, "there was a heavy wooden door between the living area and the office, which was just as well if an irate farmer came in and complained at the top of his voice about having to pay for his water through a meter!"

In the office, there was a recorder chart which showed the water level in either the water tower itself or in the reservoir at the base of the tower. Clem Rose would have to keep an eye on this and Hazel remembers going with him to the reservoir and tower site in School Lane to start the diesel-driven booster pump. This was necessary whenever the mains supply to the electrically-driven pump failed, and Hazel still recalls the loud, frightening noise of the engine inside the small booster house. There was, she thinks, a ladder that went up the centre of the tower; sometimes when the tower was full, water would splash out through the air vents. Her father kept chickens on the roof of the reservoir and grew vegetables on an allotment at the foot of the tower.

The Company employed a number of men to lay gas and water mains and carry out repairs. Hazel remembers some of their names, such as Alfie Barrett, Arthur Ireland and Fred Cole. There was a gas appliance showroom and a workshop at the rear of the office at 163 High Street. A number of fittings were stored there and the men would report each morning to be given their jobs for the day.

Clem Rose in the Selsey Gas and Water Company office (Photo courtesy of Hazel Ousley)

One of Clem Rose's innumerable jobs was to keep the plans up to date when new mains were laid. Hazel remembers that the Company gave him a fine mahogany plan chest in which to keep these drawings. He was also given a bike to enable him to travel out to deal with complaints and problems! Later the bike was replaced by a car.

As Hazel grew up, she became aware that it was not just her father working for the Company, but the family as well. As she puts it, "Although it was our home, there was no escape from work for Dad, as we lived 'over the shop'. It was all business, all the time." Everyone mucked in and Hazel herself worked for the Company when she was older, typing letters, answering the phone and preparing all the water rate demands, a job she particularly disliked! Sometimes there was a burst main and "I had to get on my bike to go and call out George Harwood the fitter, because he had no telephone in his home!"

The Directors of the Company would visit quite frequently and Hazel's mother, Dorothy, was often called upon to prepare tea for them. Hazel liked Mr Hazeldine, the Managing Director, whom she recalls as a kindly old gentleman.

The gas side of operations tended to be dominated by the Company's Petersfield office, with the London office handling mainly the water side of the business. Dealing with two sets of Directors caused a lot of problems for Hazel's father, Clem. At the time of the depression in the 1930s, she remembers going to meet him from the bus on his return from a meeting in London, at which he had been instructed to lay off some of the men. "That was one part of the job that broke his heart" she says, and for a short while, it made him rather unpopular in the close-knit community in Selsey. However, it had to be done and Clem Rose's reputation was quickly restored; even today, he is still fondly remembered for his popular personality and his activities outside work for the people of Selsey.

In 1957, Clem Rose left Selsey Water Company to join the Southern Gas Board. In appreciation of his service to the Company for the previous 31 years, the Chairman, Mr W H Bennett, presented him with an inscribed gold watch, the ceremony also being attended by the Directors, A E Whitcher, A E Crisp and W K Tate, and the Secretary, A N Gillman.

Sadly Clem Rose died four years later at the relatively young age of 59. A man of many skills at work, he was in his spare time a fine painter in oils and his daughter Hazel still has several of his paintings in pride of place on the walls of her house.

Following the passing of the Selsey Water Act 1930, improvements to the supply were soon put in hand. By 1932, a 6-inch duplication of the trunk main from the Chichester meter to Selsey was completed. In 1935, additional storage and booster pumping facilities were constructed next to the water tower in Cross Road (now School Lane). The storage comprised a 200,000 gallon reinforced concrete reservoir in two halves, which stored water delivered in bulk from Chichester, thus safeguarding supplies at times of higher demand. The stored water was boosted into the tower by an electrically powered Pulsometer pump delivering 10,000 gph. To guard against mains electricity failure, there was also a stand-by pump of the same capacity, powered by a 10 HP Ruston oil engine. Both pumps were housed in a brick building integral with the new reservoir. The pumping period was normally 4 hours per day and intended to be a maximum of 8 hours per day when demand was at its peak in the summer.

The reservoir structure and booster house still exist, having been converted for use by the local scouts.

The Drought of 1934 and Further Dissatisfaction

During the 1934 drought, public water supply restrictions were again introduced in Selsey. Owners of private wells fared little better, as the newly-formed Chichester RDC advised all such owners to boil water for consumption, owing to the risk of contamination arising from low water levels in the wells.

Selsey's dissatisfaction with its water company continued through the 1930s. At the annual parish meeting of 1936, a resolution was passed requesting Chichester RDC to promote a Parliamentary Bill to acquire Selsey Water Company in the interests of ratepayers. In July 1937, a further complaint was made to the RDC about water charges. It promised to investigate, but nothing came from either of these moves.

In June 1937, Chichester Corporation considered installing a second meter at the bulk supply point in Stockbridge Road, Chichester, presumably because of concerns about the accuracy of the original one, which by now was 30 years old! However, in September, the Selsey Company surprisingly agreed to provide a replacement 6-inch meter at its own expense.

The Company's annual report for 1937 refers to 1,853 yards of new main and 128 new connections being completed in the year. It noted that a forthcoming extension of the supply to Runcton would require a further 2,300 yards of main to be laid.

In the 1930s, Selsey continued to be developed for housing and as a holiday resort. However, the Company's report for 1939 states that the declaration of war had brought housing development to almost an entire standstill. By the following year, a similar plunge in the numbers of holiday makers visiting Selsey led to a serious decline in revenue for the Company.

Mainlaying in West Street, Selsey, 1930s (Photo courtesy of Tom Creedy)

The Post-War Era

Following the Second World War and the nationalisation of the gas industry in 1949, the Southern Gas Board took over the running of Selsey Water Company. Meanwhile, expansion continued in Selsey, but Chichester Corporation Water Department kept an eagle eye on how the undertaking was performing. On 20th September 1955, Alfred Burgess, the Corporation's Water Engineer & Manager, wrote to ask the Selsey Company to comply with its obligations under the 1930 Act, regarding sufficiency of water storage and the capability of its trunk water main to deliver the maximum demand with 140 feet pressure at the Stockbridge Road meter. The reminder followed an incident in the summer of 1955 when, between 25th and 31st July, the Corporation provided a pressure of 170 feet at Stockbridge Road, but the Selsey Company still had difficulty in maintaining supplies in Selsey.

In 1956, the Selsey Company responded to the Corporation's concerns by informing it of plans to lay 1,500 yards of 10-inch main between Green Lane, Hunston and the Anchor Inn, Sidlesham. This was not, however, done and, as problems with meeting demand persisted, the Corporation wrote again in 1958 to draw the Company's attention to its obligations. Replying to the Corporation's request, the Selsey Secretary, Arthur Gillman, said that, with the emerging national proposals to regroup local water undertakings, it was difficult, if not impossible, to make the necessary capital investment.

However, the Company did obtain budget quotations from G A Neal & Sons of Chichester for a new reservoir, of capacity ranging from 30,000 to 100,000 gallons. The largest size was quoted at just £2,850. The fact that Selsey Water Company was unable to proceed demonstrated just how constrained its finances were becoming.

Two miles of 10-inch duplication main were, however, laid from Sidlesham to just north of Selsey Ferry, but not until 1961.

The Separation of Gas and Water Operations

On 4th January 1957, the Chichester Observer reported that, from 1st January, the association between gas and water services in Selsey had ended after a period of 50 years. The two utilities were now separate and independent, and the arrangement whereby Southern Gas Board ran the Selsey Water Company ceased.

Alfred ('Freddy') Dawkins, of Burgess Hill, was appointed as local Manager in place of Clem Rose, to be responsible for all Water Company business. Prior to this appointment, he had been Chief Inspector to the Seaford, Newhaven and Ouse Valley Water Company for ten years.

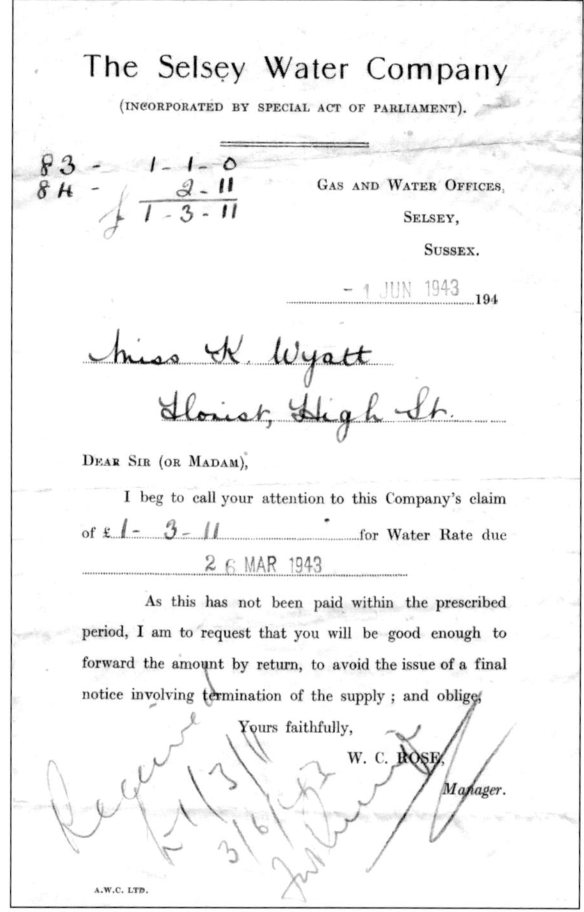

The Selsey Water Company

(INCORPORATED BY SPECIAL ACT OF PARLIAMENT).

83 - 1-1-0
84 - 2-11
£ 1-3-11

GAS AND WATER OFFICES,
SELSEY,
SUSSEX.

- 1 JUN 1943 194

Miss K. Wyatt
Florist, High St.

DEAR SIR (OR MADAM),

I beg to call your attention to this Company's claim of £ 1-3-11 for Water Rate due 26 MAR 1943

As this has not been paid within the prescribed period, I am to request that you will be good enough to forward the amount by return, to avoid the issue of a final notice involving termination of the supply; and oblige,

Yours faithfully,
W. C. ROSE,
Manager.

A.W.C. LTD.

Selsey Water Company rate demand, 1943
(Courtesy of Ruth Mariner/The Selsey Society)

The Chichester Observer of 18th January 1957 reported that the residents of Batchmere paid Chichester Corporation 2s 3d (11 pence) per 1000 gallons of water, while their neighbours at Keynor were charged 3 shillings (15 pence) per 1000 gallons by Selsey Water Company, even though the water came from the same source. The Selsey Company explained that the increases had come about because the Corporation had raised its price to them from 9d to 1 shilling per 1000 gallons and, in addition, that the Company planned new office accommodation, which had to be funded. Needless to say, the discrepancy in charges generated angry letters to the Chichester Observer!

Then another report in the Chichester Observer, of 14th August 1959, mentioned that the residents of Selsey had to pay 10 shillings (50 pence) per year for having a bath in their house, and speculated that the planned amalgamation of undertakings would end this charge.

In August 1963, only two months before the end of Selsey Water Company's existence, it had to impose a hosepipe ban. This was despite the fact that there was no shortage of water in the chalk aquifers from which supplies were originally taken. The restrictions were, in fact, imposed because of high water demand from the large influx of holidaymakers, this demand being beyond the capacity of the trunk mains supplying Selsey from Chichester. Freddy Dawkins was reported in the Chichester Observer as saying that the Company had insufficient funds to complete the laying of a trunk main of higher capacity to Selsey from Selsey Ferry, a scheme that had been started in 1961. However, he expected matters to improve after the forthcoming amalgamation with Portsmouth and Gosport Water Company and, in the same article, Leonard Simpson, PGWC's Engineer, confirmed that his Board had already approved plans for this final section of trunk main to be laid, once the amalgamation had been completed.

The Amalgamation with Portsmouth and Gosport Water Company

In due course, the Selsey Water Company was indeed taken over by PGWC in 1963, at the same time as the takeover of the undertakings of Bognor Regis UDC, Chichester Corporation and Chichester RDC.

Freddy Dawkins was still the local Manager at the time of the takeover. His office was at his house, 'South View', 5 Croft Way, Selsey. He and three other employees, Bill Gasson, Reggie Lee and Peter Newlen, were all transferred to PGWC.

Portsmouth and Gosport Water Company sign at West Meon Pumping Station, 2007.

1955-1960: A Period of Consolidation

The 1950s were a period of significant growth in population, housing and commercial business throughout the United Kingdom. In Portsmouth and Gosport, the rate of growth was probably higher than in many other towns and cities, owing to the rebuilding programmes in areas that had experienced significant bomb damage during the Second World War.

Major new developments, some of which had begun before the war, were rapidly expanded at Paulsgrove, on the mainland to the north of Portsmouth, and at Leigh Park, just to the north of Havant. Outside the Company's area at that time, the town of Fareham was also expanding rapidly.

The increasing demand for water had already necessitated the development of the Worlds End boreholes by the Portsmouth Company in the early 1950s. At the same time, the Gosport Company had developed new boreholes at its Northbrook source at Bishop's Waltham.

The National Scene

The winter of 1955/56 had been relatively dry and so groundwater levels during 1956 were very low. As a result, there were pleas across the country for consumers to 'use water wisely'. By 1957, it was reported that industry research bodies were investigating the benefits of the use of spray taps to save water.

The Ministry of Housing and Local Government (MHLG), which was responsible for overseeing public water supplies, was at that time urging small water undertakers to regroup or amalgamate, principally to ensure that rapidly increasing demands could be met and best use made of available resources. The Local Government Act 1958 gave the Minister the power to establish Water Boards, to which existing undertakers' powers could be ceded. The Water Companies' Association, which represented private water companies, made strong representations to exclude its member companies from those provisions. In the same year, the Water Act 1958 enabled the Ministry to give water undertakers temporary powers to overcome short-term deficits in supplies during periods of exceptionally low rainfall. It meant that in times of drought, undertakers could apply to the Minister for an Order permitting them to put in place temporary abstractions, suspend compensation discharges and, if necessary, supply water by standpipe or tanker.

Coincidentally, following the publication of a report by the Central Advisory Water Committee *(The Growing Demand for Water and Information on Water Resources)*, the summer of 1959 was exceptionally dry. This prompted a Ministry circular, urging water undertakings to take all possible steps to secure their supplies in the immediate future, preferably by obtaining supplies from impounding reservoirs.

Engineering Improvements

The last half of the decade was a period of consolidation and planning. With the amalgamation of the Portsmouth and Gosport companies having taken place in 1955, much was done to maintain the security of supplies. At the same time, preparations were made for the incorporation of the Fareham Undertaking and the possibility of developing further supplies in the Ems valley.

During 1956, the Havant Mill springs, which were situated in various locations within Havant, were enclosed to protect them from any possible pollution. In the same year, the Company discovered that the 36-inch steel main from Drayton across Portscreek to Portsea Island, which had been laid in preparation for the Second World War, was suffering serious corrosion. Consequently, a system of cathodic protection was installed. The system, using sacrificial anodes connected to the main, ensured that, in future, the anodes would corrode instead of the main.

Worlds End No.3 Borehole, 1962, with artesian flow

In the former Gosport area, a second main, 24 inches in diameter, was laid from Hoe Pumping Station to Shedfield Reservoir, thereby enabling more water from Northbrook and Hoe to augment Soberton, which supplied both the rural and urban areas of the former Gosport Undertaking. At West Meon, a small rural community in the upper Meon valley with no other connections to the Company's network, a second borehole was developed to provide additional security of supply. At Hoe itself, the Company installed submersible borehole pumps in the well, together with automatic controls that allowed a reduction in manning levels.

Meanwhile, in the Portsmouth area, the Company was busy carrying out improvements at Havant and Bedhampton. Work on the conversion of the Havant Pumping Station to use electric pumps commenced in 1958, whilst at Bedhampton the redundant steam engines and boilers were removed from the No. 1 Pumping Station and the chimney was demolished. Following the recommendations of Edgar Morton, the Company's consultant geologist, a third borehole was drilled at Worlds End by Messrs G Stow. This enabled the Company to increase the security of supply from the works, by ensuring that any two borehole pumps could operate with the third as a stand-by.

Immediately prior to the takeover of the Fareham Undertaking, the Board approved the laying of a new 18-inch main between the Shedfield and Hoads Hill Reservoirs. The objective was to provide more water to enable the connection of the Fareham Low Level Zone to the Company's Hoads Hill Reservoir supply.

In October 1958, the Company demolished the Havant Mill. This was the last of the mills inherited almost exactly 100 years previously; the Mill, which had been used as a store, had become uneconomical to repair.

Lowering 10-inch main in Commercial Road, Portsmouth

1957 - Centenary Celebrations

One of the highlights of the decade for the Company was the celebration of its Centenary in 1957. With the formation of both the Portsmouth and Gosport Companies having taken place in 1857, it was appropriate for the celebration to embrace the whole Company and a special programme of events was organised.

The Company staged an exhibition, showing the 'life cycle' of water from source to tap at a Careers Exhibition in Portsmouth, which was visited by over 10,000 people. During the summer, an 'At Home' week was staged on evenings and afternoons, when parties of consumers were transported from their homes to the Havant and Bedhampton Works. A colour film outlining the Company's activities was also shown.

In commemoration of the Act of Parliament which established the Company on 13th July 1857, the Directors, employees and their families were invited with many local dignitaries to a Service of Thanksgiving at Portsmouth Cathedral on 14th July 1957.

Staff outing, Portsmouth Water Company Centenary, 1957. 'In command' is Deputy Engineer, Leonard Simpson, pictured right.

The Directors entertained staff, pensioners and partners at a special dinner, an occasion that has become a tradition in the Company's calendar.

Company vehicles, 1959

During the year, the Centenary was marked by the publication of *A History of the Portsmouth and Gosport Water Supply*, written by D Halton Thomson, a former Engineer of the Company.

The Centenary celebrations were concluded at a lunch hosted by Portsmouth City Council in the presence of the Parliamentary Secretary for Housing and Local Government, the Lord Mayor of Portsmouth and the Mayor of Gosport, as well as chairmen of the local authorities supplied by the Company. The Commander-in-Chief, Portsmouth Naval Base, was also present, as were a number of dignitaries from local organisations and the Water Industry.

Company Finances

Following the amalgamation of the Portsmouth and Gosport Companies, a revaluation of rating assessments on all properties was conducted in 1955/56, to enable new values and water rates to be applied for the following charging year.

Throughout the decade, the Company continued to pay the statutory maximum dividends to its shareholders. However, the 1958 Annual Report records the fact that 'the receipts on the Capital Account have been overspent and the replenishment of resources is now a matter of some urgency'. The Directors delayed an issue of new stock because of high interest rates, but the following year's Report records the issue of new Debenture Stock.

Life at the Company

In 1957, the Company's Directors decided to reward long-serving employees with a certificate upon reaching 25 year's service. By 1963, the certificate had been replaced by an engraved watch, which was presented at the Annual Dinner. The tradition continues today, although employees are now given rather more freedom in the selection of their gift! The Directors must have been feeling particularly generous because, at the same meeting, they decided to award a gratuity of £1 for every year of completed service to retiring employees. Needless to say, that sum has increased during the last fifty years. A year later, the Directors resolved that they would send Christmas cards to all their pensioners or widows/widowers, another tradition that remains today.

In the latter part of 1957, the Directors also agreed to fund the showing of a Frost Precautions Cartoon in local cinemas. The cartoon had been prepared by the British Waterworks Association, The Water Companies' Association and the Institution of Water Engineers; little did they know how timely this advice would be, with the cold winter of 1963 not so many years away.

In December 1957, the Company, mindful of the likely need for future resources, wrote to local planners to ask them to reserve a site north of Leigh Park for water storage, which would, in time, become the proposed Havant Thicket Reservoir.

1958 saw the sudden death in service of the Secretary & Treasurer, Frank King. He was succeeded by his deputy, Eric Guymer, who played a key part in the future of the Company over the following sixteen years.

In July 1959, the Board approved the purchase of an alarm bell, at a cost of £80, due to the vulnerability of the Portsmouth Office to 'hold-up' raiders, particularly during the lunch period! Later that year, it was reported for the first time that surface water flows discharging to the swallow holes in Rowlands Castle had caused elevated turbidity at Havant & Bedhampton Springs. Temporary diversions of drainage from a local brickyard were approved by the Board, but surface water drainage to the swallow holes was a recurring problem for the Company in the years to come.

The Transfer of the Fareham Undertaking

Despite the inevitable upheaval associated with the amalgamation in 1955 of the Portsmouth and Gosport Companies, in 1957 the Directors of the new Company sought to follow the advice of Government by approaching Fareham UDC Water Undertaking about the possibility of amalgamation. At that time, Fareham UDC was experiencing considerable difficulty in maintaining supplies to its rapidly expanding population. In the early months of 1958, the Ministry granted powers for the Portsmouth and Gosport Water Company to supply a new factory and housing in Giles Close, Fareham. By early 1959, terms had been agreed with Fareham UDC to purchase its water assets, together with the transfer of six staff. Application was made to the Minister and, following the making of the Portsmouth and Gosport Water Order 1959, the Company took over responsibility for the Fareham area on 1st October that year. The acquisition of the Fareham Undertaking cost £144,000, and the benefit for the people of Fareham was a reduction in their water charges! More details are given in the chapter on the Fareham Undertaking.

Almost as soon as the area had been taken over, there were concerns about the possibility of contamination from the 'ball hydrants' used for fire-fighting in the Fareham area. Eventually the hydrants were replaced, with the Fire Authority bearing the cost of the materials.

The Ems Valley Scheme

It was as far back as 1905 that the Company had first expressed its interest in developing a source in the Ems valley. In 1944, the idea was rekindled in recommendations by H B Milner, the Company's consulting geologist. Consequently, during the development of the River Boards Act 1948, the Company made representations for the Ems valley to be included within the area of the Hampshire Rivers Board, even though it was actually in West Sussex. As a result, a local Inquiry for Hampshire was held in 1949, where Portsmouth City Council and the Hampshire Rivers Catchment Board supported the Company's views. The proposal was, however, resisted by the West Sussex authorities and the upshot was that the Minister of Health confirmed that the Ems valley was excluded from the Hampshire area.

In 1957, the Company experienced significant summertime peak demands and, had drought conditions existed, it would have been unable to meet those demands with the available supplies. At the same time, following the West Sussex Inquiry, the Ministry published proposals for dividing the West Sussex area into three separate water authority areas, one of these being the so-called 'Regnum Area', which included the Chichester, Bognor Regis and Selsey undertakings, its boundary being contiguous with that of the Company. Interestingly, the Minister's proposals conflicted with those of the Inspector reporting for Hampshire, who had recommended that the Company should consider options outside its supply area, including the Ems valley. In November 1957, the Board authorised its Engineer to hold discussions with the Engineer of the Chichester Corporation Water Department and representatives of the Brighton Corporation, who were also known to be keen to develop new sources of supply in the area. Alfred Burgess, the Engineer at Chichester, believed that new sources should be developed for the new Regnum Area.

Over the next two years, the Company held discussions about developments with the West Sussex water undertakings, without much success. The dry weather of summer 1959 galvanised the Board into action. At the end of that year, it wrote to the Minister, the Clerks of the Chichester Corporation, the Bognor Regis UDC and the Chichester RDC, outlining its intention to seek an Order authorising it to develop a new source in the Ems valley.

The Dry Summer of 1959

The summer of 1959 was one of the driest on record, with three periods of drought (defined by the Meteorological Office as a period of at least 15 consecutive days without measurable rainfall) between 4th May and 8th October. As a result, the peak weekly average for the new Company area, including the Fareham supply, was 27.59 million gallons, 19% above the annual average. In the Portsmouth area alone, the peak weekly average rose to 22.11 million gallons, which was just below the maximum recorded during the 'blitz' of January 1941, when 63 broken mains and service pipes were reported, and vast quantities of water were used by the Fire Brigade.

Had there not been average rainfall to replenish the aquifer in the preceding winter, the Company would certainly have had to impose restrictions for the first time in its history.

The exceptional demands of summer 1959 also led to distribution problems and a number of improvements were authorised. Booster stations were installed at Peel Common to improve pressures at Hill Head, at the former Hayling Island works, together with a new 15-inch main to serve the south of the island, and at Worlds End to supply Hambledon. At Hoads Hill, a booster had to be installed to ensure that Shedfield water would reach the water tower supplying the nearby properties.

Company van, July 1959, during the drought. Note the clear message on the side!

1960-1970: Amalgamation with the West Sussex Undertakings

The drought of 1959 and the rapidly rising demand for water in the early 1960s were major concerns, both for water undertakers and Government. The process for developing new supplies, requiring Parliamentary Orders, was particularly burdensome and bureaucratic, the obstacles to the proposed development of the Company's Ems valley scheme being a prime example.

Recognising the nationally growing demand for water, the Government set up the Proudman Committee, which recommended the establishment of River Authorities to take over the responsibilities of the River Boards. The new Authorities would be required to control the development and conservation of water resources. The co-ordination of the activities of the new River Authorities through a central authority, reporting to the Minister, was also recommended. The costs associated with these new Authorities were to be recovered by a levy on water users, such as statutory undertakers, industry and agriculture. A speedier system for dealing with the development and control of water abstractions was also clearly identified.

All these proposals were addressed in the Water Resources Act 1963, which established 27 new River Authorities, notionally county based, with abstraction licensing powers. Until then, the rate of abstraction from water sources had been unspecified but, for the first time, new limits of abstraction were to be included in the licences and these had to be negotiated with the River Authority. By 1966, the Hampshire and Sussex River Authorities had issued 'Licences of Right' for the Company's existing sources.

Meeting the Water Supply Needs of the South East

In the wake of the Second World War, manufacturing industry was rapidly expanding, thus increasing the need for additional water supplies. Population and personal water consumption were also rising quickly, as a result of rapidly changing hygiene habits. The customs of families sharing their weekly bath water and household washing being undertaken only on Mondays were to vanish in a very short time, as the use of washing machines and daily showers became more popular. The Ministry carried out a South East Study, which predicted a substantial growth in population between 1961 and 1981, and proposed that locally, 'Solent City', a major new conurbation, should be developed between Portsmouth and Southampton. The South East development proposals led to a detailed study being carried out by the newly formed Water Resources Board into future water demands and the need for water resource development in South East England. The Company, in conjunction with the Southampton Corporation, commissioned Herbert Lapworth Partners to consider the specific impacts of 'Solent City' for both Undertakings.

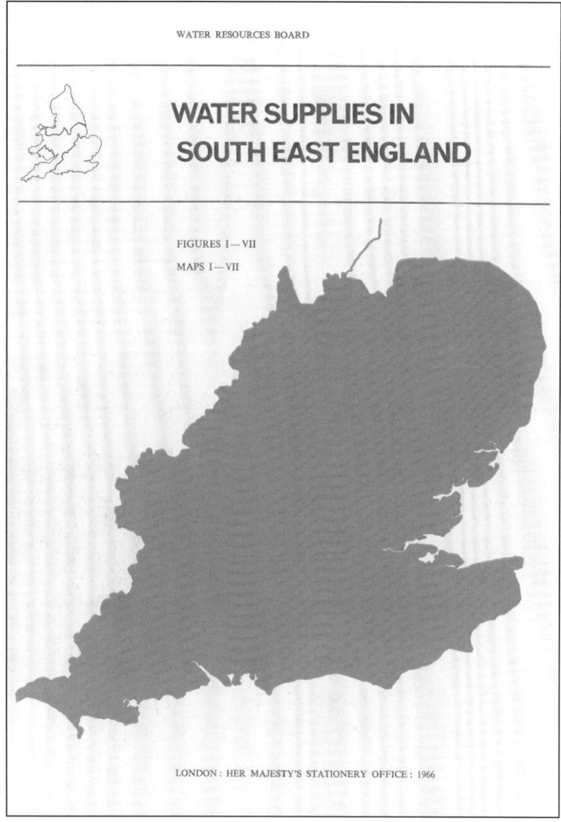

The Water Resources Board Study concluded in 1966 that Hampshire and Sussex could remain self-sufficient in water, provided that conservation measures were implemented to keep pace with rising consumption. The South Hampshire Study, carried out by Herbert Lapworth, identified a number of new resources that, with conservation measures, would allow the development of the new city to proceed.

Both water resources studies identified a number of alternative options for the Company and its neighbouring water undertakers. The schemes of greatest interest to the Company were the development of further abstractions in the Meon and Lavant valleys, as well as a proposal to abstract water from the lower reaches of the River Itchen at Gaters Mill near West End. At the time, the River Itchen development was seen as the principal resource to meet the needs of the Solent City development. Being located just above the tidal limit, the abstraction was seen as likely to cause minimal environmental impact upon the river, as well as providing ample opportunity for further extension as development in South Hampshire continued.

The studies also identified the potential for the development of pumped storage reservoirs at Havant Thicket and Southleigh Forest, which would be filled during the winter by surplus spring water from Havant and Bedhampton. Whilst neither of the reservoirs has yet been needed, the purchase of the necessary land, as will be seen later, has provided the Company with the basis for securing its long-term supply needs well beyond 2007.

Press reports from 1966 make reference to desalination schemes and the construction of a barrage across the entrance of Chichester Harbour as other possibilities.

The Amalgamation with the West Sussex Undertakings

Ever since 1905, the Company had fostered plans to develop further resources in the Ems valley, but neighbouring undertakings to the east at Chichester, Worthing and Brighton had thwarted such proposals. In 1957, the West Sussex Survey, which considered the future of water supplies for the county, appeared to rule out any possibility of the Company developing a source here, a conclusion that was accepted by Ministers. Most organisations in West Sussex seemed keen to reserve their resources for the future needs of their own county and favoured amalgamation of the four local undertakers into the 'Regnum Water Board', which had been proposed in the 1957 Survey.

In October 1959, experience of that summer's drought led the Board, yet again, to seek powers to develop a new source in the Ems valley. The Engineer was instructed to notify the neighbouring organisations of this intention.

It must have come as quite a surprise to those involved at Portsmouth and Gosport Water Company (PGWC) in 1960, to receive an approach from Mr Reginald Martin, the Chairman of the Water Committee at Bognor Regis UDC, who appeared to favour the Company taking over the Bognor Regis water supplies. Despite previous rebuttals, his approach encouraged the Company to pursue the amalgamation strategy vigorously. By April 1961, the Directors had agreed terms with the Chichester Corporation and, by January 1962, Bognor Regis UDC had also accepted the Company's offer. Terms were finalised with the Chichester RDC in June 1962, and with the Selsey Water Company in December 1962.

Of course, each of the organisations received financial recompense for the sale of their assets, a significant benefit during times when financing the provision of new housing was difficult. The benefit for residents was the fact that the Company's water charges were lower than those of the predecessor organisations. This fact was soon forgotten when they realised that it was more difficult to pay their water bills locally; local newspaper reports refer to complaints about the sixpence levied by the banks for the payment of bills!

With terms agreed, a Parliamentary Order was needed to enable the transfer to be formally completed. It was not until March 1963 that an Inquiry was held and, following the recommendations of the Inquiry Inspector, the Company took over responsibility for the 'Regnum Area' on 1st October 1963.

Despite approval of the takeover in 1963, the urgency of meeting the growing demand for water had to be satisfied before formalities could be completed. Ministerial approval was finally received, in 1962, for the Company to put down an exploratory borehole at Walderton in the Ems Valley, and a similar approval was granted to Bognor Regis UDC to develop a new borehole at Westergate Woods to supplement the wells at Eastergate.

The Development of New Resources

Meeting the rising demand from a growing population was proving to be a challenge for most water undertakers and PGWC was no exception. In 1962, high demand led the Board to consider the imposition of hosepipe bans, but these were narrowly avoided, although only as a result of appeals in the press by the Engineer, Reg Hall, for customers to use less water. High demand did, however, accentuate the need for the Company to develop new sources.

Other water undertakers were having similar problems and the Brighton and Worthing Corporations put down exploratory boreholes in 1966 at Binsted and Madehurst, within the Company's area of supply.

Further dry weather at the end of the decade resulted in the record peak day demand being broken in 1969, when 51.8 million gallons were supplied.

The Ems Valley Scheme (Walderton)

Following the submission of a draft Order for a new source in the Ems valley, a Local Inquiry was held during 1961, as it had been impossible to reach agreement with the objecting authorities. The outcome was that the Company was granted an Order by the Minister, but for a rate of abstraction limited to 2 million gallons per day.

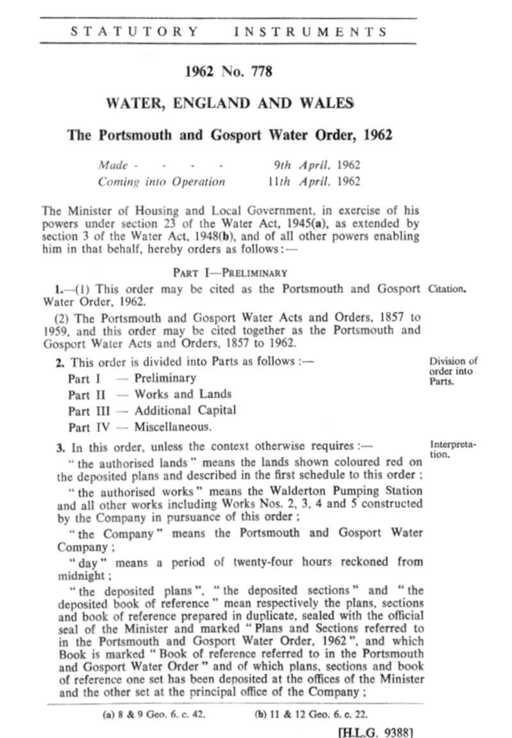

STATUTORY INSTRUMENTS

1962 No. 778

WATER, ENGLAND AND WALES

The Portsmouth and Gosport Water Order, 1962

Made - - - - *9th April*, 1962
Coming into Operation *11th April*, 1962

The Minister of Housing and Local Government, in exercise of his powers under section 23 of the Water Act, 1945(**a**), as extended by section 3 of the Water Act, 1948(**b**), and of all other powers enabling him in that behalf, hereby orders as follows:—

PART I—PRELIMINARY

1.—(1) This order may be cited as the Portsmouth and Gosport Water Order, 1962. Citation.

(2) The Portsmouth and Gosport Water Acts and Orders, 1857 to 1959, and this order may be cited together as the Portsmouth and Gosport Water Acts and Orders, 1857 to 1962.

2. This order is divided into Parts as follows :— Division of order into Parts.

Part I — Preliminary
Part II — Works and Lands
Part III — Additional Capital
Part IV — Miscellaneous.

3. In this order, unless the context otherwise requires :— Interpretation.

"the authorised lands" means the lands shown coloured red on the deposited plans and described in the first schedule to this order ;

"the authorised works" means the Walderton Pumping Station and all other works including Works Nos. 2, 3, 4 and 5 constructed by the Company in pursuance of this order ;

"the Company" means the Portsmouth and Gosport Water Company ;

"day" means a period of twenty-four hours reckoned from midnight ;

"the deposited plans", "the deposited sections" and "the deposited book of reference" mean respectively the plans, sections and book of reference prepared in duplicate, sealed with the official seal of the Minister and marked "Plans and Sections referred to in the Portsmouth and Gosport Water Order, 1962", and which Book is marked "Book of reference referred to in the Portsmouth and Gosport Water Order" and of which plans, sections and book of reference one set has been deposited at the offices of the Minister and the other set at the principal office of the Company ;

(**a**) 8 & 9 Geo. 6. c. 42. (**b**) 11 & 12 Geo. 6. c. 22.

[H.L.G. 9388]

By early 1962, the Company had approved tenders from George Stow of Henley-on-Thames for the construction of three boreholes at Walderton. Confident of a yield in excess of 2 million gallons per day, the Company installed one 33-inch and two 36-inch diameter boreholes. At the same time, approval was given to seek tenders for the construction of Racton Service Reservoir, which would receive water from Walderton and supply Emsworth and the rapidly expanding areas to the north of Havant.

West Sussex County Council was concerned about the rural nature of the area and recommended the appointment of an architect to undertake the design. The Board authorised the Engineer, Reg Hall, to employ an architect to design a pumping station building that would 'blend with the local surroundings'. Whether or not there was any disagreement during the course of the design is unclear, but the finished building displays few, if any, 'rural features'. The architect was never asked to prepare any more designs for the Company!

By March 1963, water from Walderton was already being pumped into supply, despite the fact that the Racton Reservoir and the trunk mains from Walderton to Racton and onwards into Havant, were incomplete. At Walderton, as for a number of the new sources developed in the 1960s, the Company initially installed simple electrical starters and controls in a large 'garden shed', with the disinfection equipment in another shed alongside. With the urgency for additional water, the source could then be utilised while the construction of the permanent buildings took place.

Mainlaying at Walderton, October 1962

As a result of the dry winter of 1964/65 and the possibility of a water shortage the following summer, the Company applied to the Minister of Housing and Local Government for a Drought Order to temporarily increase the abstraction at Walderton to 5 million gallons per day. Although the Drought Order was granted for six months from 2nd July 1965, a wet summer ensued, and the powers were not needed, other than for a brief period to augment the Farlington supply area while a burst on the 36-inch pumping main from Havant to Farlington was repaired. However, the availability of more water at Walderton had been confirmed by the original test pumping, and so the Company persuaded the Sussex River Authority to collaborate in a series of long-term pumping tests. The continuous tests ran from July 1966 through to the autumn of 1967 while the River Authority undertook a hydrometric study of the effects of pumping upon other water features in the Ems valley.

By the latter part of 1967, the tests had been completed and the Company applied for a licence of up to 8 million gallons per day. This proposal would make Walderton the Company's second largest source at that time. The application was advertised and a meeting of the Sussex River Authority was held in early 1968 to hear the objections; by that time, the Company had agreed various compensatory measures with the objectors and the licence terms were issued. One important condition was the requirement for the Company to make a compensation discharge of mains water to the River Ems at Westbourne, when flows in the river fell below a specified amount. The discharge continues to be used when groundwater levels are at their lowest, usually during the autumn and early winter of dry years.

Thus a scheme first promoted in 1905 had finally been completed! The result was that the source at Woodmancote, to the north-east of Emsworth, which had been used for many years as the principal source for the Chichester RDC area and had provided up to 1 million gallons per day, was relegated to use as a stand-by source.

Walderton Pumping Station, May 1965

Westergate

Since the 1890s, the principal source for Bognor Regis UDC and its predecessors had been the wells at Eastergate, near Fontwell. The growth in housing and population forecast in the early 1960s had forced the Bognor Undertaking to seek additional supplies, even though discussions about amalgamations were taking place with the Company and others in the 'Regnum Area'. Driven by the drought of 1959, and the subsequent advice of Government that undertakings should 'take all steps to secure their supplies in the immediate future', the UDC put down a 24-inch borehole in early 1962 at Westergate Woods, a site near Norton to the west of Fontwell. Following successful test pumping, it applied for an Order for the new source later that year, even though by that time agreement on the purchase by the Company had, to all intents and purposes, been reached.

Throughout the development of the source, the Company was kept informed about the progress of the scheme. After receiving the necessary Order, temporary pumping plant and controls were installed at the site, but it was not until 1967 that a further borehole was put down, together with the construction of the permanent pumping station building.

Westergate Pumping Station, 1983

The second borehole enabled the licensed yield to be increased to a maximum of just less than 5 million gallons per day, with both boreholes operating concurrently. The source, therefore, became a valuable alternative to the supply from Eastergate.

The fashion for unusual designs during the 1960s appeared to be at its height. At Westergate, where there had been wooden garden sheds for a number of years, architect Bruce Carter of Thomas Makins suggested that the 'wooden' theme be retained, with wooden tiles or 'shingles' used as the cladding to a timber-framed structure with sloping walls. Maintaining the building would be a constant headache for the Company's building maintenance staff!

Lavant

As was the case at Bognor Regis, plans for further sources to supply the Chichester and Selsey areas were being prepared by Chichester Corporation during the amalgamation negotiations. At that time, Fishbourne and Funtington were the sole sources for the city of Chichester and the bulk supply to Selsey. A potential source at the junction of the Lavant and Chilgrove valleys, just north of Lavant village, had been identified for investigation. More details are given in the chapter about the Chichester Corporation Undertaking. In February 1964, application was made to the Ministry, after agreement had been reached with the Brighton and Worthing Undertakings to resolve their objections. By October of that year, an Order authorising abstraction at the rate of up to 5 million gallons per day had been received.

The delays that had dogged the development of other sites were not repeated at Lavant, and the whole scheme, which involved the drilling of three boreholes, the construction of the permanent pumping station building and a pumping main to a second service reservoir at Chalkpit Lane, was completed in 1967. As had been the case at Walderton, a local firm of architects, Tyler and Dixon of Chichester, designed the building. The design incorporated a number of low-level windows, which soon encouraged considerable vandalism. Having smashed the windows with scaffold poles on one occasion, vandals then opened the valves on oil storage tanks inside the building, requiring a major clean-up operation. Even replacing the windows with aluminium sheet did not deter vandalism and the Company finally resorted to re-cladding the building in 1978; this time Bruce Carter of Thomas Makins was the architect and no windows were included!

Northbrook

Northbrook Pumping Station, at Bishop's Waltham, had been originally developed to serve the local area in 1894. Having changed ownership several times, it became part of the Gosport Waterworks Company in 1941. In the early 1950s, a further borehole was constructed with a yield of over one million gallons per day, far in excess of the needs of Bishop's Waltham. A main was therefore laid to Hoe to transfer the surplus water to Shedfield Reservoir, which at that time was the principal reservoir serving the naval establishments on the Gosport peninsula. Such was the success of this new borehole that a further borehole was constructed with a daily yield of 1.5 million gallons.

Reconstruction of Northbrook Pumping Station, February 1962

In 1960, in response to the Ministry's recommendations to increase supplies following the 1959 drought, the Company sought to maximise the potential of Northbrook by deepening the No. 2 borehole and drilling a third borehole to the same depth and diameter. This increased the yield of Northbrook from 2.5 to 6 million gallons per day. The buildings on the site were extended to incorporate new electrical controls, the work being largely completed by the end of 1962.

The Northbrook Pumping Station, 1983

A tragedy occurred during the laying of the new main between Northbrook and Hoe. While guiding a pipe into the trench in July 1961, a crane jib came into contact with overhead electricity cables and Dennis Cox, one of the Company's employees from Emsworth, was electrocuted and died instantly.

Lovedean

Until the 1950s, the Company had supplied the 'country' area north of Portsdown Hill by pumping water from Farlington Works to the George Reservoir and gravitating supplies from there to areas such as Waterlooville, Cowplain, Catherington, Horndean and Clanfield. The supplies had been augmented by the development of Worlds End Pumping Station in the early 1950s. In expectation of significant residential development in many of these areas, the Company decided to seek a source in the upper part of the South Downs, as identified in the earlier resource studies. It was, however, cautious of the potential to adversely affect the yield of the springs at Havant and Bedhampton. By September 1963, a site had been located in the Lovedean valley opposite the 'Bird in Hand' inn. In July 1964, test pumping was successfully completed and the Board approved the development of the site in September. An interesting and, with hindsight, not altogether surprising phenomenon was noticed during the development at Lovedean. During the course of the usual acidisation of the new boreholes to maximise the yield, within only 48 hours a change in pH (acidity/alkalinity) was recorded at Havant & Bedhampton Springs, confirming initial suspicions that the Lovedean source was within the springs catchment.

An Order authorising the abstraction of up to 3 million gallons per day was made in February 1965. In now familiar fashion, a temporary supply was set up using power supplies, controls and disinfection equipment in 'garden sheds', while the pumping station building and service reservoir were constructed. Once again, Thomas Makins was commissioned to design the building, this time in a 'spiral' shape, which was different from anything before. John King, Supply Engineer at the time, recalls that Bruce Carter had chosen a very rustic brick for the building. Apparently the contractor's bricklayer complained that "it was like laying a whole load of old leather shoes!" It was not until late 1967 that the permanent works were completed.

Borehole drilling at Lovedean, 1966

As was the case at Havant and Bedhampton Springs, the Company found that heavy rain brought a sharp rise in turbidity at Lovedean, a phenomenon that had been resolved by the construction of the Farlington Filtration Works in 1910. The Company had not anticipated such an effect at a borehole source and so, for many years, it was necessary to carefully monitor turbidity at the works following heavy rainfall. On such occasions, the source would have to be temporarily shut down for short periods until the turbidity had fallen, with supplies being maintained from the George Reservoirs. In later years, it became necessary for the Clanfield and Catherington Reservoir Zones, normally supplied from Lovedean, to be temporarily fed from Fort Nelson Reservoir whenever turbidity rose.

West Street, Soberton

Buoyed by the success at Northbrook, and guided by the work of the new Hampshire River Authority, the Company decided to seek further sources in the Meon valley. Since the wells and adits at Soberton had already been extended several times over the previous fifty years, the Company decided, in 1964, to drill a new 24-inch borehole on a nearby site between the A32 Droxford Road and the River Meon, conveniently located near the existing infrastructure. Initial test pumping results from the new borehole appeared favourable with a yield of 1.5 million gallons per day, but further tests in combination with the existing Soberton pumps revealed a reduction in yield from the existing wells! Overall, there was no increase in the total works yield and the new borehole was abandoned.

West Street Pumping Station, 1983

Advance work for the 1966 Resources Study had already identified the potential for another source in the Meon valley. Undaunted by failure at Soberton, the Company sought another site close to the river at West Street, in Soberton village. According to Pete Dulson, the Area Supply Superintendent, there were initially many complaints about the flooding caused during test pumping; however before long the Company was being praised because local householders found that, with lower groundwater levels, they were able to install damp courses in their houses. By the middle of 1965, approval had been obtained from the Ministry for the funding of the work and, by the autumn, satisfactory test pumping at up to four million gallons per day had been completed. Application was then made to the Hampshire River Authority for an abstraction licence and two further boreholes were constructed on the site. At that time, the output from Soberton was pumped to Shedfield Reservoirs, near Swanmore, before transfer to Hoads Hill but, with the development of a second source, a new 24-inch main was laid to deliver the combined output of West Street and Soberton directly to Hoads Hill Reservoir.

The West Street source came into operation in summer 1969.

Improvements at Existing Source Works

It had been during the 1950s that, to improve the flexibility of source operation and reduce manpower, the Company, like the rest of the Industry, had begun the conversion from steam-driven pumps to electrically-driven units.

The felling of Havant Pumping Station chimney, 1961

In 1958, the Company replaced the steam engines at Havant Pumping Station but, by the end of the 1950s, many of the its other sources, albeit with electrically-driven pumps, were still being operated under manual control by staff dedicated solely to a particular site. In the 1960s, there was a gradual change from manual to automatic control. This required fewer staff to operate sources and led to cost savings, always a high priority for a company with low charges! In all cases, reductions were achieved by redeployment of staff to other duties; redundancy was very much a last resort.

The first automation scheme was the redevelopment of Hoe, which entailed the replacement of the single horizontal spindle pump with a submersible pump and motor, automatically controlled by a water level signal from the reservoirs at Shedfield.

Success at Hoe was closely followed, in 1961, by the automation of the Maindell Works, which had been inherited from Fareham UDC in 1959. Fortunately, the UDC had installed submersible pumps during modernisation in 1955, and so the costs of conversion to automatic control were relatively modest at £5,150.

Following the modernisation of Havant Pumping Station, the Board decided to upgrade the Bedhampton Works in 1963. Since the Second World War, the Bedhampton No. 2 Pumping Station, using diesel pumping plant, had been routinely used to deliver water to Farlington, the steam-driven No. 1 Pumping Station having been 'mothballed'. A new electrically-driven No. 1 Pumping Station was built alongside the Victorian buildings, with new suction wells collecting water

Hoe Pumping Station, 1966

Soberton Pumping Station, 1969

from the various spring basins to supply horizontally mounted centrifugal pumps. Two new pumps rated at five and eight million gallons per day were installed in 1965 at an overall cost of £29,000. On completion, the No. 2 Pumping Station was relegated to stand-by use.

In 1967, Soberton Pumping Station was automated and, since the microbiological quality of the source had always been unreliable, the Board decided that a superchlorination system should be installed to improve the effectiveness of disinfection.

Distribution Network Improvements

Just as new resources were needed to support growing demand from industry and households, so the distribution network began to struggle to maintain adequate pressures. The problems were exacerbated for the Company at that time since, in the space of less than ten years, it had inherited several independent networks with no interconnections to help make best use of the available resources. It had also negotiated new tariffs with the Southern Electricity Board, which enabled it to purchase cheap 'off-peak' electricity, but meant that, for several hours of the day, it could not operate many of its main sources.

Inspecting a burst 24-inch pumping main, Bedhampton, 20th February 1964

Help for Hayling

The hot summer of 1959 and the consequent record demand had already revealed the need for improvements, the first of which was the laying of a 15-inch main on Hayling Island, together with the installation of booster pumps at the former Hayling Island Works. Further problems in the developing south-western end of Hayling Island prompted the laying of a 15-inch main from the Hayling Works to Station Road, and a further 12-inch mains extension in Station Road itself. That work was not finally completed until January 1967.

Hill Head and Stubbington

Continuing problems of low pressure in the Hill Head and Stubbington areas led the Company to improve capacity to the south of Fareham by the laying of a new 18-inch main from Hoads Hill Reservoirs to Fareham, together with the construction of a booster station on the reservoir outlet in 1962. The Company believed that the construction of the booster station would defer the need for new trunk mains for a considerable time.

Rural Boosters

A number of smaller booster stations to serve small rural communities were also improved at West Marden, Walderton and Titchfield Lane, to the north of Wickham.

Selsey

In the lead-up to the takeover of the West Sussex Undertakings in 1963, PGWC had already begun laying additional mains, with a new 15-inch main being laid from Sidlesham to Selsey to augment the single 10-inch main, which provided the bulk supply from the Chichester Corporation. In the summer of 1963, just prior to the Company taking over its supplies, the town of Selsey suffered a hosepipe ban, principally due to the inability of the 10-inch main to meet demand. The new main was not finished in time to avoid the ban!

Major Improvements for the Gosport Peninsula

By the autumn of 1964, the Company had identified the need for a number of major reinforcements of the infrastructure serving the Gosport peninsula. A computer model, developed by the Water Research Association, was used for the first time to design the trunk mains improvements. A £580,000 scheme was developed, which included a new 36-inch main from Hoads Hill to Fareham,

Laying 30-inch main, Fareham to Rowner, alongside the railway line to Gosport, 16th September 1966

reducing in size to 30-inch between Fareham and Rowner, and then to 24-inch as far as Privett Road, close to the old Bury Cross Works. Further improvements comprised a 20-inch supply off the new 36-inch main to Portchester from Fareham, as well as 8-inch and 12-inch mains to Elson, Bury Cross, Stubbington and Lee-on-the-Solent. Work started on the scheme in 1965 and was not finally completed until 1969, at a lower cost than the original estimate!

Chichester and Bognor Regis

In the Company's new East District (comprising the former West Sussex Undertakings taken over in 1963), continuous pumping from some of the Chichester sources was required just to maintain adequate water pressures. Improvements were authorised, comprising a new 24/18-inch supply to Fordwater (north of Chichester) from the Lavant Reservoir site, where a second reservoir was constructed. To improve the capability to fill the new reservoir from the Fishbourne Works, a new 18-inch main was laid in Salthill Road, Fishbourne. As the Witterings area still experienced poor pressure, a 15-inch main was laid from Birdham to East Wittering.

Supplies in Bognor Regis were suffering from similar problems and trunk mains from Flansham to Middleton (18-inch), Aldwick to Pagham (10-inch) and Victoria Drive, Bognor Regis (12-inch), were also laid during 1967 and 1968.

Construction of Lavant No.2 Reservoir, 1968

Portsdown Hill

In 1968, the Board authorised a complete reorganisation of the supplies serving the Palmerston Forts on Portsdown Hill, whilst accommodating the planned development of the Crookhorn Estate, between Widley and Bedhampton. The scheme comprised the construction of a new service reservoir adjacent to Fort Southwick, together with new mains and new boosters at the George Reservoir and an additional booster system to supply the Admiralty Surface Weapons Establishment. The scheme was not finally completed until 1972.

The Great Freeze of 1963

Those who experienced it will never forget the extremely hard winter of 1962/63. The conditions were particularly memorable for those who had to maintain water supplies at a time of prolonged low temperatures and deep snow. The cold weather began with heavy snowfall on Boxing Day in 1962 and, from then on, freezing temperatures were experienced for most of the next three months.

During this period, the Company suffered 140 broken mains and, in total, 6,280 premises were reported as being without water. Help was given in emergency repairs to service pipes in 5,880 cases (some as outlined below) and, in all, 2,340 stopcocks were also repaired. Where individual service pipes were frozen, the Company erected 350 standposts on fire hydrants on a daily basis; in cases where there was no convenient hydrant, water was delivered by tanker.

Dave Morris, who was at that time employed as a Company Plumber, recalls, "It was almost impossible for householders to get local plumbers to help them when bursts occurred. It wasn't the Company's responsibility to help them, but we used to get called to assist them to stop the leak by bending over the end of the damaged pipes, which fortunately were lead and so fairly malleable. We would then wrap tallow around the end and tie it with string. It was then up to the householder to try to get a plumber to make a permanent repair. On many occasions, this left them without water for days. In one instance, I remember us being out at Hambledon and, so desperate were people for water, that we went to some of the local wells and collected water by bucket! During that three-month period, all I can remember is working very long hours; it seemed like every night that we'd get home at about 11 pm and then be back at work by 7.30am the next day."

Almost all routine distribution maintenance work was postponed, partly because the frozen ground was so hard that it was very difficult to excavate to do any work, but also to avoid any more supplies freezing than already existed.

The late George Slater, Senior Assistant Engineer at the time, clearly remembered what water operations staff were up against: -

"It was the practice of the Company to use a crutch-top stopcock, which was placed inside the stopcock box, within easy reach of the hand. It was usual to lay the service on to a building site before the builder had done any plumbing, and usually the builder pulled up the tail of the pipe including the stopcock, and used this as his building supply. This inevitably led to the service between the stopcock and the house being laid at a shallow depth, thus leaving it liable to freezing in cold weather. This practice very much came home to roost in 1963 during the most severe period of cold weather the Company had ever experienced. It became very cold with heavy snow on Boxing Day, 1962 and the cold weather persisted into the middle of March.

On Boxing Day itself, there were nearly 40 broken mains, mostly in the older areas of Portsmouth. At the beginning of 1963, we had 6,000 houses frozen up and without water and a delivery service had to be organised, using tanks mounted on lorries. One evening, the television news showed the Metropolitan Water Board defrosting frozen services with a DC generator. It was decided to try this method in our area, and one Saturday morning I went with a generator to the Berg Estate in Waterlooville. On the first service I defrosted, I set the house on fire, as well as that of the next-door neighbours! The problem that hadn't been thought of was that the current produced by the generator found its way to earth via the earth connection on the immersion heater in the airing cupboard. This inevitably resulted in this length of cable turning into an electric fire that immediately set fire to the clothes in the airing cupboard!

The Company staff commenced working a five-day week from 1st January 1963, but I was unable to have a Saturday off until well into March that year. After my experience on the Berg Estate, we did defrost many hundreds of frozen services with the use of transformers by limiting the current and disconnecting any earth wires in the house. As a result of our experiences at the beginning of 1963, the Company immediately adopted the Southampton Pattern stopcock, a sturdier design without a 'crutch handle' and tightened up on the Water Byelaws, insisting that builders set up an insulated standpost before allowing any connection to the Company's mains.

At the beginning of March, the weather gradually warmed up, and the last item to be unfrozen was the 3-inch main in Mill Lane, Bedhampton. This happened on 15th March 1963."

Stan Leggett, who was an Inspector with Chichester Corporation Water Department, also remembered that time. "I was called out on Christmas Day 1962, to deal with problems caused by the freeze-up. In one incident, a householder in West Wittering asked me to visit a large house next door that was only occupied in the summer. Looking through the window, I saw furniture floating around inside the house, which had been flooded by a burst service pipe!"

The late Roy Etherington, who was at that time a Water Inspector in the Fareham area, recalled it being a time of continuous call-outs for days and weeks on end. On one call, he came across the heart-breaking sight of an old man sitting alone in front of a fireplace, from which a mixture of filthy water and soot was pouring, due to a burst pipe upstairs discharging water into the chimney flue. Roy made a pot of tea and called Social Services to take over.

He visited one house at the top of Miller Drive, Fareham, in response to a late night call. On completing the job and leaving the house, he found that his van had disappeared, having slid down the hill on the ice!

In the same area, one Sunday afternoon, he remembered: "I was called to repair a stopcock which had blown out, shooting water up into the air. At the time we all wore long rubberised mackintoshes. After getting soaked doing the job, I took off my mackintosh, which was frozen solid by now, and stood it up on its own beside the van – a strange sight. But it didn't prompt the people having tea in front of the fire in the house to bring me a cup!"

Improvements at Farlington Filtration Works

The exceptionally cold winter of 1963 caused many problems at Farlington. Normal procedure was for the slow sand filters to be cleaned in strict rotation by draining each bed and skimming off the top layer of sand by hand shovel into barrows; this process would take the Farlington staff about a week. Once the dirty sand had been removed, the bed would be refilled and then returned to service. During the winter of 1962/63, with temperatures rarely rising above freezing, the top surface of the wet sand would freeze solid, making it almost impossible for the dirty sand to be skimmed off. Even if the sand could be removed, it was almost impossible to operate the normal cleaning process and the frozen surface in the bed caused problems when it was refilled with water; it was very difficult to restart filtration.

Len Jones, Assistant Superintendent at that time, recalls, "With two filter beds being simultaneously frozen, the Works staff dared not drain any more beds. So, with throughput in the remaining beds being reduced as the sand became clogged, there was a considerable quandary. The Superintendent, George Davis, and I developed a specially fabricated rake which, if it was regularly dragged across the surface of the empty bed, would prevent the surface freezing solid. However, our invention left us with the task of ensuring that the raking operation was maintained around the clock. We didn't get a decent night's sleep for weeks!"

The growing demand for water in the Portsmouth area, coupled with the problems experienced that winter, quickly led to proposals being prepared to improve the treatment capacity at Farlington. By January 1964, the Company had accepted a tender from the Paterson Candy Filter Company for the provision of rapid gravity filters. Instead of the sand having to be skimmed manually and put through a sand washer, the new filter beds of gravel and sand would be washed automatically using an air scour and backwash system, thus greatly reducing the manual labour required. This was to be a valuable investment, given that labour costs rose rapidly in the years following. The new plant was officially opened in July 1966.

Company Finances

The amalgamation with the West Sussex Undertakings, the subsequent development of new resources, and the necessary distribution improvements, inevitably put significant strain on the Company's finances. On several occasions in the early part of the 1960s, there were issues of Debenture and Redeemable Preference Stock, which raised over £3m. Throughout the decade, the Company continued to try to restrain charges to consumers, but that restraint was severely tested when the Government decided to amend taxation arrangements as a result of the Finance Act 1965.

In 1965, it was reported that the Company's Retirement Benefits Scheme was in deficit and, consequently, additional payments were made into it.

In 1969, for the first time, the Company was required to pay abstraction licence charges of just over £31,000 to the River Authorities. At the same time, new training levies were introduced, while inflation was beginning to rise rapidly. The Government's Prices and Incomes Policy urged water undertakers to maintain strict control of prices. However, by 1970, the Company was forced to draw upon its reserves, and a wage increase of 20% in the same year led to charges rising by a similar amount in July.

Life at the Company

At the beginning of the 1960s, the Portsmouth and Gosport Water Company Board consisted of eight Directors, all of whom had been Directors of the Portsmouth and Gosport Companies. Over the decade, there were a number of changes owing to the death of Philip Childs, the Chairman, in 1960, and the election, following his retirement as Engineer in 1963, of Reg Hall. By 1970, the Board had shrunk to just five members, following the deaths of Sidney Raffety, Herbert Cooke and Reginald Page, the Deputy Chairman and one-time Portsmouth City Analyst.

A New Engineering Staff Structure

The expansion of the Company in 1963, led to some significant changes in its organisational structure, particularly in the Engineer's Department. Following the amalgamation with the 'Regnum Area' Undertakings, and the retirement of Reg Hall, the restructuring resulted in the promotion of the Deputy Engineer, Len Simpson, to the post of Chief Engineer, with George Slater, previously Senior Assistant Engineer, as his Deputy.

R W (Reg) Hall, Engineer, 1950-1963 (Photo courtesy of CIWEM)

A number of new senior posts were created, with John King, who had previously been Engineering Assistant, being appointed Supply Engineer and Alfred Burgess, the Engineer & Manager at the Chichester Corporation Water Department, becoming the new Distribution Engineer.

New Distribution Depots for Gosport, Bognor Regis and Chichester

The amalgamation of the Portsmouth and Gosport Companies in 1955 had resulted in much of the administrative work of the new combined Company being undertaken at the Head Office in Commercial Road, Portsmouth. As the Gosport Company's Office at High Street, Gosport, was surplus to requirements, in February 1962 the remaining distribution staff were relocated to new accommodation at the defunct Bury Cross Works in Privett Road. At the same time, the Company decided that it would no longer receive water rate payments at the Gosport High Street Office. Gosport councillors were incensed by the decision, since it resulted in residents either having to travel to Portsmouth, which in the 1960s was not very convenient, or else having to pay by bank credit and incur bank charges. Despite the ferocity of the arguments made by a number of councillors and residents in the local press, the Company resisted any change to its policy. By 1965, Gosport Town Council had agreed that it would collect rates on behalf of the Company at its offices to assuage the feelings of local residents, and this practice continued for a number of years afterwards.

Bognor Regis District Office and Depot, 1960s

Almost as soon as the ink was dry on the agreements to purchase the 'Regnum Area' Undertakings in West Sussex, the Company was planning the administrative arrangements for what would become its new 'East District'. By the autumn of 1964, it had constructed a new District Office and Depot at Amberley Drive in Bognor Regis, as a base from which to maintain the network of the former Bognor Regis UDC. Peter Harvey, who had worked at the Chichester Corporation, became the Manager of the East District. At Fishbourne, a depot was set up in some disused parts of the pumping station and, although they were controlled from the Bognor Regis Office, the staff were responsible for maintaining the networks of the former Chichester Corporation,

Chichester RDC and Selsey Water Company. The Company's newly acquired staff were able to vacate temporary offices at Bognor Regis Town Hall and the Chichester Corporation's Tower Street depot.

George Slater makes a presentation to Peter Harvey on his departure from the Company in December 1965

New Working Practices

The 1960s brought a number of changes to the working practices in all walks of life and the Water Industry was no exception.

With electrical pumping plant replacing oil or steam-driven plant at many sources and modern controls at the new borehole sites, the Company was able to automate the operation of these works and reduce manpower in the Supply Department. The installation of a system of 'automatic warning devices', today better known as telemetry, which relayed information to a new central Control Room at Havant, enabled the Company to reduce the number of pumping station attendants from 25 in 1963 to just four some five years later. Mobile maintenance technicians were then charged with the responsibility of attending to faults relayed from the works to the Control Room via the telemetry system. Doug Corbin, who was Mechanical and Electrical Engineer from 1959 to 1986, recalls that the system used a modified burglar alarm that would dial up the Control Room at Havant and play a gramophone record confirming the alarm! The first one was installed at George Reservoir and gradually they became more sophisticated as they were introduced across the Company's area. Doug says, "I visited a number of other water companies, whose systems had cost much more than the £50,000 that the Company had spent."

The Distribution Department was also undergoing significant change, obtaining modern equipment such as mechanical excavators and thrust-boring machines, which made the tasks associated with mains repairs, mainlaying and servicelaying much quicker. It was only at this time that the Company was beginning to provide motor vehicles to many of its Distribution staff; in the 1950s, there were many turncocks using bicycles and the mains repair gangs were still using handcarts. The Board minutes from that era are littered with references to the purchase of new vehicles; so many were there that the Company's coach painter, Lew Stent, had the sole duty of turning out all the vehicles in their brown and gold livery.

Some of the Company's vehicles in 1964 with, left, Motor Vehicle Supervisor Reg Woolrich and right, Mr Rickard, chief salesman of Central Garage

At the same time, the Ministry was urging water undertakers to develop greater productivity in the Industry by introducing what were commonly referred to as 'bonus schemes'. It was very much a period when the Company management held the 'upper hand'. Dave Morris, who was a Plumber at the Portsmouth Depot, recalls " The clocking-in machine was rigidly policed by Jock McIntyre, Chief Turncock, and Charlie Smith, Gangs Foreman. If you were even one minute late clocking on at 7.30, you were recorded as being late. If it happened a second time in the same week, you were sent home and got no pay."

To improve communications, the Company purchased a radio system, which for the first time, enabled operational staff to keep in touch with their Depot and the Control Room, as well as each other.

Radio van in use, 1960s. Left to right: Jack Bennett, Fred Smith and (on excavator) Brian Plumstead

Following the Industrial Training Act 1964, Industry leaders decided that there would be significant benefit in setting up joint training facilities and the first Training Council for the Water Supply Industry (with many subsequent changes of name) was set up. Many Company employees were trained at the residential training centres developed in the 1960s; subsequently several Company staff lectured on the courses. Recognising the need to develop its workforce, the Company began a number of trade apprenticeships for waterworks craftsmen, primarily in the Distribution Department.

The Introduction of Bonus Schemes

Following proposals set out in the Prices and Incomes Board Report 29, the Company asked PA Management Consultants to investigate the possibility of implementing productivity schemes. The consultants' report, in January 1968, recommended the setting up of a Work Study Department and Maurice Croxon, from Stevenage Borough Council, joined the Company as Chief Work Study Officer in June 1968. A department with two Assistant Officers, an Observer Clerk and two Workers' Representatives, from the trade unions, was quickly set up alongside a Joint Productivity Committee, consisting of Management, Employee and Trade Union representatives. A good degree of co-operation was achieved and the first productivity scheme was implemented in the Meter Repair Workshop in November 1968. A scheme to cover the Mainlaying and Mains Maintenance activities was introduced in the middle of 1969, and further schemes were rapidly developed, either by the Work Study Department or PA Consultants, to cover most of the Company's manual trades. A novel scheme, introduced for the Inspection and Waste Department in early 1970, incorporated two key elements in the calculation of the bonus payment. Not surprisingly, the first was related to the actual productivity of individuals, but the second element was subject to a monthly calculation of the amount of leakage from the distribution network; in other words, as leakage levels were reduced, so the bonus payments increased. Inevitably, there were many debates about the leakage calculations!

Maurice Croxon himself recalls, "There was little doubt that the schemes increased overall productivity and they were used by the Company to reduce staffing levels. However, there always seemed to be accusations that 'Work Study was running the Company'!"

A new Head Office

The Company's Offices at Commercial Road, Portsmouth, were opened in May 1884 and sufficed for 83 years. The late George Slater described why they were eventually relocated to Havant and the details of the move. In his words: -

"After the expansion of the Company into Sussex in 1963, alterations were made at the Head Office to increase the available office space, but this was not particularly successful, as people were crowded into the back entrance. The Directors, at a Board Meeting held at Worlds End Pumping Station in 1965, therefore decided to relocate the offices to the Havant Works. At this Board Meeting, the Secretary & Treasurer, Eric Guymer, explained that, if the Admiralty agreed to abandon an agreement of 1906 under which they were supplied with water at the price of 6d ($2^1/_2$ pence) per thousand gallons, and agreed to pay the Company's standard rate, this would mitigate the cost of the new development. In due course, Eric was able to successfully negotiate this amendment!

For some time, the Company had been considering computerisation, but at the time of the construction of the new building, the particular model of computer had not been decided upon. Space was provided for a large machine, an IBM 360 Model, on the first floor with the input section accommodated on the ground floor. In the event, the new computer was much smaller than had been envisaged and it became possible to include both on the first floor! The ground floor thus became available for the printing section, which was another new venture for the Company. The cost of the new buildings at Havant, that is the office block, the workshops and stores, was £530,000.

The move to Havant took place in September 1967. This had been carefully planned with White & Company, a local removals firm, to fully occupy one day, but such was the enthusiasm for the move by the staff that, by lunchtime, the operation was virtually completed. Included in the new office complex was a staff canteen, the first time the Company had provided catering, and at this time the cost of a two-course meal was 2s 6d ($12^1/_2$ p). The new complex also included a brand new Social Club. This had previously been located in an old pumping station that had been knocked down to provide for a stores extension. At the opening night of the new Club, 300 people attended and there was absolute chaos!"

The new Head Office at Havant, 1967

The reception desk at Havant Head Office. Left: Mary Morrison, right: Tony Ludlow

Norman Hudson, who was Engineering Assistant at the time of the move (and later became Chief Distribution Engineer), recalls: "It was very cramped at Commercial Road towards the end. Eventually staff took over what were originally two flats at the top of the building. One had been occupied by the caretaker and the other by Jack Bennett (who worked in the Drawing Office) and his father, who was Superintendent at the Portsmouth Depot. This gave opportunities to go up and have a coffee there, or else in the Southdown bus depot over the road!

After the move to Havant from Commercial Road, it was a great improvement for office space. An awful lot of material was thrown out in the move, which ideally one would like to have saved, but it was impossible. Places were allocated at the new office beforehand, furniture was numbered and up it all came. George Slater, then Deputy Engineer, was in charge of the office move".

The Drawing Office 1969. In the corner office (and insert) is Chief Draughtsman, Stan Drew. Others, left to right are: Mick Wiggins, Bob Simmonds, Janet Simpkins, Don Pindar and Jeff Etherington

Chris Whatley, a carpenter at the time and subsequently Building Maintenance Superintendent, recalls "At the time there was a rumour that the Directors were to have a banqueting suite on the top floor of the building and each of them was to have his own toilet and shower! The truth was that they shared a toilet and the only other concession was that their offices were carpeted."

Not everything was entirely successful at the new offices. The new fountain, in the centre of the roundabout at the entrance sprayed customers paying their bills even in the slightest wind and a 'waterwheel' alongside the main entrance doors never worked properly. The waterwheel was quickly removed, but the fountain was replaced some years later with the outlet bellmouth pipes from the demolished filter beds at Farlington. The old Commercial Road Offices were demolished in the later redevelopment of Portsmouth city centre.

The relocation of the Head Office to Havant resulted in the need for a new base to be found for the staff responsible for everyday distribution maintenance in Portsmouth. Part of the Portsbridge

Booster Station, on the north side of Portscreek, was converted to enable Mains and Services gangs and teams of Inspectors to operate from a new depot in close proximity to Portsea Island. The conversion was completed in 1968 and remained in use until the 1990s.

The First Computer

The Computer Room, Havant Head Office, with operator Joyce Neville

It was in 1966, in connection with the development of the new Head Office, that a decision was taken to purchase the Company's first computer. This was principally required to simplify the billing process. Until then, the Company had used an Addressograph system developed in 1914 by the then Secretary, Richard Bishop. The system, referred to as a 'Negative Posting System', and requiring new 'plates' to be prepared each time the water rate changed, had been widely adopted by a number of other water undertakers. It meant that, because of the labour-intensive process of producing new plates, the Company was reluctant to raise its charges! Eventually, rising inflation in the late 1960s meant that charges had to rise and so a simpler system for sending out bills to customers had to be found.

Although an IBM machine had originally been chosen, John Batty, former Managing Director, recalls that, at a late stage, the Company changed its mind and chose a Univac 9300, which was found to be significantly smaller in size and hence took up much less space in the new offices. However, it wasn't until 1969 that the first bills were produced on the new computer! The new computer had just 8 kilobytes of memory, a mere fraction of the capacity of portable computers and other technology in common use in 2007.

Initially the Computer Section was set up without specialist help, but it soon became clear that trained computer staff would be needed and Tony Perry joined the Company in 1969. By this time, the

Customer Billing System was well advanced and he began to set up the other 'mainframe' systems, many of which, while much updated, are still in use. Whilst he was not involved in the original billing system, he eventually became the Company's Chief Revenue Officer, retiring in 1997.

Introduction of uPVC Pipes

In the mid-1960s, the corrosion of old cast iron pipes, the Industry's standard material for over 150 years, was causing significant problems. Burst mains were commonplace and the cost of repairs, both during and outside normal working hours, was rising. The answer seemed to be a new material, uPVC (unplasticised polyvinyl chloride) pipe, which was corrosion resistant, much lighter and easier to lay. It was a by-product of the oil industry and so was also competitively priced. Norman Hudson, then Distribution Engineer, recalls "I instigated the recommendation to George Slater that the Company should adopt uPVC as its preferred mains material. At the time, we had no inkling of the problems that would eventually emerge, and would of course have acted differently in hindsight. What we did know was that the corrosion and failure of cast iron pipes was becoming a big problem and incurring high costs for the Company, and something really did need to be done. The only alternative to cast iron and uPVC was steel, which would have posed similar problems to cast iron in due course and was thus not suitable. I visited the factory of Yorkshire Plastics, our first supplier of uPVC pipes, and looked at the manufacturing process and quality tests that were carried out - it seemed a very attractive material. Although the larger diameter uPVC pipes subsequently caused major problems of bursting, the smaller mains were satisfactory and many remain in service today."

Computerised Network Analysis

In 1968, impressed with the capabilities of the computer programme developed by the Water Research Association to predict the performance of mains networks, the Company committed itself to a joint venture with five other companies to purchase a 'Network Analyser'. The Company's commitment to buy the computer equipment cost £145 per annum over a five-year period.

The Network Analyser was used to design further improvement schemes in 1969, the principal one being a new 24-inch main between Littleheath Reservoir and Bognor Regis (laid in three stages). The linking of the Hambledon supply to the trunk main between Lovedean and Clanfield Reservoir and a small distribution improvement in the Meon valley followed quickly.

Water Quality

Until the 1960s, the Company checked the quality of its supplies by sending fortnightly samples from the distribution network to the Counties Public Health Laboratories in London. Annual Reports from the time confirmed that "the water is of the highest standard of bacterial purity, indicative of a wholesome water suitable for drinking and domestic purposes".

The development of a Water Quality Department

A new post of Chief Chemist and Bacteriologist was created to enable the Company to conduct its own analysis of water samples. The Company appointed Tom Jobling to this post and he started work in April 1964, in a newly created laboratory adjacent to Havant Pumping Station. The first samples were analysed on 22nd June of that year. Subsequently, more frequent sampling and analysis for both chemical and microbiological parameters was conducted on the basis of new World Health Organisation recommendations. The following year's Engineer's Report contained, for the first time, a separate section prepared by the Chief Chemist and Bacteriologist. This summarised the details of the samples taken, the results of the analyses and 'a comprehensive picture of the normal nature and quality of the various waters supplied by the Company'. It also gave some insight into some of the quality concerns raised by customers.

Fluoridation Proposals

In 1963, the Government published recommendations that water undertakers should fluoridate water supplies to improve the dental health of the population. These proposals were to start a debate that continues to cause considerable conflict amongst dental professionals and opposing pressure groups,

Tom Jobling in the new Laboratory, 1967. In the background, left, is Barry Abrahams and at the microscope is Roger Nash

even today. Initially, many local authorities were in favour of fluoridation and wrote to the Company to urge it to adopt the proposals. There was much heated debate in the press and, one assumes, in many council chambers. It was not long before many councils retracted their pleas, in the face of strong opposition.

The Need for further Water Resources

As has been outlined earlier, domestic demand was rising rapidly as household habits changed during the 1960s. The Company's annual Engineering Reports show that personal consumption (including leakage) rose from 32.8 gallons per head per day in 1959/60, to 44.9 gallons per head per day in 1969/70, a 37% increase in just ten years. Coupled with rising population and up to 5,000 new properties per annum being connected in the middle of the decade, the Company was concerned that it would not be able to keep up with rising demand. This concern led to the development of the Inspection and Waste Department Bonus Scheme, which reduced leakage levels in the short term. However, the Company recognised that, in the longer term, new resources would be needed too.

Havant Thicket Winter Storage Reservoir

Throughout the 1960s, demand rose rapidly. Although the development of the borehole sites was keeping pace with increasing demand, the need remained to develop major new resources, especially if the planned 'Solent City' was to materialise.

It was in 1961, during the negotiations for the Ems valley scheme, that mention was first made of the possibility of storing the surplus yield from the Company's Havant and Bedhampton Springs. It had been known for many years that, although in drought summers the yield of the springs might only be sufficient to supply Portsmouth, the yield in all but the driest winters was far in excess of the Company's requirements. Thus, for many months of the year, despite the springs abstractions, there would be very significant quantities of water overflowing into Langstone Harbour; the proposal was, therefore, that a reservoir site be sought, where some of the surplus yield could be stored and used to augment the springs during peak summer demand.

By 1962, the Company had identified what appeared to be a suitable site at Havant Thicket, just north of Leigh Park. A soils investigation proved the site to be suitable for a reservoir and, in January 1963, the Board authorised the Engineer to begin negotiations to purchase the site. By the end of the year, Hampshire County Council had granted planning permission and the Company was close to agreeing purchase terms with the Forestry Commission, the owners of the land. Yet again, the Company was wasting no time in planning for new resources, although in due course, the scheme was to be deferred in favour of the River Itchen Scheme, described below.

The Company was also involved in the 1966 Water Resources Board investigation, which identified Southleigh Forest, an area to the north of Emsworth, as another potential reservoir site. The Company decided to purchase this site too, the negotiations being completed by early 1966. In 1969, the Board approved a 'self-financing scheme' that enabled the woodland at Havant Thicket to be cleared in stages and the land made available for grazing.

The River Itchen Scheme

The studies by the Water Resources Board and Herbert Lapworth had identified not only the possibility of developing winter storage reservoirs, but also the availability of significant quantities of water from the River Itchen. For water quality reasons, the Company was keen to develop an abstraction point just upstream of the main sewage treatment works serving Eastleigh. However, the River Authority wanted to maintain river flows to encourage spawning salmon and this meant that their preferred abstraction point was at Gaters Mill, near West End. Just above the tidal limit at Woodmill, the abstraction at Gaters Mill was expected to have minimal environmental impact on river life. Its proximity to Southampton Airport meant that it would also be ideally situated to meet demand from the proposed 'Solent City'. Despite the Company's best efforts, the River Authority would not be persuaded otherwise.

However, always keen to seize the initiative, the Company's Board approved a proposal in September 1967 to abstract and treat 15 million gallons per day from the river at Gaters Mill.

Phase I of the scheme was to consist of a river intake works, with screens and low lift pumps delivering water to a nearby treatment works. In addition, there would be a treated water reservoir, high lift pumping plant and a nine-mile, 40-inch pumping main to a new service reservoir at Hoads Hill, near Wickham. This phase was estimated to cost £1.875m. Negotiations for the rights to develop the chosen site had already commenced with the Hampshire River and Planning Authorities and with local land and fishery owners. At the same time, the Board approved a proposal to install a pilot treatment plant to determine the treatment process best suited for dealing with the worst pollution conditions. The intention was to have the works completed and commissioned by 1972.

Phase II, which was expected to follow three or fours year later, comprised the construction of a booster pumping station at Hoads Hill, together with a 2.7-mile, 36-inch diameter pumping main to a new service reservoir adjacent to Fort Nelson on Portsdown Hill. Water would then gravitate to the rapidly growing Waterlooville area via a new 36-inch trunk main and to Portchester via a new 20-inch main.

The project programme anticipated the completion of pilot trials by early 1969, a licence application to the Hampshire River Authority by June and an application to the Ministry for a Parliamentary Order at the same time. The trials were completed, as planned, in March that year, and Paterson Candy International was commissioned to prepare the detailed treatment works design. By July, the Hampshire River Authority had issued an abstraction licence for 10 million gallons per day, despite a number of objections having been received. However, the application to the Ministry took much longer to resolve, with a Public Inquiry being held on 2nd December 1969 and the Order not being finally made until 14th October 1970.

Details of the development of the engineering aspects of the River Itchen Scheme are covered in the next chapter.

1970-80: Rampant Inflation followed by Economic Recession

Although demand continued to rise at a rapid rate at the beginning of the 1970s, that rate slowed during the decade as a result of a number of factors. The first was the drought which affected most of the country in 1976. It resulted not only in a reduction in overall demand, but also the realisation that it was important for consumers to value their water supplies. This applied not only to domestic consumers, but also to major commercial users who, recognising the financial value of the savings in 1976, made them a permanent feature of their operations. Another factor was the inflationary impact of rising charges which, together with the oil and power crises, drove the nation's manufacturing industry to carefully examine its operating costs. Many industries began to look for efficiencies in their processes, including their demands for water. Towards the end of the decade, the country was affected by economic recession, which resulted in significant changes in the manufacturing base throughout the UK. In Portsmouth, a great many traditional industries began to disappear.

The Establishment of Regional Water Authorities and Further Changes in the Industry

In 1970, the Ministry of Housing and Local Government became the Department of the Environment (DoE) and, within a year, its Central Advisory Water Committee had recommended the amalgamation of many water boards and local authority water undertakings into ten new Regional Water Authorities. The Water Act 1973 led to the establishment of the new authorities in April 1974, with the statutory water companies remaining in existence, despite the Labour Government's desire to nationalise them. Although that desire surfaced from time to time during the decade, the Water Companies' Association lobbied hard for the 'status quo' to be maintained.

The creation of the Regional Water Authorities and a central governing body called the National Water Council to oversee the management of the Industry provided the focus for employee terms and conditions to be negotiated and agreed on a national basis. That arrangement was in place for 15 years and eventually created many local tensions, but it has to be remembered that the 1970s was a decade when trade unions were able to exert considerable power.

Following Government pressure to provide pension arrangements for all employees, the Water Companies' Association (WCA) set up a consolidated Pension Scheme in 1973, to which it was encouraging all its members to contribute. The Company had maintained its own Scheme since 1925 and, despite some pressure, it decided to retain its own Scheme for existing employees, whilst new employees were required to join the WCA Scheme. This was to be an important decision as is described in later chapters, although the Trustees at the time might not have realised just how important.

In 1977, the Government obtained Parliamentary approval for the Water Equalisation Charges Act with the intention, over a period of years, of adjusting water charges to be the same across the country. Responsible for some of the lowest charges in the industry, the Board was incensed, but there was little that it could do except raise charges to meet the statutory levy paid to the Government. In 1978, charges to Portsmouth consumers had to rise by 21.4% in order to pay a levy of £556,000! Fortunately, the new Conservative Government repealed the Act soon after its election in 1979, and the requirement to pay equalisation levies ceased after 1982.

Company Structure and Finances

Board and Management Changes

In 1974, Eric Guymer, Secretary & Treasurer since 1958, retired after 47 years' service with the Company. In recognition of his valuable experience, Eric was appointed a Non-Executive Director and remained a Board member until 1992. The Board then decided, for the first time in its history, to appoint an Engineer & Manager. Leonard Simpson, who was already Engineer, was appointed to the new post, and Fred Bailey, the Assistant Secretary, became the new Secretary & Treasurer.

Engineer & Manager Leonard Simpson, centre, at his retirement. Left is Eric Guymer, right is Jack Bennett

The post of Engineer & Manager was to be a short-lived arrangement, as Leonard Simpson retired in 1976. George Slater, the Deputy Engineer, who had joined the Company in 1950, was appointed Chief Engineer.

Chairman of the Board, Leonard Glanville, died in November 1975. His successor, David Childs, was awarded the OBE in 1977 for, among other things, his services to the Industry. The Safety and Training Officer, Jack Bennett, was awarded the Queen's Silver Jubilee Medal at the same time.

Financial Pressures

In the previous chapter, reference has been made to the Government's attempts to control inflation in the late 1960s. The demands for higher wages eventually led to a 20% increase in charges in 1970. Despite the Company's efforts to improve efficiencies in its operations, a further rise of 30% was necessary in 1972!

The Annual Report for 1973 referred to the additional administrative burdens which were expected from the imposition of Value Added Tax (VAT) from 1st April. The next year, a massive 45% increase in charges followed, again due mainly to 'raging inflation'.

In 1976, the Company raised capital through a £5m issue of Redeemable Preference Stock, partly to replace stock recently redeemed, but also to provide the capital for investment in further links between the supply networks.

By 1979, the Company had applied to the Department of the Environment (DoE) for an Order to increase the Company's authorised capital, from £20.4m to £30m, in advance of a further £5m issue of capital stock in 1979.

Droughts in the 1970s

The summer of 1969 had been very dry and the following year, the yields of sources had fallen to record lows. Even more extreme conditions were to come, which were to test the Company's ability to maintain supplies.

A warning in 1973

Until the commissioning of the River Itchen scheme in 1973, the Company had been entirely dependent upon its groundwater supplies from the springs, wells and boreholes. The yield of these sources would vary considerably during the year, the yield being dictated by groundwater levels in the South Downs chalk.

At the beginning of the winter of 1972/73, rainfall was well below average. Fortunately a wet December resulted in some recharge of the aquifer, but below-average rainfall throughout 1973 led to groundwater levels in the summer and autumn falling to the lowest level recorded since the drought of 1933/34. However, the Company had already been alert to the situation in the autumn of 1972 and, although it was confident that it would be able to partially commission the new River Itchen scheme, negotiations took place with the Southampton Corporation for a potential temporary supply from the Corporation's network into the new Itchen pumping main at Boorley Green.

Mindful of the anticipated future development of the proposed 'Solent City', as well as the possibility of increasing the abstraction at Gaters Mill, these negotiations spurred the Company to consider taking over responsibility for Southampton's water supplies. It was around this time that legislation was being considered for setting up new Regional Water Authorities and it seemed that Southampton City Council preferred 'nationalisation' to selling its assets to a private company. Nothing further came of the idea.

In June 1973, as groundwater levels continued to fall, the Company took the unusual step of appealing to its customers to conserve supplies, first by fixing stickers to its vans and then by making direct appeals on BBC Radio Solent. A number of temporary distribution connections were made, primarily to enable more water from the new Fort Nelson Reservoir to augment supplies to Portsmouth, Southwick and Worlds End. Formal restrictions were avoided and heavy rainfall finally came in December 1973. Groundwater levels rose rapidly at the end of January and, by the summer of 1974, the resource situation was back to normal.

The Drought of 1976 - A Major Challenge to the Industry

Having survived quite narrowly in 1973, the Company's Board was far from complacent and a number of measures outlined elsewhere in this chapter were approved. Unfortunately, none of them was completed in time for the next drought in 1976, one that would affect a much larger area than just that of the Company. The lack of rainfall first became apparent in the latter part of the summer of 1975, with prolonged hot, dry weather that resulted in record water demand for the Company and many other water undertakers. Worse was to follow, with less than 47% of long-term average rainfall throughout the winter of 1975/76. The conditions were so dry that the Company's groundwater level monitoring borehole on the Hampshire/Sussex border at Idsworth recorded no recharge of the chalk aquifer at all. The record at Idsworth, which had been maintained since 1932, had only recorded no winter recharge on one previous occasion, and that was in the drought period of 1933/34.

In anticipation of difficulties in meeting demand, the Company recommissioned the sources at Hoe, Woodmancote and Slindon, which had been mothballed some years earlier, but provided significant and very valuable additional yield.

By April 1976, the Board had already authorised the Engineer to ban hosepipes and sprinklers, if necessary, albeit after prior consultation with the Chairman.

It needs to be remembered that, at this stage in the Company's history, there were still relatively few interconnections between the supply systems inherited from predecessor undertakers. By the end of May, and despite the recommissioning of Slindon source, the situation in the East District was so serious that a hosepipe ban was necessary in the Arun District Council area, and this came into force from 1st June. The June Board Minutes record that even Fontwell Park Racecourse was refused permission to water the course from the Company's supply.

During June, the situation across the whole country became so serious that the possibility of standpipes in the streets was being contemplated in certain areas. This galvanised the Industry nationally and, in conjunction with the national media, a country-wide campaign urged consumers to save water. It highlighted the problems that were facing the Industry and this heightened awareness had a very significant impact upon demand from both domestic and commercial consumers. Although the Company still appeared to have sufficient resources, it extended its hosepipe ban at the beginning of July 1976 to cover the whole area of supply to help enforce the restrictions imposed by neighbouring companies. The Company also took steps to reduce pressures in certain supply zones where this was possible. Although not essential, staff were sent out in the evenings on 'hosepipe patrols'. Although there is no recollection of any prosecution of customers for using their hosepipes during bans, a number of staff recall customers trying to hide hosepipes down their trousers or under their jumpers once they saw the patrols approaching! Dave Morris, a Company Inspector at that time, recalls that, on one occasion, while carrying out a mains flushing exercise after a 'dirty water incident', he and his colleagues came in for much criticism from local residents, incensed at the apparent waste of water.

The national media picked up the drought story and, across the country, householders placed bricks in toilet cisterns to reduce the amount of water used in flushing, while plants were watered with washing-up water. Then finally, in August, the Government appointed a Minister for Drought, Denis Howell MP, to manage the crisis. The whole process had a dramatic effect, with demand some 30%

lower than normally expected by the end of August. The appointment of the Minister seemed to have the desired effect; almost immediately the rains came! By the end of September, groundwater levels had begun to rise again, although it was not until October that the Company finally lifted its hosepipe ban. By the end of August, the Company's rain gauge at Havant showed that, in the previous twelve months, there had been only 38.6% of the long-term average rainfall.

Average demand for the year turned out to be 10% less than the previous year and the Board noted, at its September meeting, that the lower demand from commercial customers would reduce the Company's revenue. The reductions in commercial demand achieved by large businesses became permanent losses in revenue.

In November, having suspended charges for the use of garden hosepipes during the drought, the Board decided that it would not reinstate the hosepipe licence charge.

The River Itchen Scheme

In July 1969, an abstraction licence was issued by the Hampshire River Authority, and planning permission was granted by Hampshire County Council in April 1970. However, work on the scheme could not commence until a Ministerial Order confirmed the outcome of the Public Inquiry, held in December 1969. In anticipation, the Company had already let a provisional contract to Shellabear Price Contractors Ltd (a local company with a long association with Portsmouth Water) and work started on site almost immediately after the Order was made on 14th October 1970.

The scheme had been conceived in two phases. However, owing to the delay with the Ministerial Order and the still-rising demand for water, the Company decided, in December 1970, to proceed as quickly as possible with Phase II immediately after Phase I, with overall completion being programmed for 1974.

Phase I

The elements of Phase I of the scheme, designed for a throughput of 15 million gallons per day, were as follows: -

- ***River Intake and Low Lift Pumping Station***, sited just upstream of Gaters Mill, comprising six separate intakes, floating booms to exclude debris, coarse bar screens and fine mesh rotating drum screens, with space for eight fixed-speed pumps of different duties. These allowed a wide range of abstraction rates to be delivered to the treatment works. A facility for chlorine dosing was included to begin the disinfection process.

The Intake and Low Lift Pumping Station at Gaters Mill, River Itchen, 1973

- ***A Treatment Works*** consisting of two stages of treatment. The first stage, of clarification, incorporated a flash mixer and contact tank for chemical coagulation, together with two banks of eight pyramidal clarifiers. The second stage, filtration, was carried out in six rapid gravity sand filters. The chemical building incorporated chemical storage facilities, the dosing plant for the treatment process, as well as electrical controls and displays.

- Three ***Sludge Disposal Tanks***, together with sludge thickening plant, lagoons and drying beds enabled the solids to be removed, with the improved washwater returned to the main treatment process.

The clarifiers at the River Itchen Treatment Works

- A 2 million gallon capacity chlorine ***Contact Tank*** for disinfection.

The High Lift Pumping Station

Laying the River Itchen 40-inch pumping main at Moor Green

- A ***High Lift Pumping Station*** with facility for eight horizontally mounted centrifugal pumps, providing a range of duties to deliver up 15 million gallons per day to Hoads Hill Service Reservoirs. The pumping station also contained the washwater pumps for filter washing.

- A 40-inch diameter steel ***pumping main***, 9 miles long, from the Works to Hoads Hill, where a second ***service reservoir*** was constructed.

The scheme, which was probably the largest undertaken since the development of the original Farlington Filtration Works and Reservoirs in the early 1900s, was managed by the Company's engineering staff led by Deputy Chief Engineer, George Slater. Internal staff, external consultants and contractors, as outlined below, carried out separate elements: -

- Kenneth Severn Associates carried out the detailed design of the intake, treatment works and pumping stations, with architectural input from Thomas Makins.

- The main contractor for the construction work, both at the River Itchen and Hoads Hill sites, was Shellabear Price Contractors Ltd

- The 40-inch steel pumping main was laid by four supply gangs, headed by George Biggs, Jim Gregory, Frank New and Jack Bennett.

- Paterson Candy International supplied the treatment plant, instrumentation and controls, most of which were installed by the Company's mechanical and electrical staff.

Whilst the capacity of the works was 15 million gallons per day, sufficient space was provided on the site for doubling the capacity at some later date.

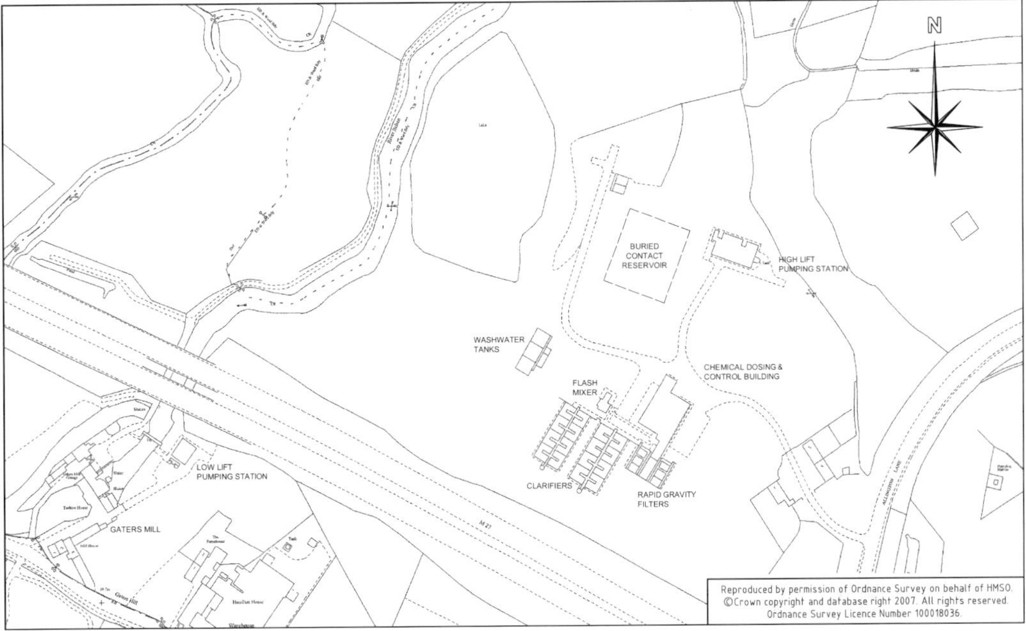

Layout of the River Itchen Water Treatment Works

Phase II

Phase II was developed to provide urgently needed supplies to the rapidly expanding areas in and around Waterlooville, and to eventually allow an emergency transfer to be made via Portchester to the Farlington supply area. Until then, the area had been wholly dependent upon the Havant & Bedhampton Springs for its supply. Whilst the springs had not failed the Company in over a century, there was increasing concern that a pollution incident in the very large catchment area might potentially contaminate supplies. John King, Supply Engineer at the time, recalls that a temporary over-ground pipeline was laid along the military road on the top of Portsdown Hill in order to be able to augment the supply to Farlington during the 1973 drought.

Phase II, which closely followed the completion of Phase I, therefore consisted of the following elements:

- A new 10 million gallon service reservoir constructed by Shellabear Price Construction Ltd, adjacent to Fort Nelson on Portsdown Hill.

- A 2.6 mile section of 36-inch diameter steel pumping main from Hoads Hill to Fort Nelson Reservoir, laid by the Company's own supply staff.

- A new booster pumping station at Hoads Hill Reservoirs, to deliver 8 million gallons per day from Hoads Hill to Fort Nelson Reservoir, constructed by Shellabear Price and using Weir pumps.

- Two new gravity distribution mains, the first being a 36-inch trunk main from Fort Nelson Reservoir to Waterlooville. The second, a 20-inch cast iron main to Portchester, not only enabled new developments at high elevation to be supplied, but also could support the Farlington supply area. Both mains were laid by direct labour staff.

Phase I of the Scheme was officially opened on 4th October 1973 by Sir John Cockram, the Chairman of the Water Companies' Association. Phase II was finally completed and brought into service in 1974, although not until some temporary connections had been made to enable sections of the 36-inch main to be used to alleviate the drought during the dry autumn of 1973.

Unforeseen Problems

The commissioning of the River Itchen supply was not without a number of setbacks and many of them did not come to light for a number of years, as will be covered later.

The first problem was the reaction of the Company's customers in the Gosport area to the introduction of treated river water to a system which had, until then, been entirely based upon groundwater supplies. Although the base flow of the river was largely groundwater derived, upstream of the Gaters Mill intake there were a number of watercress beds and fish farms, each abstracting water and discharging effluents. In addition, Eastleigh Sewage Treatment Works at Chickenhall Lane was just 3 kilometres upstream, together with a number of surface water discharges from industrial sites. As a result, the chemical composition of the river water was markedly different from a chalk borehole supply. Immediately the new Works was commissioned, there were a number of complaints from customers, who detected an 'earthy taste'. These were largely from those with sensitive palates, and in time, most customers became accustomed to the new supply. However, there were a number of subsequent occasions when activities upstream of the Gaters Mill abstraction, such as weed cutting carried out by water bailiffs, would lead to a fresh set of taste complaints.

In other parts of the country, a number of pollution incidents affected river abstractions and discharges. It was not long after commissioning that the Company was similarly affected. The intake had to be shut down for 24 hours in November 1975 following a chemical spillage in Eastleigh. Worse was to follow, when the river was polluted by a manure spillage in May 1976, at the most critical period during the drought, when supplies could not be suspended. Through judicious treatment, a shutdown was avoided on that occasion, but it was clear that the Company needed some protection from the dangers of future incidents. Consideration was given to the installation of 'bankside storage' that would enable the Gaters Mill intake to be closed from time to time without having to suspend treatment. This option was adopted, but negotiations for the land and difficulties with ground conditions at the chosen site at nearby Highwood delayed the start of reservoir construction until 1980.

Despite the difficulties experienced with taste from the River Itchen Works, a rather more disturbing issue came to light in 1979. A residential Study Centre at Stubbington, run by the Hampshire

Education Committee, reported that a number of visiting students had reported digestive upsets. Although accusations were made that the problems had only been experienced since the commissioning of the River Itchen Works, extensive sampling was never able to attribute any cause.

The Development of Further Resources

Despite record water consumption in the summer of 1970, at the beginning of the decade the Company believed that it was well placed to meet the increasing demands from planned housing developments. This confidence arose from the planned completion of the River Itchen Scheme and the possibility of the subsequent development of Havant Thicket Reservoir.

Borehole drilling at Brickkiln, March 1976

In October 1973, as groundwater levels began to fall to record levels, the Sussex River Authority, who were responsible for water resource planning, advised the Company that it planned to seek a potential new source in the Lavant valley to the north of Chichester. In due course, the newly formed Southern Water Authority (which took over responsibility for water resource planning following the Water Act 1973) took up that proposal. The boreholes, sited near Brick Kiln Farm in the Chilgrove valley, were developed jointly by the Company and the Authority. They were not completed until early 1976, when discussions were held with the Authority about the possible emergency use of the new boreholes during the drought. In the event, the hosepipe bans and nationwide publicity resulted in such a demand reduction that the boreholes were not required. However, in due course, the Company applied for an abstraction licence for the new boreholes at Brickkiln.

By July 1977, frustrated by the failure of Southern Water Authority to issue an abstraction licence, the Board, nevertheless, approved a scheme for the construction of a permanent pumping station at Brickkiln. Situated in the Chilgrove valley, a very rural part of Sussex, it became apparent, when the Company approached local planners, that the building needed to be unobtrusive. Their first suggestion was that the Company should build it a mile away, not understanding the fact that the location was the result of the local hydrogeology! The Company's architect, Bruce Carter of Thomas Makins, in conjunction with the

Brickkiln Pumping Station, built in the style of a Sussex barn

Supply Engineer, John King, therefore resolved to develop the building in the style of a Sussex barn, using flint walls and clay tiles. The design found favour with the local planners and Brickkiln Pumping Station was opened in September 1979, the abstraction licence having finally been granted in July 1977.

The traditional materials used did not go unnoticed as, one night in 1983, all the Sussex clay tiles on one side of the roof were stolen. By the time they were recovered by police some months later, the Company had already replaced them.

Improvements to Existing Sources

Eastergate

In 1973, the Company embarked upon improvements at Eastergate, which still used the direct current pumps installed by the Bognor Regis Undertaking. New alternating current submersible pumps were installed in the well, together with a new mains power supply. Owing to the varying microbiological quality of the raw water at the site, the Company also installed a new contact main and the facility to superchlorinate the supply to improve disinfection. The contact main ensured that the high dose of chlorine was in contact with the water for a specified time to ensure that the supply was adequately disinfected. Downstream of the contact main, the chlorine content was reduced to the normal level by adding a small dose of sulphur dioxide.

Maindell

Although only used infrequently, the source at Maindell had provided valuable support during the 1976 drought and, in 1978, the Board decided to 'reactivate' Maindell. With coliform bacteria frequently present in the raw water, it was necessary to lay a contact main with disinfection being provided by a system of superchlorination and dechlorination similar to that at Eastergate. The work was completed in 1979.

Alternative Power Supplies

The 1970s marked a period of considerable industrial relations unrest throughout the United Kingdom. The trade unions wielded considerable power and many industries suffered strikes by workers in support of better pay and conditions. The Company and the Water Industry were not immune and, throughout the decade, difficulties were experienced in maintaining supplies. One of the most significant issues from outside the Water Industry was the impact caused by strikes in the power industry. In 1978, these led the Company to decide that it would invest in stand-by diesel generators at 50% of its sources, so that it could maintain pumping even when mains electricity supplies were interrupted.

Distribution Network Improvements

Having provided additional and much needed new resources, the Company remained aware of the limitations of the local infrastructure inherited from its predecessors. It therefore set about linking parts of these separate networks to enable it to maintain supplies during emergencies.

The Nelson to Farlington Link

The construction of the River Itchen Scheme had already begun the process of linking supplies between the Hoads Hill Reservoirs, serving Gosport and Fareham, and the Waterlooville area. This was followed by a new supply from Fort Nelson Reservoir into Portchester, which was extended in 1976 by laying a 500mm diameter main parallel with the railway line to Cosham, where it connected to the trunk mains from Farlington to Portsmouth. Thus, a high capacity alternative supply from the West District sources to Portsmouth had been provided.

Alternative Supplies for the Lovedean area

From its inception in the mid-1960s, the Lovedean source had suffered from elevated turbidity after heavy rain, in a similar manner to the springs at Havant and Bedhampton. A monitor had already been installed at Lovedean to warn of rising turbidity and there were a number of occasions each year when the source had to be shut down. On such occasions, the supplies to the Cowplain, Catherington and Clanfield areas were maintained from George Reservoir, which was already 'stretched'. The Cowplain Booster Station, which had previously transferred water from George Reservoir further northwards, had already been abandoned. Fortunately, the new 36-inch main laid from Fort Nelson Reservoir to Waterlooville allowed an additional 20-inch extension to be laid from Waterlooville to Lovedean Works. The new main meant that the reservoir at Fort Nelson, at a similar level to that of Lovedean Reservoir, could maintain supplies to the Clanfield pumps when shutdowns occurred at Lovedean.

A Link between Chichester and Bognor Regis

The low groundwater levels of 1973 and the consequent impact on source yields had revealed the frailties of the independent systems developed by the Company's predecessors, particularly in West Sussex. The difficulties in maintaining supplies to Bognor Regis and the surrounding area from the Eastergate and Westergate sources had led the Company to lay a trunk main between the Chichester network and that of Bognor Regis. However, the main was not completed until 1977, too late to help overcome the problems experienced in the 1976 drought.

As well as authorising the laying of that 600mm diameter link from Lagness to Rose Green, the Board authorised improved links to Selsey and the Witterings, with 450mm diameter mains being laid from Lagness to each location. These improvements were completed in 1978.

The Hampshire/Sussex Link

The experiences of the 1976 Drought resulted in yet more links between local networks. In 1977, the Board resolved that the Walderton source in the Ems valley, which had been primarily developed to augment supplies in the Havant area, could transfer water eastwards, thereby supporting supplies to the Chichester area from Fishbourne, Funtington and the Lavant valley sources. An 800mm diameter fibre reinforced cement main was laid eastwards from the Racton Reservoirs via Funtington Works to link to the Lavant trunk main in Salthill Road, Fishbourne. Low lift booster pumps were installed at Funtington to pump water from Racton into the slightly more elevated Lavant Zone.

The scheme was not without problems, as it was found to be impossible to achieve a successful pressure test on the main to prove its watertightness. The first thing that was done was to split the

Laying the Racton 800mm main, 1978

main into separate sections and a leak was identified between Adsdean and Funtington. Inspection of the line of the main, by now buried, failed to reveal the location of the leak, as did several water diviners who had assured staff that they would be successful! John Cogley, who was then Assistant Engineer, recounts: "We were at the stage when we thought we were going to have to dig up every joint, as we were convinced that a joint rubber must have been displaced. It was then suggested that we use a substance occasionally used by the gas industry called ethyl mercaptan, which has a pungent smell of rotting cabbage. We had to completely drain the main, add a very small phial of this chemical, and then pump up the main with compressed air, the idea being that we would be able to smell the location where the leak was occurring. We walked up and down the main several times, but nowhere could we detect the smell; of course we then had to get rid of the air in the main which was pretty foul smelling. Fortunately, the area is heavily used for pig farming and so we didn't get any complaints! We then refilled the main to drive out the air and when it was retested, it passed! We never found the leak and could only assume that the application of compressed air had reseated the joint rubber."

Bognor Regis Improvement Scheme

In 1971, poor pressures in Bognor Regis forced the Company to lay a new trunk main from Littleheath Reservoir to North Bersted, a distance of over five miles. With uPVC pipe at that time the much favoured material for mainlaying, the pipes were purchased from Chemidus Wavin. The Company's supply staff were already heavily involved in laying the mains associated with the River Itchen Scheme and so A L J Davis (Public Works) Ltd were contracted to lay the new main, the first time that the Company had employed a mainlaying contractor. The cross-country scheme was largely uneventful, but in November a major burst occurred during the course of testing the pipeline. Two further bursts occurred in early 1972, after the main had been commissioned. On each occasion, around 1.5 million gallons of water were lost and there was very significant damage to crops in the affected fields. The Company's costs were reimbursed by Chemidus Wavin.

Worse was to occur in May and June 1973, when four more bursts occurred, just when the Company could least afford the loss of water. On each occasion that a burst occurred, the pipes either completely disintegrated or alternatively long slivers were found in and around the massive crater left by the escape of water. One burst occurred at Aldingbourne, close to the Portsmouth to Brighton railway line, and John Reed, former East District Distribution Manager, recalls that the trains had to be stopped until the shards of pipe, which were sticking up out of the ballast between the rails, had been removed. The craters were often 15 to 20 ft across and often up to 10 ft deep. By October 1978, thirteen bursts had occurred on the main, two sections of it having been badly affected. So unreliable were these sections of main that the Company decided that they should be isolated and action taken against Chemidus Wavin. It was in May 1980, after threatening legal action, that the Company finally agreed a financial settlement with Chemidus Wavin under which it was reimbursed the cost of the pipes. At the same time, the Board approved the renewal of a 2.3 kilometre section of the main, between Aldingbourne and Lidsey.

Further problems were to occur in the 1980s and these are covered in the next chapter.

The Chilgrove Scheme

The villages of Compton and Marden had, for many years, been solely dependent for their water supplies upon the West Marden Booster, developed by Chichester RDC. As demands were increasing, an alternative supply was considered prudent. By 1970, a scheme had been approved for new booster arrangements at Lavant to pump water to a new high-level reservoir at Appledown, near North Marden.

The development of the Lavant source had already permitted a rationalisation of some of the rural supplies laid by Chichester RDC in the early 1950s. The Chilgrove valley, north-west of Lavant, and the villages of Compton and North Marden, included some very long agricultural supply pipes. The new scheme allowed a number of these supplies to be considerably shortened.

The new Appledown Reservoir, which replaced one built by Chichester RDC in 1951, was completed in 1975, but it caused a considerable stir in the locality. Not only were there concerns that the site, high up in the Downs, might have significant archaeological interest, but also, when the telemetry building was constructed on top of it, the Company came in for heavy criticism because of the building's insensitive design in such an exposed position in an Area of Outstanding Natural Beauty! Faced with mounting criticism from the local press and planners, who had referred to it as resembling a 'Second World War blockhouse', the Company replaced the telemetry building with a more modest low-level structure and a screen of trees was planted around the reservoir.

Chichester Observ

No. 5,302 FRIDAY, FEBRUARY 27, 1976 7p Est

UNDER FIRE FROM CONSERVATIONISTS: THE 'BLOCKHOUSE' ON APPLEDOWN HILL

This new Portsmouth Water Company pumping station on Appledown Hill, in the Mardens, near Chichester, has sparked an outburst from conservationists over its situation high on the Downs. Letter on page 2; story on page 16.

Courtesy of The Chichester Observer

The Development of additional Service Reservoir storage

The networks inherited from the Gosport, Fareham and West Sussex undertakings incorporated limited storage in service reservoirs, which operated as 'balancing tanks'. The source pumps delivered water to the network at a fairly constant rate, while the service reservoir provided additional water during peak demand periods in the daytime. The lost volume in the reservoir would be replenished during the night time when demands subsided. At many sites, the total volume of storage was relatively small and the Company had to rely upon several sources pumping 'round the clock'. This proved to be uneconomical, especially as a number of special 'off-peak' energy tariffs had been negotiated with the local Electricity Board. Thus the Company embarked upon a programme of increasing service reservoir storage, at most sites, to between one and two days' supply. This would enable it to maximise 'off-peak' pumping, whilst also improving the security of supplies in the event of major failures of power, mains or plant. The maximum 'two days' storage rule was applied if only a single treatment works served the reservoir. At other sites served by more than one works, a minimum of one day's storage was considered sufficient.

Construction of Fir Down No.2 Reservoir

Upon completion of the River Itchen Scheme, there was an almost continuous programme of new service reservoir construction to provide additional storage capacity during the late 1970s and early 1980s. The first, in 1973/74, was ***Racton No.2***, near Walderton, where capacity increased from 13.6 to 33.6 million litres. This was followed in 1975/76, by the construction of ***Littleheath No.2***, at the principal reservoir site serving the Bognor Regis area. A new service reservoir at ***Highdown*** to serve the rural areas north of Mid Lavant, near Chichester, was completed in 1977, with a second reservoir at ***Clanfield*** constructed a year later. At ***Street End***, to the north of Bishop's Waltham, a second reservoir was completed in 1979, followed by a new reservoir for the ***West Meon*** area in the same year. The programme was largely completed by a second reservoir at ***Fir Down***, near Droxford, in 1981, and a new reservoir at ***Madehurst*** the following year. At ***Farlington***, additional reservoir storage was provided in conjunction with the redevelopment of the treatment works as described below.

Inlet pipework, Littleheath No.2 Reservoir

By the beginning of the 1970s, the Company had developed a long-term relationship with Shellabear Price Contractors Ltd, the firm having constructed the River Itchen Works and the two service reservoirs at Hoads Hill and Fort Nelson. Unusually at that time, when most water undertakers would carry out the detailed

'onstruction of Nelson Reservoir

designs for new reservoirs using their own design staff, the Company had let 'design and construct' contracts, a feature that would not become fashionable for the Industry until the 1990s!

On behalf of Shellabear Price, Kenneth Severn Associates undertook the design work, their principal designer being Geoff Watts. Although many of the designs were traditional 'propped cantilever' reinforced concrete structures, their detailing was unusual at that time, in that most of them had no sealant or waterbar in any of the construction joints in the reservoir. At Hoads Hill and Fort Nelson, two reservoirs that were deeper than normally considered economic, Geoff Watts used a novel 'cranked' wall design in an attempt to minimise the steel reinforcement needed for the walls; the design proved to be successful.

Construction of Hoads Hill No.2 Reservoir

Shellabear Price's Construction Manager, Ken Boxall, was responsible for those schemes throughout the decade and beyond; his Site Manager, Peter Muldowney, became such a familiar part of the Company that he rented some of its land for several years after his retirement!

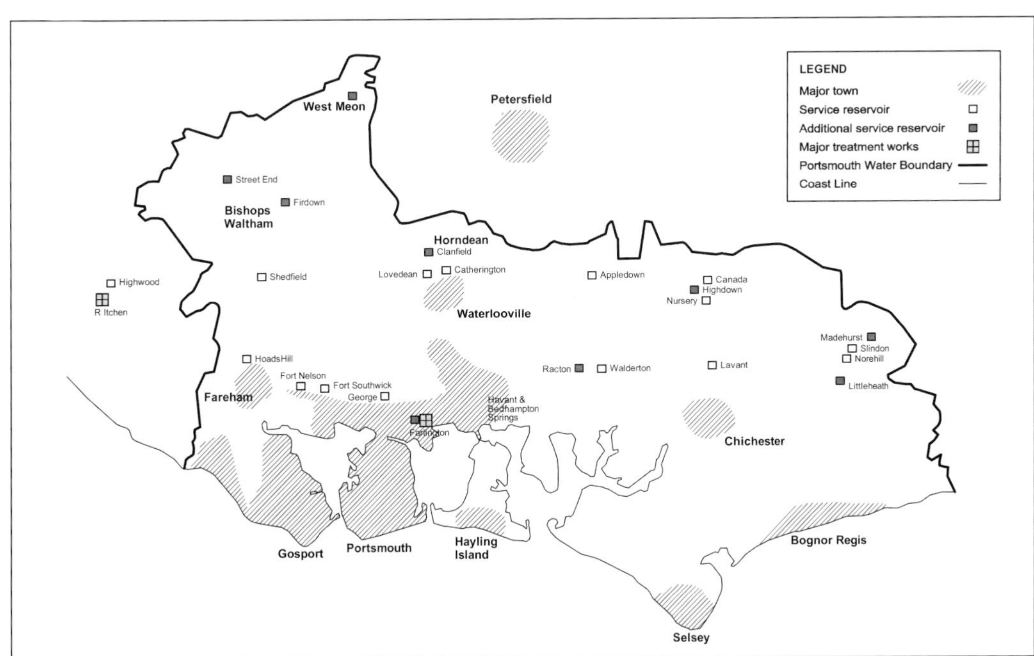

Additional service reservoir construction, 1970s

Refurbishment of Farlington Water Treatment Works 1978-82

The design of the filter beds and reservoirs at Farlington, constructed in the early 1900s, was unusual, because of their location on the southern slope of Portsdown Hill. The No. 3 and No. 4 Reservoirs had been designed such that approximately 50% of the slow sand filters were supported by the barrel vaulted brick roofs of the reservoirs. In the latter part of the 1970s, staff at the Farlington Works had noted that the walls of the slow sand filter beds were cracked in a number of places; there were concerns that they might be leaking into the treated water reservoirs below and therefore that not all the water was undergoing proper filtration. Consequently, an inspection was arranged and the Works Superintendent, Len Jones, recalls Deputy Chief Engineer, John King, and New Works Engineer, Mike Leplar, being lowered into a boat that had been specially 'chlorinated' to ensure that it did not contaminate the treated drinking water in the reservoir. Apparently, they returned from their inspection 'absolutely drenched', having found that, as suspected, water was pouring through cracks in the floors and walls of the filter beds into the reservoirs below.

Faced with the prospect of major reconstruction work on slow sand filters that were already 70 years old, it was decided, instead, that a further bank of eight rapid gravity filters would be added to the existing five, and that the old slow sand filters would be abandoned. A waterproof membrane was applied to the reservoir roofs to ensure that rainwater could not contaminate the treated water below. A contract was awarded to Paterson Candy Holst in December 1978. At the same time, the volume of treated water storage at Farlington was increased to the equivalent of two days' supply by building a new No. 6 Reservoir holding 38.7 million litres. This was yet another reservoir constructed by Shellabear Price! The design included an eastern wall designed to accommodate future extension of the reservoir.

Construction of Farlington No.6 Reservoir and new rapid gravity filters

The abandonment of the slow sand filters brought to an end the era of skimming and washing the filter sand by hand. The staffing of the Company's largest works could now be reduced to just one Superintendent and two assistants, who were responsible for daytime working and out-of-hours emergency cover.

The Construction of the A3 (M) Motorway

The construction of the new motorway bypassing the A3 London to Portsmouth Road, between Clanfield and Bedhampton, caused the Company considerable problems. Not surprisingly given the scale of the scheme, a number of major trunk mains diversions were needed to accommodate the new road, but the biggest problems were related to the construction work itself.

At the outset, the Company expressed concerns that the work might have an impact upon the Havant & Bedhampton Springs. The Department of Transport was not of the same view. However, soon after the commencement of the scheme, contractors needed to pump significant quantities of water away from the site. It was the discharge of this wastewater to 'swallow holes' in the Horndean and Clanfield areas which caused major problems. On these occasions, the wastewater would cause turbid (cloudy) water to be received at the Havant & Bedhampton Springs, thus causing significant difficulties with treatment at the Farlington Treatment Works. On one occasion the staff at the works noticed that the water had turned red! Considerable liaison was needed with the County Council and its contractor to avoid further problems. The experience resulted in several studies by university groups who confirmed, using tracer tests, the long-held suspicion that there was very rapid 'conduit flow' of surface water between the swallow holes and the springs.

The Growing Importance of Water Quality

By 1970, a routine had been established in the Company's Laboratory for analysis of water samples from sources, treatment works and service reservoirs. In addition, samples were taken from households in the main centres of population, in accordance with World Health Organisation guidelines.

New water mains were tested under pressure and sterilised by water quality staff. It was a requirement that microbiological samples from any new main should be satisfactory before it was commissioned and the households and premises connected. By 1978, the Company had introduced a policy that required a satisfactory microbiological sample not only from new mains, but also in all cases where the inside of the main had been exposed during a repair.

In 1972, the Company was alerted to the presence of cyanide deposits in a waste disposal site at Slindon, 'up-catchment' of the Eastergate and Westergate sources. As a precaution, an observation borehole was installed at Fontwell, between the tip and the sources, and this was sampled on a regular basis for many years afterwards. No cyanide was ever found in the samples!

On one occasion in 1975, the Navy's Fire-fighting Training School, at HMS Phoenix, was responsible for a pollution event, when it managed to pump oil into the Company's mains via an illegal cross-connection within the site. The problem was resolved by a major flushing exercise in and around the Hilsea and Stamshaw areas of Portsmouth; the incident received considerable local press coverage.

In 1975, the Department of the Environment (DoE) commissioned a National Lead Survey, since the World Health Organisation had expressed concerns about lead levels in drinking water supplies. Only two samples in the Company survey were found to exceed the safe limits as, generally, the hard waters found in the south of England were less prone to plumbosolvency.

For the first time, the Chief Chemist and Bacteriologist reported in 1976 that nitrate levels had risen significantly at Westergate and Eastergate. Whilst not of major concern at that time, they were to rise much higher in later years. In the same year, possibly as a result of low groundwater levels, the Company suffered saltwater intrusion at Fishbourne during high tides. On several occasions the source had to be temporarily shut down.

Life at the Company in the 1970s

Having automated many of the Company's sourceworks, there were fewer staff at pumping stations and increased use of electronic equipment, which required staff with more technical maintenance skills. Consequently, mechanical and electrical craftsmen were recruited and employed as Pumping Station Technicians.

The Company also realised that greater technical skills were required by its distribution staff and a significant number of new apprentices were recruited as 'waterworks craftsmen'. These staff were sent on day release courses to local colleges to learn plumbing skills which, at that time, were still important in the everyday maintenance of the mains and services network.

Observatories at Clanfield Reservoirs

In 1971, the Board agreed to allow a local astronomical group to use some of its land adjacent to the Clanfield Reservoirs. This arrangement, which continues today, has enabled the Hampshire Astronomical Group to make use of this location away from urban lighting as a prime site for its activities.

The late 1960s had seen the introduction of bonus schemes in several areas of the Company's manual work. During the early 1970s, new schemes were introduced by the Work Study Department for Stores, Servicelayers, Inspectors and Waste, Vehicle Repairers and Lorry Drivers, and Pumping Station Attendants. The Inspectors and Waste Bonus Scheme, which based its payments upon leakage levels, was so successful that, in the early 1970s, the Company's Annual Reports refer to the fact that rising demand had levelled off as waste detection was proving so effective! Leakage reductions were not achieved without significant effort and cost. All the inspectors and their supervisors were required to take part in 'night tests', when leakage investigations were much more effective. The staff went out on test from midnight until 4 am, paid at double time rates, but were still expected to be back at work four hours later. Inevitably, there was pressure for them to have a longer rest period and eventually the Company agreed to give the staff an extra four hours paid 'sleeping time'. The night tests also caused other problems, as on numerous occasions well-meaning members of the public would report the fact that they had seen men with metal bars (valve keys!) roaming the streets. "Oh, it's you lot again", was the usual response when a police car would turn up to investigate!

The 1970s was a period of high inflation and considerable conflict between trade unions and management in many walks of life. The new National Joint Council negotiated substantial pay rises in 1974, and on several other occasions during the decade. In addition, the trade unions exercised their power from time to time by calling strikes or withdrawing standby cover when disputes broke out at local level.

An Inspector 'listening for a leak'

Aerial view of Farlington Treatment Works after demolition of the slow sand filters

1980-1990: The Emergence of Customer Power

The 1980s were a decade of changing attitudes in the Water Industry. The ten Regional Water Authorities established in 1973 were public bodies that operated in a similar manner to local authorities. They supplied water to the majority of England and Wales, with 28 smaller 'water only' companies, such as Portsmouth Water Company, supplying the rest. Consumers largely believed that water and sewerage services should be in public ownership, since water supply and sewerage were essentially seen as a public service. Over the next ten years, the Government radically changed the financing and ownership of the Industry, although the public's view remained much the same!

As new water companies began to make profits, so the general public began to demand greater levels of service. Consumers demanded to be treated as customers!

The Introduction of Household Metering

In the latter part of the 1970s, the Labour Government had sought to rationalise the wide range of water charges that existed across England and Wales. The setting up of the new Water Authorities in 1973 had resulted in charges within each authority supply area being standardised, but differences still existed between the authorities themselves and those water companies unaffected by the Water Industry reorganisation. At that time, most commercial businesses were charged by volume through a metered supply, whilst domestic households and many offices and shops were charged according to the rateable value of the property.

With a newly elected Conservative Government wishing to encourage customer choice, new policies were introduced to enable universal metering to become available to customers. The cost of providing and installing a new meter was chargeable to the customer and so only those likely to make considerable savings in charges were tempted to switch tariff; many offices and shops, with high rateable values, took up this option in the early years. The Company also introduced a 'standing charge', a fee for maintaining the availability of the service regardless of rateable value or volume of water used.

With the lowest charges in England and Wales, there was less financial incentive for the Company's customers to opt for a meter. In the early years, therefore, the take-up of domestic meters was very low.

Consumer Consultative Committees

By 1982, as part of its programme to control inflation, the Government was pressing the Industry to restrain water charge increases. It proposed to dissolve the powerful National Water Council, the Industry's governing body. It also proffered the idea of setting up consumer consultative bodies to ensure that consumers, or customers as they were now being called, could express their views on the operation of the authorities and companies. By January 1984, Consumer Consultative Committees, based on county council boundaries, had been established. Representatives were appointed by Government. They were obliged to act on behalf of customers and to see that the Industry responded to customers' views. The Company was represented on two committees, because its area of supply covered parts of both Hampshire and West Sussex.

Interestingly, the records show that, in 1986, the Company commissioned its first 'public relations' brochure from Polymedia Ltd of Fareham. The Company's desire to improve communications with its customers was a theme that would develop much further over the coming 20 years.

Company Structure and Finances in the 1980s

At the beginning of the decade, subtle changes in the Company's management structure occurred with Assistant Distribution Engineer, Tim Jackson, being appointed Supply Engineer; until then supply issues had been dealt with by John King, the Deputy Chief Engineer.

At Board level, the long-serving former Engineer, Reg Hall, died in 1980. Consequently Fred Bailey, the Secretary & Treasurer, and George Slater, the Chief Engineer, were appointed as Directors.

In 1983, Nick Roadnight, the Deputy Chief Accountant, took on the additional role of Registrar from Geoff Smith, who had succeeded the retiring George Greene, the Company's long-serving Stores Controller.

Both Nick and Tim were selected for the first Water Companies' Senior Management Programme in 1985, an intensive and very demanding management training exercise aimed at developing a number of senior managers across all the water companies. A similar training programme had already begun for the water authority staff. Soon afterwards, in September 1986, George Slater retired at the age of 65, although he remained a Director for another ten years. He was succeeded as Chief Engineer by John King, with Tim Jackson appointed as his deputy. As had been the case for his predecessors, Tim retained his supply responsibilities and the post of Supply Engineer disappeared again for some years.

When Fred Bailey retired as Secretary & Treasurer in November 1988 after 49 years in the Industry, his deputy, John Batty, succeeded him. Nick Roadnight was appointed Deputy Secretary & Treasurer. Like George Slater, Fred remained a Company Director for many years to follow.

Tim Jackson (right) with the Mayor of Portsmouth at the River Itchen Treatment Works, July 1986

Company Finances

The Government decided to abolish the Water Equalisation levies after 1981 and the saving of an annual payment of over £500,000 did much to constrain rises in water charges during the early 1980s. The Government's tight control on inflation also had a major impact and it was not until 1988 that a significant rise in charges of 9.8% was imposed. A much larger rise was implemented in 1989, in the lead-up to the privatisation of the Industry, and even though the Chairman, David Childs, and Secretary & Treasurer, John Batty, were summoned to see Michael Howard, the Secretary of State for the Environment, there was little he could do to persuade the Company to reduce the impact.

During the course of the decade, Preference and Debenture Stock were redeemed and replaced by new issues from time to time. With a rather more modest capital programme than previously, there was no necessity for the Company to apply for authorisation to raise the level of capital issued.

Other Staff

In 1987, Farlington Works Superintendent, Len Jones, was awarded the British Empire Medal for his services to the Company over the previous 37 years.

The Rise and Fall of Industrial Relations problems

In Britain, the 1970s had been a decade when the trade unions were able to exert considerable power in support of their demands for the recognition of employees' rights. As that decade progressed, union power even surfaced in the Water Industry, which had, until then, been relatively trouble free. The election of a Conservative Government under Margaret Thatcher in 1979 saw a marked reversal of trade union power, but it was well into the 1980s before this change had an impact on the Water Industry.

The National Joint Councils

Following the creation of the new Water Authorities in 1973, the Company had been obliged to participate in new National Joint Councils for Staff, Craftsmen and Manual Workers. The Councils were formed of management and trade union representatives, who were responsible for determining the rates of pay, terms and conditions for staff working in the Water Industry in England and Wales. National conditions did not always suit local circumstances and the decisions made did not always satisfy either party at the Company!

The Deterioration in Relations

During the previous decade, with the trade unions able to exert considerable power, there had already been a number of local disputes over what might seem relatively insignificant events today; the sharing of 'sea boot socks' and the availability of soft toilet paper are just two such examples which staff recall! One-day strikes, walkouts and withdrawal of stand-by cover became frequent occurrences and much management time was spent in negotiating settlements to local disputes with trade union officials.

The impact was felt across the Company, as there was a gradual reduction in many of the long-held staff welfare provisions; annual staff outings ceased, the frequency of dinner dances was reduced and the Company closed the staff canteen, although this was mainly due to under-use by staff. However, in 1983, matters came to a head when, at a national level, manual workers' union representatives called a strike in support of their annual pay claim. What was expected to be a short, sharp strike of a few days actually lasted five weeks. The repercussions changed local working practices and the future of industrial relations, both at national and local level.

The National Water Strike of 1983

The strike began in January of that year, with all the Company's distribution maintenance and supply operators being called out by their unions. A 'Union Shop Agreement' at the time obliged all manual and craft staff to be members of one of several trade unions. It meant that if they were expelled from their union, they were at risk of losing their job. Regardless of their personal circumstances and views, all manual and craft staff were obliged by the unions to comply with the call to strike. The Company had to make alternative arrangements to cover their activities in order to maintain water supplies during the strike. Almost all non-emergency work was cancelled.

Although the supply operators were on strike, the Area and Works Supply Superintendents were classed as non-manual staff, as were the Mechanical and Electrical Technicians. Since they were not on strike, it fell to them to ensure that all the treatment works and reservoirs continued to operate during the strike. Pete Dulson, Western Area Supply Superintendent, remembers it being a rather lonely existence, since he was left to run the Western Supply Area on his own. It was somewhat arduous too, as he was on duty every day for the length of the five-week strike!

Maintaining the distribution network was rather more difficult. Distribution Supervisors and Superintendents were not normally expected to operate valves on the network, nor were they expected to carry out excavations to repair burst mains, valves and other apparatus. Their trade union had instructed them to work as usual, but not to carry out work normally done by others. As the strike had begun during the winter, there were inevitably problems caused by broken mains. The Company had already postponed all non-emergency work, including the provision of new mains and service connections to building sites; fortunately, the country was in the grip of recession and so the demand for this work was relatively low at that time. The Company asked its managers to provide emergency cover and, for the next five weeks, a small handful of staff was dedicated to responding to emergency calls of all types. When broken mains were reported, these staff would attempt to 'throttle' the valves controlling the leak to try to maintain customers' supplies, whilst avoiding potential damage to property from escaping water. Where this was not possible and the main had to be 'shut in', emergency standposts would be erected close by and customers affected were asked to collect their water. Managers and Supervisors were not expected to carry out excavations to repair and restore supplies.

After some five weeks, a national settlement was finally agreed and the employees, having been without pay throughout that period, returned to work. So eager were they to return that all the broken mains were repaired on the first day back at work! During those five weeks, it had become apparent to managers that, prior to the strike, there had obviously been many occasions when non-emergency work had been undertaken at premium overtime rates. As soon as the strike was over, a new policy was introduced, requiring emergency repairs to be authorised by management. This resulted in a very significant reduction in overtime payments to manual and craft employees in the months and years that followed.

The Company Chairman best summed up the whole experience in the following year's Annual Report, "it has been a sad and salutary period in the industry's history with an outcome in which no one gained and some consumers suffered considerable inconvenience." The Chairman went on to congratulate the management and supervisory staff, who had ensured that only about 100 households were deprived of a piped water supply. Whilst the experience led to some initial bitterness, it paved the way, in due course, for better industrial relations in the years ahead.

The Return to Local Negotiations

The fact that the Company had managed to maintain supplies to all but a small number of customers for such a long period inevitably reduced the power of the trade unions, not only at Portsmouth Water but also throughout the Water Industry. By 1988, the National Joint Councils, which had determined terms and conditions for the whole Industry, were abolished. From then on, the Company and its local trade union representatives took on that responsibility.

Progress towards Privatisation

Monopolies and Mergers Commission Referral

The Conservative Government was elected in 1979 with a manifesto that aimed to radically change the national economy. It very quickly set about the privatisation of many industries whose public status had become part of the fabric of Britain. The telephone service (then run by the Post Office), the gas industry and British Leyland were some of the many large organisations 'sold off' to encourage private investment and to rid the Government of its direct responsibilities in major business entities.

By 1985, plans to privatise the Water Industry were already beginning to find favour, although private companies already supplied water to approximately 25% of households in England and Wales. In May 1985, the Secretary of State for Trade and Industry asked the Monopolies and Mergers Commission (MMC) to investigate the affairs of the water undertakings in the south-east of England, paying particular attention to:

- Whether Southern Water Authority or any of the private companies could improve their efficiency and thereby reduce costs without significantly affecting the quality of service provided.

- Whether the Authority or the companies were pursuing a course of conduct that operated against the public interest.

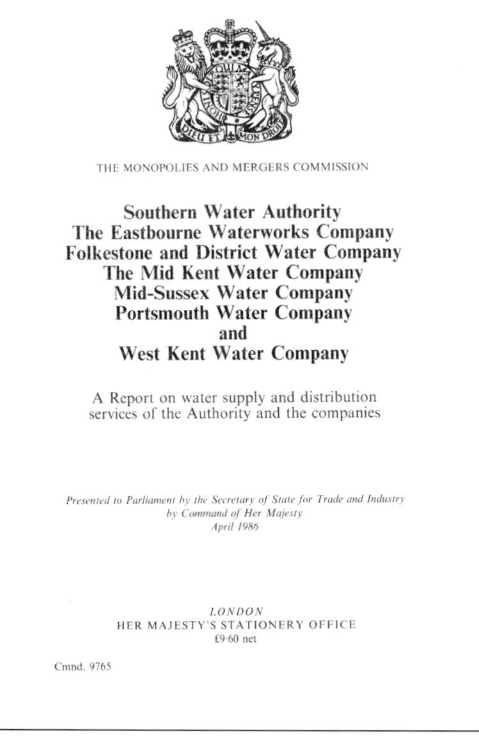

THE MONOPOLIES AND MERGERS COMMISSION

Southern Water Authority
The Eastbourne Waterworks Company
Folkestone and District Water Company
The Mid Kent Water Company
Mid-Sussex Water Company
Portsmouth Water Company
and
West Kent Water Company

A Report on water supply and distribution services of the Authority and the companies

Presented to Parliament by the Secretary of State for Trade and Industry by Command of Her Majesty April 1986

LONDON
HER MAJESTY'S STATIONERY OFFICE
£9·60 net

Cmnd. 9765

At the time, the referral came as a surprise to the Industry. However, in hindsight, it might well have provided the Government with the opportunity to study the Industry in detail and to help develop its privatisation plans.

Members and officials of the MMC visited the Company's offices and submissions were invited from a wide range of organisations with an interest in the water supply business. Hearings were held in London, where the trade unions were also invited to give evidence. The consultants, Peat, Marwick and Mitchell, who gave advice on investment planning and operational control issues, assisted the Commission.

The marked differences in financial control between the statutory water companies and Southern Water Authority were very evident and this caused the Commission some difficulty in comparing the two. Although the companies were monopolies, the Commission appeared to be impressed by the fact that boards and management teams were motivated by 'a mixture of pride of performance in providing an essential service and a natural sensitivity to local opinion which would be quick to criticise unreasonable charges or inferior service'. Not only was it difficult to compare financial performance, but it was also difficult, because of geographical factors, to compare the operations of each organisation. Whilst the Commission recognised the collaborative work done by the Authority and companies on water resources, it did raise concerns about leakage levels and the potential for demand management.

It took the Commission almost eleven months to produce its final report, which was presented to Parliament in April 1986. Overall the Commission was relatively complimentary about the Industry's performance. John Batty, Deputy Secretary & Treasurer at the time, recalls that the Chief Officers were rather disappointed that, although the Company had been praised during the investigation, such comments were not included in the final report. In total, there were 41 recommendations, many of which were specific to the operations of Southern Water Authority. There were, however, a few which would have an impact upon the Company in the future, these being: -

- The statutory companies should set formal objectives, quantified targets and measure their performance. The objectives were expected to incorporate charging and resource strategies.

- The statutory companies should adopt similar levels of service indicators to those used by Southern Water Authority, as well as a common system of complaint recording.

- A system of priority based budgeting should be used to review costs.

- Companies should review staffing levels with a view to improving efficiency.

- The companies were urged to improve their methods for estimating the costs and benefits associated with leakage control.

- The companies should regularly compare in-house costs with those from outside contractors.

Corporate Plans

Whether prompted by the MMC referral or not, the Company produced the first of its Corporate Plans in 1986. The purpose of the Plan was to:

- provide information about the Company and its methods of working;

- set out formal policies; and

- provide readily identifiable targets for management and employees.

The Plan was intended to be a working document and it looked forward over five years; it was expected to be updated every year.

The Plan set out the Company's main objectives, as well as the standards and policies, which applied to its activities. Important targets and performance indicators were set out for day-to-day operations. The Plan also set out capital investment proposals for the five-year period ahead. Annual updates were expected, the first being in 1987, but the demands of privatisation reshaped the plans and so no further updates were produced.

The Statutory Water Company Model

Prior to 1989, the Company was a 'statutory company' and was governed by the relevant Acts and Orders passed by Parliament. Those Acts and Orders restricted the level of financial reserves in the Company; the reserves were used to even out peaks and troughs in capital and maintenance expenditure. A maximum level of reserves could be held and, if the Company enjoyed a profitable year, it had to use the surplus from that year to reduce customers' charges in the following year.

In order to raise finance for capital investment, the Company would have to issue stocks, either debenture or preference, on which a fixed dividend would be paid to the stockholder. The benefit for the investor was the fact that there was very low risk involved and the level of dividend was fixed for the period of investment.

Prior to the 1980s, it was customary for little of the stock issued by water companies to carry voting rights. Ordinary shares, which held voting rights and hence gave their owners a say in the Company's affairs, were relatively few in number and the valuation of those shares in the early 1980s was only about £500,000, a very small sum by comparison with the Company's value today.

Much was made of the statutory water company model in the 1986 MMC investigation of the companies in the south-east of England, but little of it appeared to find favour with either the Commission or the Government.

The Lead-up to Privatisation

By 1986, there was already talk of privatisation in the Industry, following the Government's promise in its manifesto of 1979 and the subsequent floating of British Telecom and British Gas. There were concerns about the Company's independence, as there seemed possibilities that either a large Regional Water Authority or a foreign investor might be able to buy up voting shares at relatively low cost. There was also the possibility that, if the statutory rules restricting profits and dividends were relaxed by privatisation, the value of the Company might rise significantly. This did not go unnoticed by the Trustees of the Portsmouth Water Company Retirement Benefit Scheme (hereafter referred to as the Scheme). They realised the significant investment potential for the Scheme.

In making its plans to privatise the Water Authorities, the Government rejected the statutory company model that had served the companies so well. It became apparent that the impending legislation would enable fixed dividend limits to be removed to allow increases in profitability, so that the 28 listed statutory water companies could compete for capital in the new environment. It created considerable interest in the future of the companies, especially from French utility companies. In all, seventeen companies were taken over in the period just prior to 1989!

Concerned at the imminent threat to the Company's independence and the potential impact on members of the Scheme, the Trustees, with the consent of the Company and in expectation of an excellent investment return, embarked upon an active investment programme to acquire a substantial holding of the voting equity. At the time, the investment represented a small proportion of the Scheme's assets. It was so successful that the Trustees invested in other water companies too!

A major investment took place on 8th June 1987, when the Company made a new issue of £2m voting

Redeemable Preference Stock, in accordance with the Water Act. The issue was taken up entirely by the Scheme, and this gave the Trustees 37% of the voting rights, which rose to 55% following the redemption some time later of further voting stock. Under Rule 9 of the Stock Exchange Code on Takeovers and Mergers, the Scheme was required to make a bid for the remainder of the voting stock. The Scheme made its offer according to the Rules at the highest price it had previously paid, which by that time was one third of the market price. The Company recommended its shareholders not to accept the offer as a higher price could be obtained by selling on the market. The majority of the 300 shareholders rejected the offer, but there were six who accepted!

Having bought shares in 1986 at 35p each, the value of the Scheme's investment was such that by 1988 each was worth 675p!

The Water Act 1989

Following the passing of the Water Act in 1989, it became obvious that it would be difficult to raise capital in the future, as many investors did not understand the statutory water company model. So in August 1990, Portsmouth Water converted to a public limited company (plc), listed on the Stock Exchange. Freed from the strictures of the old statutory company legislation, the Company had much greater freedom in its finances and operations. Nevertheless, its long held prudence ensured that it would not develop any risky ventures for the foreseeable future. It therefore continued to focus its attention firmly on maintaining public water supplies to its customers.

New Regulators to control the industry

The legislation setting up the 'privatised' regime for the industry introduced a system of regulation to avoid the risk of abuse of the companies' monopoly position. This new system of regulation established the Office of Water Services (Ofwat), the Drinking Water Inspectorate (DWI) and the National Rivers Authority (NRA). The Department of the Environment (DoE) was involved in setting charges for the first ten years of the new companies' licence periods. Ofwat was principally charged with ensuring that the companies could 'finance their functions', while charging customers only as much as was required to maintain and, where necessary, enhance existing levels of service.

Asset Management Plans

Investors in the new companies needed to have some idea of the condition of their assets, the associated future capital investment requirement, the water quality obligations and the need to meet new demand for water. All the authorities and statutory companies therefore had to prepare Asset Management Plans (AMPs) to cover the first ten years of the new regime. These AMPs were also used to help the DoE, pending the creation of Ofwat, set the water charges for each company. Depending on the level of future operating costs and investment, the new companies were permitted to vary their annual charges by a fixed percentage, known as the 'K' factor, in relation to RPI, the retail price index (ie inflation).

By the end of the 1980s, many of the Company's treatment works and pumping stations contained pumps, plant and equipment more than 25 years old; much of this was out-dated or obsolete. At the same time, concerns were growing about the problem of bursts and leaks in the old cast iron mains that comprised the great majority of the mains network.

The Company engaged consultants, Rofe, Kennard & Lapworth, to prepare its first AMP. Their reports identified the need to carry out the following:

- A new source in West Sussex to meet a projected demand increase.
- Additional capacity at the River Itchen Treatment Works.
- Modernisation of a number of pumping stations and treatment works.
- Additional service reservoir capacity.
- Service reservoir refurbishment.
- Refurbishment of office and depot buildings.
- The renewal of approximately 1% (or 32 kilometres) of the water mains network per annum.

The AMP1 submission, as it became known, was used to determine the total investment required for asset maintenance, water quality improvements and growth in water demand. However, with a few exceptions, it did not break the total investment down between individual sites and schemes, nor did it determine a method for deriving a programme of mains replacements. All of that was a job for the Company and is described later.

Resource Developments and Improvements

Although overall demand grew to a maximum in 1983 when, during July, the all-time peak daily and weekly figures of 297 and 277 million litres per day respectively were recorded, the 1980s saw a fall in commercial demand matched by a slow growth in domestic demand. By the end of the decade, overall demand was at about the same level as ten years earlier. Consequently, there was little urgency for the development of new sources, although the dry period, which affected south-east of England from 1988 to 1992, was to challenge the Company. This is outlined later in the chapter.

Highwood Reservoir (River Itchen Works)

The Company had already recognised in the mid-1970s that a bankside storage reservoir would be needed to avoid shutting down the River Itchen Works whenever a pollution incident occurred on the river. Several other companies had suffered similar incidents and it had been recommended nationally that storage of around seven days should be provided. However, the travel time of water through the whole Itchen catchment was much less than seven days and, given the Company's continual desire for economy, the Board approved a scheme to construct a reservoir of three days' works capacity in woodland adjacent to Allington

Aerial view of Highwood Reservoir

Lane, no more than half a mile from the Works. Rofe, Kennard & Lapworth, consulting engineers, designed the reservoir; as was the case with many schemes of the previous 10 years, it was constructed by Shellabear Price Contractors.

Aerial view of the River Itchen Treatment Works, during construction of the adjacent M27 motorway

Sadly, almost as soon as it had been commissioned, the reservoir developed algal growth. Warmer river temperatures coinciding with low river flows and nutrients in the effluent from the upstream Eastleigh Sewage Treatment Works exacerbated the difficulties during the summer. Almost immediately, the residents of Gosport and Fareham (who received Itchen water via the Hoads Hill Reservoirs) complained of 'earthy' or 'musty' tastes. On several occasions, the complaints grew to such an extent that the Company was forced to cease using the large compartment of the reservoir throughout the summer. In the summer of 1984, the Company received over 600 telephone complaints about the unpleasant taste! In that summer and many thereafter, the isolation of the large compartment of the reservoir meant that pollution protection was severely reduced for several months. In order to address the problem, in 1988 the Company replaced the sand and gravel in three of the six rapid gravity filters at the Itchen Works with granular activated carbon (GAC), the same material used in domestic jug filters. So successful was this change that the remaining filters were upgraded the following year. For the time being, the taste problems that had resulted from the development of Highwood Reservoir were over.

The Catherington Scheme

When the Company took over responsibility for the 'country area' to the north of Portsdown Hill in the 1930s, it had been necessary to boost supplies at Cowplain in order to supply Horndean, Catherington and Clanfield. In the 1950s, a service reservoir had been constructed at Clanfield at such a high level that most of those areas could then be supplied from it by gravity. The development of Lovedean Pumping Station in the 1960s led to the abandonment of Cowplain Booster, with Clanfield Reservoir then being supplied from boosters on the outlet of the Lovedean Service Reservoir, which served the lower levels in the Cowplain area. Unfortunately, this meant that many intermediate properties in Horndean and Catherington were also supplied from Clanfield and these suffered extremely high pressures. This led to complaints from customers about water hammer and noise in pipes; it also meant that there could be higher leakage levels.

In 1982, a new reservoir was constructed on the site of a small inherited reservoir at Catherington, together with a new pumping main and boosters pumping from Lovedean. This was yet another reservoir constructed by Shellabear Price to their by now routine structural design. However, a departure from long-standing practice was the laying of the pumping main by a contractor, instead of by direct labour staff. By 1982, the Company had reduced its labour strength through 'natural wastage' and so there were insufficient staff to take on the work. Tenders for the mainlaying works were invited from local contractors. Solent Excavations Ltd was the successful tenderer, thereby starting a long association with the Company that has continued through to 2007.

Pumping Station Refurbishments

In the mid 1980s, the Company embarked upon refurbishment work at some of its older pumping stations.

The new Eastergate Pumping Station

At Eastergate, which had not been updated since the takeover of the Bognor Regis undertaking, the old pumping station building was in a fairly poor state of repair. A new architect, James W Harper & Associates, was appointed, and following competitive tendering, a contract was let to E A Chiverton, of Bognor Regis, for the construction of the new building and other on-site works. A new building was constructed alongside the existing building to house all the electrical and treatment equipment. The original building was then demolished, leaving the covered well and its three submersible pumps more easily accessible for routine maintenance and repair.

Solent Excavations carried out underground mains alterations and ductwork, whilst the electrical switchgear and controls were installed by the Company's mechanical and electrical staff. The scheme was finally completed in 1986.

A minor refurbishment was carried out at Funtington, with new booster pumps being installed to increase the transfer capacity from the Racton to Lavant Reservoir zones, ie the link between the Hampshire and Sussex sources. There followed a major refurbishment scheme at Fishbourne, another site that had remained largely untouched since its takeover in 1963. This refurbishment dovetailed with the Distribution Department Review in 1987, after which Fishbourne became the operating depot for the East District. Therefore, not only was the pumping station refurbished, but a new office and depot were also constructed on the site.

The scheme was completed when staff moved into the new depot in 1990. The move enabled the Company to sell the old depot at Amberley Drive, Bognor Regis, for a new housing development.

Havant Springs

At the Head Office site, the enclosures surrounding many of the separate springs and connecting channels had been in place since the 19th century. By the 1980s, they had deteriorated and, rather than undertake major repairs, the Company decided to construct individual spring enclosures around each, much like those that already existed for the Havant Town Springs. The enclosures had the added benefit of inhibiting weed growth during the summer, whilst protecting the spring water from contamination, either airborne or from the wildlife inhabiting the site. The work was carried out in two stages, with completion of the final stage in 1991.

Distribution Network Improvements

As mentioned earlier, there was relatively little increase in the annual average demand for water during the decade. The Company's efforts to maximise the efficiency of the supply system were focused on improving the distribution network to minimise low pressure complaints. A number of schemes were developed, some using newly available computerised network models, others using traditional engineering calculations.

Portsmouth Reinforcement Mains

In the early 1980s, major housing development began at the former Portsmouth Airport site, one of the few remaining open spaces on Portsea Island. At that time, the trunk mains supplying water to the Island were the 36-inch main laid in 1939 on the north-east side and several mains passing underneath Portscreek through the Hilsea Tunnel in the north-west. A 30-inch main from Norway Road to the Coach and Horses roundabout at Hilsea linked both supplies, but from here the major supplies into the city were principally on the western side of the Island.

The new development on the airport site was expected to exacerbate the problems on the eastern side of the Island, especially in parts of Eastney, where poor pressure and complaints from customers were already a regular occurrence. The potential costs of major trunk mains reinforcements in such a congested urban area were significant. Thus in 1986 the Company commenced a network study, using new computer software called Watnet, developed by the WRc, the Industry's research body.

Laying the Portsmouth Reinforcement Main at Copnor Bridge, April 1989

The study and the associated field trials took several months to complete and resulted in a decision to lay a 7-kilometre length of 600mm diameter main from the 36-inch main at its crossing of the Portsmouth to Waterloo railway line in Airport Service Road to Highland Road in Southsea. The mainlaying was let in three separate contracts and the final section of main in Winter Road was commissioned in 1992.

Improvements for Havant, Emsworth and Hayling Island

For a number of years, water from Walderton had augmented supplies to much of Havant, Emsworth and Hayling Island. While this arrangement ensured that the southern end of Hayling Island received adequate pressure, the rest of the network on the northern part of the Island and the towns on the coastal mainland received pressures considerably higher than necessary. During the 1980s, trunk mains improvements were put in place to ensure that supplies to Hayling Island could be maintained from the Farlington Reservoirs. A new 450mm main was laid from Bedhampton to Langstone in 1983, followed in 1988 by a further section laid across Langstone Creek below the mud in the harbour. A long section of 450mm main was laid from the site of the former Hayling Works to Eastoke in 1989/90 to alleviate the long-standing pressure problems affecting the far south-eastern extremity of the Island's distribution network.

Solent Excavations Ltd laying the new 450mm main across Langston Creek, 1988

On completion of these schemes, the Company rezoned the whole area on to Farlington Reservoir, enabling leakage in the Zone to be reduced.

Replacing uPVC Trunk Mains

As already outlined, the Company experienced a number of bursts on the 24-inch uPVC main laid between Littleheath and Lidsey during the 1970s. The failures were initially believed to be due to manufacturing faults, but unfortunately failures began to occur on several other large diameter uPVC mains, particularly the one in Waterlooville between Hambledon Road and Lovedean. The burst on this main led to a further claim against the manufacturer, which was eventually settled out of court in 1989. Some of these failures were investigated by the WRc, which confirmed that the material was susceptible to the impact of sharp objects, such as stones in the backfill material or even the temporary supports that had been used during mainlaying. The failures led to the use of uPVC pipes being discontinued for all but small diameter distribution mains. In light of the significant flood damage caused in the aftermath of such failures, the Company embarked upon a major programme of replacements during the 1980s. The key mains renewed are outlined below:

- Littleheath to Lidsey – 24-inch uPVC main replaced with 600mm and 450mm ductile iron mains in several stages between 1983 and 1986.

- Hambledon Road to Lovedean Lane – 20-inch uPVC main replaced with 450mm FRC main.

- Mile End Road, Portsmouth – 16-inch and 10-inch uPVC mains replaced with a single 450mm ductile iron main.

Despite the problems experienced with the 24-inch uPVC main from Littleheath Reservoir to Lidsey, not all the main was renewed immediately. The section from Aldingbourne to Lidsey, which had the worst burst record, was renewed in 1983.

However, one further burst gave rise to great consternation. At 7 am on 28th November 1985, the Operations Centre Controller at Havant noticed that the level in Littleheath Reservoir was dropping rapidly, suggesting that a trunk mains burst might have occurred. He called out the Area Trunk Mains Inspector, Chris Taft, who located the burst in Littleheath Road, Fontwell and the 24-inch main north of the A27 was isolated by 7.45 am. Further investigation with Distribution Assistant, Ken Baldwin, revealed that massive subsidence had occurred over a considerable length of the road. Parts of the area were already known to suffer unexplained subsidence. It was never confirmed whether this had caused the burst, or whether there had been another unexplained failure of the pipe itself.

Fractured uPVC main, Fontwell, 1985

Split uPVC pipe with, beyond, 'craters' in the field resulting from ground subsidence

The result was that a number of houses in the road were severely undermined, as was the road and the adjoining fields. Those who witnessed the damage recall the area looking as though it had been hit by a wartime bombing raid. The road itself had to be closed to traffic and the Company had to make safe the adjacent 18-inch main, which was maintaining supplies to the reservoir. In due course, the 18-inch main was relaid with special tie-bar joints to minimise the risk of failure from future ground movement. The road had to be reconstructed several months later.

The damage to nearby properties eventually became the subject of a legal battle for compensation, which was not eased by the Company's insurers deeming that the previous settlement with Chemidus Wavin had invalidated the insurance cover. This meant that the Company had to bear the direct costs of remedial works for the properties in Littleheath Road. The legal dispute with the owners was not finally resolved until June 1992.

The failure spurred the Company into action and two further sections of the main were relaid in 1986. However, the final section of renewal between Lidsey and North Bersted was only completed in 1990. It allowed the supply to Aldwick and Pagham to be transferred from the Lavant Zone to the lower pressure Littleheath Zone.

Improvements for Bedhampton, Soberton and Stubbington

Solent Excavations Ltd laying 600mm main at Havant Road, Farlington

The summer of 1988 was hot and dry and the sustained demand for domestic garden watering led to many customer complaints about low pressure during the early evening and at weekends. Accordingly, in September, the Board gave prompt approval for new trunk mains at the following locations:

- A new 600mm ductile iron main from Farlington Reservoirs to the 'Forty Acres' roundabout at Bedhampton to improve pressures in Bedhampton and Leigh Park.

- A 600mm ductile iron main from Soberton Works to Mislingford to reduce pressure losses on the pumping mains from Soberton and West Street.

- A 600mm FRC main from the 30-inch main at Meadow Walk in Bridgemary to Peel Common to avoid low pressures in Hill Head and Stubbington.

These schemes were all completed by 1991.

Mains Renewals

Until 1987, mains renewal schemes were not a regular part of the Company's mainlaying programmes. Individual sections of mains susceptible to bursts or other problems were renewed, but the length of new mains being laid to serve housing developments vastly exceeded the lengths being renewed each year. It was recognised that the Company would be storing up significant problems for the future, if it did not begin to invest in its infrastructure, much of which dated from the 19th century in Portsmouth and Gosport. Thus the first mains renewal programme began.

In the first year, the Company renewed just over 11 kilometres of mains. However, by 1989, a regular programme of works was being prepared on an annual basis and in that year, 16 kilometres were renewed at a cost of £1.28m. Within a further two years, the programme had grown to 38 kilometres per annum at a cost each year of over £3m.

Life at the Company in the 1980s

New Bonus Schemes

In the early 1980s, the Company was becoming dissatisfied with the bonus schemes introduced in the previous years, although Maurice Croxon, former Chief Work Study Officer, recalls that the Mainlaying and Servicelaying Scheme had lasted much longer than most in the Industry! Many of them required considerable administrative support and there were many disputes about interpretation adding to industrial relations problems. As a result, simplified 'Efficiency Payment Schemes', which were dependent upon group rather than individual performance, were introduced in most departments during the decade. It took many months of negotiation to implement a simplified scheme for the Mains and Services Department, which in the end lasted only two years. The implementation of the Single Table Agreement, which is covered later, dispensed with all of the Efficiency Payment Schemes and consequently the Work Study Department was also disbanded.

A New Mains Material

Since the late 1960s, the Company had been using uPVC as its preferred material for water mains. uPVC pipes had the advantage of being corrosion resistant and very light to transport and lay; their relative flexibility minimised problems with ground movement that often caused cast iron pipes to fracture during cold or prolonged dry weather. During the twenty years that they had been in regular use, it had become apparent that there was a tendency for uPVC pipes to become brittle over time. Catastrophic failures would occasionally occur, often accompanied by flooding of customers' properties. As outlined in a previous chapter, the use of this material for trunk mains had already led to major problems with bursts.

Over the same 20-year period, the Company and the Water Industry generally had been using two types of black polyethylene pipes for service connections, in place of lead, galvanised steel and copper pipes. The low density polyethylene (LDPE) pipe had thicker walls and was more flexible, whilst high density polyethylene (HDPE) pipe was thinner, but less flexible; both pipes could be connected using mechanical compression fittings, which required considerably less skill than that needed to connect metal pipes. One other major benefit was that, as both pipes had the same outside diameter, connections between each could easily be made, with only a change of internal insert needed.

The flexibility and corrosion resistance of polyethylene pipe were major benefits. These factors led manufacturers, in conjunction with the Industry research body, the Water Research Centre (later WRc), to develop a new pipe for water mains. Medium density polyethylene (MDPE) pipe was already being used by the gas industry to overcome the major safety concerns which had come to light in the 1970s, following a number of explosions resulting from leaks on cast iron gas mains. The Gas Industry had been forced to develop a much more flexible material that was corrosion resistant. The same material was further developed to withstand the much higher internal pressures in water mains. With more and more utility apparatus being installed in public highways, a simple system of identification was also needed. Thus blue MDPE water pipe became a common sight on mainlaying schemes across the country. Gas pipes were yellow!

Initially the Company was a little apprehensive about adopting another new plastic pipe, given its experiences with uPVC mains. One significant difference with MDPE pipe was the method of jointing. In the past, water mains had been laid by jointing short sections of pipe together; old cast iron pipes normally had 'run lead' joints, which required considerable labour, skill and time to make. More recently, ductile iron and uPVC pipes had been jointed using 'spigots' and 'sockets' with a rubber sealing ring, simpler to use but not always entirely foolproof!

Leakage from pipe joints was and continues to be a very significant problem for both the gas and water industries. MDPE pipes developed for the Water Industry, like those used in the gas industry, had a butt-welding jointing system, which entailed welding the pipes end to end, with heated plates being used to locally melt the ends of the pipes being joined. Another form of joint developed was the electrofusion coupling, incorporating an electrical coil within the jointing collar. The joint would be made by applying an electric current for a specified period to weld the collar to the pipe. At first, the Company standardised on the use of electrofusion joints for all its small diameter mainlaying, but a number of teething problems occurred, particularly the need for all parts of the joint to be scrupulously clean; not an easy task in a wet trench! Whilst electrofusion jointing was the standard method adopted for the Company's staff, the contractors, many of whom had worked in the gas industry, could offer substantial financial savings by butt fusing pipes, and so both methods of jointing were used.

Butt fusion of polyethylene pipes

At the same time, the different types of black polyethylene service pipes were replaced by a standard blue MDPE pipe, made from the same material as was used for mains. The outside diameter remained the same as the previous specifications and so mechanical connectors could be used for all types of polyethylene pipe. The era of 'wiping joints' on lead pipes to make connections came to an end in the 1980s. During the same era, the practice of 're-running' leaking lead joints on old cast iron pipes using molten lead was phased out by the introduction of joint leak clamps.

Larger Diameter Mains

Although the Company was adopting MDPE as the standard material for its small diameter mains in place of uPVC, it had considerable trepidation about using anything other than tried and tested materials for larger diameter mains. The standard material for all mains of 200mm (8-inch) diameter was usually ductile iron, an improvement upon the grey cast iron pipes used for more than 100 years until the 1960s. Ductile iron was more flexible and much less likely to suffer the brittle failures associated with grey iron. Its superior strength meant that pipes could be manufactured with much thinner walls; however, this quickly led to corrosion problems and eventual leaks, if the pipes were laid in aggressive clay soils, such as existed across much of a central swathe of the Company's area. The Company therefore decided to use external polythene sleeving on all ductile iron pipes. Later on the manufacturers were to add zinc coatings to improve the corrosion resistance of the pipes. The Company also continued to use fibre reinforced cement (FRC) pipes; whilst this material did not corrode, making it ideal for use in clay soils, it was susceptible to differential movement and third party damage. Thus, in urban locations, where other utility excavations were anticipated, ductile iron pipes were used, while FRC pipes were laid in rural areas.

The Use of Mainlaying Contractors

Increasing concerns about the productivity of Company staff, coupled with growing pressures to reduce leakage levels with quicker response times, led to more mains being laid by contract. In July 1983, a period mainlaying contract was awarded to A H Ball Ltd, of Farnham, Surrey. The contract was based on a schedule of standard rates that could be used to calculate contractual payments for varied schemes across the Company's area.

The Company and the contractor each appointed supervisors to oversee the planning and execution of the work. The Company's supervisor, Mick 'Happy' Parsons, ensured that the work met the specified standards and agreed the work records with Julian Ball, the contractor's representative. By 1985, the Company had decided that the use of mainlaying contractors should become a permanent arrangement and it invited competitive tenders from a number of other contractors, in an attempt to ensure that it received value for money. The lowest tender was that of Avon Lippiatt Hobbs (ALH), a contractor based in Westbury. Given that they were also the current Southern Gas contractor, there appeared to be some potential financial benefits in awarding them the contract, including the possibility that ALH might be able to undertake 'dual-lay' works on new housing sites, where both gas and water mains were required. Ultimately, the perceived benefit was not realised, because co-ordination between the Company and Southern Gas proved difficult. There also seemed to be many sites where the respective mains could not follow identical routes. In the end, the financial savings were insufficient to justify overcoming the practical problems and the arrangement was dropped.

The Introduction of Reinstatement Contractors

The vast majority of the Company's distribution network was, and still is, laid in the public highways of Hampshire and West Sussex. For many years, the local highway authorities had been entirely responsible for the maintenance of road and footway surfaces throughout England and Wales. A system of notices under the Public Utilities Streetworks Act 1950 governed the arrangements for utilities to carry out work in highways. It also prescribed how highway authorities could recover, from utilities, the costs they incurred in reinstating the surface of the highway, after utility works had been carried out.

Whilst those arrangements had been largely effective in 1950, thirty years later, with much greater volumes of traffic and substantially higher levels of utility maintenance, many difficulties were apparent. The first was the often long delay between the utilities notifying the highway authority that reinstatement was needed and the time when it was finally undertaken; in the intervening period, the utilities were responsible for maintaining the temporary surfacing and for any damage to vehicles and pedestrians from faulty work. In the drive for economies, questions were being asked about the charges that local authorities were levying for reinstatement work. The highway authorities were unhappy too, as there appeared to be little or no co-ordination of the utility activity, with sometimes two or more organisations working in a street at the same time. Highway authorities were also dissatisfied with the poor standard of trench backfilling by the utilities and they were unwilling to resurface until they could be sure that there would be no further subsidence of trenches.

By the late 1970s, informal arrangements had been set up in several local highway authorities to attempt to programme roadworks to minimise traffic disruption. In the early 1980s, the local gas and water utilities had managed to persuade the highway authorities to allow them to undertake their own trench reinstatement, while guaranteeing the trench against subsidence and maintaining the surfacing for a two-year period after completion. It was not without costs, as the utilities had to pay for the inspection of the reinstatement works by the highway authorities during that two-year period. This new arrangement, which allowed the gas and water industries to employ their own contractors, would lead many years later to a change in the legislation governing road reinstatement works.

In 1976, the Company employed a local surfacing contractor, D J Frankham Ltd, based near Fontwell, to undertake the work, first in the Company's East District and subsequently across the whole supply area.

New Mobile Radios

For many years, the Company maintained contact with its mobile workforce through a VHF radio system using a National Frequency Plan for the Water Industry. By 1987, the system being used was more than 25 years old and over 100 mobile radios were 'fighting' for a single channel in order to make contact. Interference from foreign radios was a common problem and there were prolonged periods when the system was unusable.

The Company became the first water undertaking to give up its industry frequency in favour of a commercial 'Band Three' system, which used the frequencies previously reserved for the defunct black and white television channels! An initial trial was very successful, the coverage from Chillerton Down on the Isle of Wight being reasonably coincident with the Company area, and in 1988 new radios were installed. It proved to be much more reliable, so much so that its use was extended to supply and water quality staff.

The Distribution Review

Following the retirement of Norman Hudson in 1986 and the subsequent appointment of Andy Neve as Distribution Engineer with John Cogley as his deputy, a major review of operational practices in the Distribution Department was begun in 1987. The work was undertaken by a small group of distribution staff on a part-time basis over a period of 12 months.

The Review considered not only the organisational structure of the Department, but also the need for efficiencies in the staffing, methods and materials used in the everyday operation and maintenance of the distribution network. The main outcomes of the Review are outlined below:

- New policy documents were produced to ensure consistency of operational practices across the Distribution Department.

- The three Distribution Managers were provided with administrative support to allow more effective day-to-day management of the workforce.

- The number of area supervisors was reduced and byelaw enforcement was allocated to staff with this sole duty.

- A new Distribution technical support team was set up.

- The routine repair of all but large meters was discontinued.

- The Havant Distribution Manager was provided with a centralised depot and the satellite depot at Portsbridge was closed.

The Distribution Review Group continued to investigate improvements and, in due course, there were staffing reductions in the Control Room (now the 24-hour Operations Centre) and a reduction in the frequency of meter reading for small and low consumption meters. In addition, the functions of the Bognor Regis District Office and Depot were relocated to a site at Fishbourne, more central to the East District. For similar reasons, the Gosport Office and Depot were later relocated to Maindell at Fareham in 1994. The Company was able to sell both vacated sites for housing development.

Maindell Depot, Fareham

At first the Review was not entirely popular with many of the staff, since it represented a big change to the way in which they operated, but many remarked afterwards that change had been long overdue.

New Stopcock Combination Boxes

Since the 'Great Freeze' of 1963, the Company had been installing 'Southampton Pattern' stopcocks on customers' supply pipes. These were considered to be much more robust than the 'crutch' type previously used.

A major shift in policy was initiated in 1987 when the Government decided that rateable values, used for calculating council and water rates would no longer be issued for new properties, At the same time it decided that, from April 2000, water undertakers would no longer have the right to charge customers on the basis of the rateable value of the property. Many undertakers decided to charge all new customers by meter; however, in recognition of the cost and the administrative burden, all of which would ultimately be borne by its customers, the Company decided against compulsorily metering new households. Instead it gave customers the choice between a measured and unmeasured supply. It did, however, decide to install a new Stopcock Combination Box at the boundary of each property; this box could allow a meter to be easily 'screwed in' at a later date, if the customer should choose to be metered. Alternatively, the customer could pay a standard licence fee, based on average rateable value, that would simplify the Company's billing procedures.

Some years later, the original legislation was repealed to allow rateable values to continue to be used for water charges.

Havant Thicket Reservoir

In 1984, with the Havant Thicket Reservoir no longer on the immediate horizon, the Company was persuaded to join with a number of local authorities in establishing a country park at Leigh Park. It was based around the 'Pleasure Grounds' established by Sir George Staunton in the 1800s and, since part of the reservoir site was originally within the estate, the Company joined the Park Management Committee.

Water Quality Issues

Two major incidents in 1989, in other parts of the country, raised concerns about the Company's supplies. At Camelford in Cornwall, a delivery error at South West Water's Lowermoor Water Treatment Works resulted in residents receiving water with very high aluminium content for a number of days. The ensuing publicity about alleged illnesses among local inhabitants caused a number of water companies to replace the aluminium-based chemicals used at treatment works with iron compounds. The Company decided to impose additional controls, such as on-line monitors, at the River Itchen and Farlington Works, where aluminium-based chemicals were used.

The second incident occurred as a result of a filtration problem at Thames Water's Farmoor Water Treatment Works near Oxford, following which some residents in the area supplied by the Works were affected by severe sickness and diarrhoea. The cause was a microscopic organism called cryptosporidium, until then not associated with public water supplies in the UK. The organism normally inhabits the gut of animals and humans and can cause unpleasant and prolonged bouts of sickness and diarrhoea. The subsequent Government-sponsored investigation, chaired by Sir John Badenoch, resulted in much stricter operating controls at surface water treatment works in the years ahead.

River Itchen Works

As outlined elsewhere, the commissioning of Highwood Reservoir led to a number of taste problems. In 1988, warm weather led to a rise in the alkalinity of the water in the reservoir and caused treatment difficulties at the Itchen Works. Elevated concentrations of aluminium were found in the treated water leaving the Works, although once it had mixed with the borehole supplies at Hoads Hill Reservoir, aluminium levels were within safe limits. The Company quickly installed a sulphuric acid dosing plant to enable the pH (acidity/alkalinity) of the water to be accurately controlled, thereby improving the efficiency of treatment and reducing aluminium levels.

A new problem appeared at the Itchen Works in 1989, in the form of what appeared to be 'small red worms' in the filter beds. Although deemed to be harmless, the worms were in fact midge fly larvae. It transpired that still conditions on the water surface of each filter were an ideal breeding ground for the midge flies. A relatively simple solution was found, using horticultural spray irrigation systems installed over the filters, which provided a fine mist of water. This deterred midge flies from landing on the walls of the filters and laying their eggs.

Farlington

A new phenomenon at Farlington came to light following prolonged dry weather in 1989. Heavy rainfall occurred in December and, as usual, alum was added in response to a rise in turbidity in the spring water from Havant and Bedhampton. The alum dose was switched off as the turbidity returned to normal levels; however, some while later, customers in the Farlington Reservoir Zone complained that their water was a 'yellowish' colour. Although the regulatory colour standard of 20 Hazen units had not been exceeded, it seemed that the cause was a high level of humic acid in the 'first flush' of organic matter into the swallow holes in the springs catchment. Fortunately the slight colour was only detectable to a small number of residents (mainly those with white baths!) and new monitoring arrangements were put in place at the Farlington Works to prevent a repeat of the problems.

Water sample ready for analysis in the laboratory

Nitrates

During the decade, routine monitoring began to reveal a worrying rise in nitrate levels in some supplies. Nitrates from fertilisers used in intensive farming since the Second World War were believed to be the primary cause for the increase. Whilst levels remained within safe limits, heavy winter rainfall resulted in significant, sustained rises in nitrates at West Meon, Eastergate, Fishbourne and especially at Westergate, where the legal limit was nearly exceeded.

New Water Quality Regulations

Until 1989, the Company's sampling and analytical programme was based upon the European Drinking Water Directive 1992 and 'The Bacteriological Examination of Drinking Water Supplies 1982', published by the DoE. Privatisation and the need for strict regulation of drinking water quality led to the introduction of the Water Supply (Water Quality) Regulations 1989. These regulations prescribed the frequency of sampling and analysis of all treatment works, service reservoirs and customers' supplies. In addition, the Regulations set down new standards for certain parameters and these placed further obligations upon the Water Industry.

A halving of the lead standard from 100 to 50 micrograms/litre resulted in the Company committing itself to an Undertaking, under Section 19 of the Water Act 1989, to investigate whether the new standard might be exceeded at customers' taps. The outcome is outlined in a later chapter. Another new requirement was for a minimum of 50% of samples from each supply zone to be taken from customers' taps at randomly selected addresses. A computer program was developed to enable this to be done.

Some Unexpected Challenges!

The Great Storm of 1987

16th October 1987 will long be remembered by those living in Hampshire, Sussex and Kent. Despite concerns raised, weather forecasters had been confident that the southern counties of England would be largely unaffected by a storm gathering in the Atlantic the previous day.

It finally crossed those counties in a few brief hours early the next morning, yet it took weeks and months for the communities affected to recover from the devastation caused. It was estimated that, in the counties affected, approximately 25% of the mature tree stock was lost during the storm. Fallen trees caused very significant traffic disruption and blocked roads, isolating many rural areas. The greatest disruption was associated with the majority of overhead power and telecommunications lines, which were brought down by falling branches.

No major mains failures were caused, but the uprooting of large trees damaged a number of customer supply pipes. It was the loss of the overhead cables that presented the biggest problems for the Company. Its policy of providing its own private underground control cables between pumping

Excavator damaged by fallen tree in Havant Head Office grounds during the 1987 hurricane

stations and service reservoirs meant that the control systems were unaffected. However with no power at the pumping station, the pumps would not operate! Moreover, as there was little or no telecommunications contact, the telemetry system in the Operations Centre could not receive status signals or alarms from either the pumping stations or the reservoirs.

Emergency contact with both British Telecom and Southern Electricity was almost impossible, as many of the undamaged telephone lines were engaged. For several days, the Company was left to fend largely for itself. Southern Electricity reconnected mains power supplies often without any prior warning and this led to a number of occasions when major rezoning was completed to maintain supplies, only to find that power to a pumping station had been restored and water supplies had to be reverted back to normal. Throughout the period, the Company's supply staff ensured that the larger treatment works remained in operation, mostly through continued use of the stand-by power generators installed for that very purpose. Many supply staff spent long hours manning the sources, a reminder of the practice that had been largely superseded twenty years previously!

Pete Bridger, Eastern Area Supply Superintendent, recalls "It was impossible for us to know what was happening at the sources and the reservoirs and it was extremely difficult for us to get to many of the sites because the roads were blocked by fallen trees. Neither could we make contact with the Operations Centre at Havant. The first four days were the most critical. Every day I would arrange to meet my staff, Ian Crees, John Champion and Don Wells, at a certain location and we would report back to each other on what we had found and then agree an action plan and the rota for the next 24 hours. At several sites we had to run generators because there was no mains power, but some of them did not have much fuel storage. Because we couldn't drive to the site, we had to lug large containers of diesel fuel over fallen trees to keep the generators running. The last site where power was restored was at Madehurst, which was ten days after the storm."

In the Western Area, the Supply Superintendent, Pete Dulson, remembers that it was 17 days after the storm that power was finally restored at Northbrook. Fortunately he was able to maintain supplies by running the Hoe source, which was not so badly affected.

At all the sourceworks, there were many fallen trees. At Soberton, 16 of the pines planted when the site was developed in 1906 were brought down. John Polkinghorne, Area Supply Superintendent for the Central Area, recalls that the removal of the fallen trees was a long job. John says, "The trees had basically been uprooted. When we came to cut them up, the trunk would have a habit of returning to the vertical once it was disconnected from the rest of the tree. Steve Chandler, one of the staff on the chain saw, had just returned to work following an injury. He was standing on the trunk the first time this occurred and was promptly thrown off, causing a second period of time off for a further injury!"

Whilst water supplies to customers were largely unaffected by the incident, the experience did result in the installation of new stand-by power generation at Hoe and Funtington Pumping Stations.

The Wecock Incident

In 1988, the Company experienced considerable problems at the Wecock Farm Estate, north of Waterlooville, comprising some 2,000 houses built by Portsmouth City Council in the early 1970s. The area was served from the Nelson Reservoir Zone and, following several bursts on the 8-inch uPVC mains on the estate, a programme of mains renewals commenced in 1987. During the renewal work, bacteriological samples taken from two sections of new main were unsatisfactory, despite prolonged flushing. Resulting investigations of the existing network supplying the renewed mains also revealed unsatisfactory quality. Initially, the renewed mains were thought to be the cause of the quality problem and so all these mains were swabbed and rechlorinated on Wednesday 12th October. The existing network was then flushed.

While these actions did bring about an improvement in water quality, analysis of the samples revealed small numbers of bacteria called 'citrobacter', which could have been of faecal origin, suggesting that more harmful organisms could also be present. The local Medical Officers of Health were informed and occupants of the 500 affected properties were advised to boil all drinking water. Notices were delivered by hand to every property and the advice was publicised through the local press and radio. The affected areas were isolated and supplied only from parts of the network known to be clear of bacteria.

Flushing and sampling was carried out daily until Monday 17th October when, following a marked improvement in quality, it appeared that the problem had cleared. Further sampling, however, revealed the continued existence of bacteria and that now an adjoining part of the network was also affected. This area, serving approximately 180 properties, was isolated on Wednesday 19th October, and the occupants, along with those in the 500 previously affected properties, were advised to boil their water.

It was apparent that flushing alone had been unsuccessful and so a programme for swabbing and further flushing of every section of main within the affected area was commenced on Saturday 22nd October. This was reasonably successful, bringing about a marked improvement in water quality almost immediately, although an 'environmental' strain of bacteria, pseudomonas, had started to appear in most samples.

Water quality in most of the affected areas continued to improve, although a small area of around 70 properties still gave unsatisfactory results. Chlorination and flushing were carried out by Saturday 29th October, and, with the exception of one property, three consecutive clear samples were obtained from the remainder of the area. On Wednesday 2nd November, households were advised that there was no longer the need to boil drinking water, except for the single property with continuing poor quality water. The communication pipe to this property was relaid on 3rd November and the supply pipe was chlorinated and flushed.

At the same time, the chlorine dose was increased at the River Itchen Works and Soberton Pumping Station, which supplied much of the water to the estate. The final property was cleared of the need to boil drinking water on Thursday 10th November. For several weeks, staff of the distribution department and laboratory worked long hours to resolve the problem. The subsequent investigation noted the numbers of bursts that had occurred on the estate and the possibility that some soil might have entered the mains and lain dormant, until being disturbed by mains renewal activity. Low levels of chlorine in the network were also considered to have been a possible contributory factor.

As a result of the incident a number of recommendations were implemented:

- A strict procedure for witnessing and recording the swabbing of new mains was introduced.

- Where a new main failed bacteriological tests, three consecutive clear samples were to be obtained before the main was classed as 'fit for service'.

- The policy of leaving repaired mains charged with chlorinated water for a minimum of one hour before flushing and returning to service was reaffirmed.

- The reinforcement of the policy of ensuring the presence of 'free' chlorine within all parts of the distribution network, in order to combat any bacteria that might enter.

Everyone involved with the incident recalls the remarkable stoicism of the residents involved. At times, the estate was referred to as 'looking like the Somme', since there was a multitude of excavations, left open to enable the mains to be swabbed, chlorinated and flushed. Some youngsters took great delight in releasing the hoses used for the flushing work and there were a number of opportunists who blamed all sorts of things on the problem. Considering the fact that they were also forced to boil their supplies before drinking, some of them for three weeks, the residents remained remarkably good-hearted throughout.

A Cold Winter

In January 1987, a period of almost three weeks of cold weather resulted in considerable problems for thousands of customers. Not only was there a significant rise in the number of mains bursts, but also many individual households found themselves without water for long periods. This was then followed by a further rush of calls for help once the pipes thawed and customers found that they could not isolate their supply. There were two principal causes.

The first, mainly affecting older households, many on Portsea Island, was due to old service pipes that had been laid at shallow depths, with consequent freezing of water in the pipe during the cold nights, depriving properties of a supply. Until 1963, it had often been the practice to lay service pipes at shallow depths in order to provide customers and plumbers with easy access to the Company's stopcock.

The second cause was insufficient frost protection to pipework and cisterns in roof storage spaces. Where these froze and subsequently burst, considerable internal damage was caused before the supply could be isolated. In many older properties, there were also no internal stopcock and the householders either had to find and operate the Company's outside stopcock, or call the Company for help.

The Company's inspectors, who spent many hours helping customers, had some consolation in the significant overtime payments, which were welcomed just after Christmas!

The Company therefore encouraged customers to ensure that they had access to an easily operable internal stopcock and, during the following year, it employed local plumbers to install internal stopcocks in households throughout the area for a standard fee.

The Dry Summer of 1989

Although record demands had been recorded in the summer of 1983, most of the summers in the 1980s were unremarkable.

The latter part of the summer of 1988 had, however, been relatively hot and the autumn remained dry. It was followed by a dry winter, with virtually no aquifer recharge; however average rainfall occurred during the spring and, as well as prompting some late aquifer recharge, it also constrained the garden watering of the season's bedding plants! Groundwater levels, however, remained low and the dry period continued until 1992. While it led to hosepipe bans in other parts of the south-east, the Company avoided the need for any restrictions, although regular pleas were made in the local press for customers to be economical in their use of water.

The prolonged dry weather and low yields from sources resulted in many of the Company's stand-by sources being brought into use in 1989 and, given the potential for shortages in the future, investigations were begun to locate new sources of supply. Late in 1989, approval was granted for new exploratory boreholes to be sunk at Slindon and Tangmere.

1990 – 2000: Water Privatisation and the Arrival of Regulation

The Water Act 1989 removed the financial shackles that had restrained investment in the Water Industry for more than twenty years. Whilst central Government was keen to see private investment used to improve the industry's infrastructure and services, the monopoly position of the companies needed some form of regulation to ensure that they acted in the public interest. Although smaller 'water-only' firms like Portsmouth were already private statutory water companies, the so-called 'big ten' water authorities (which dealt with water supply, sewerage and sewage treatment), changed from public bodies to private companies.

It was not until August 1990 that, in order to adapt better to the new water regulatory regime, Portsmouth Water changed its status from statutory water company to public limited company (plc).

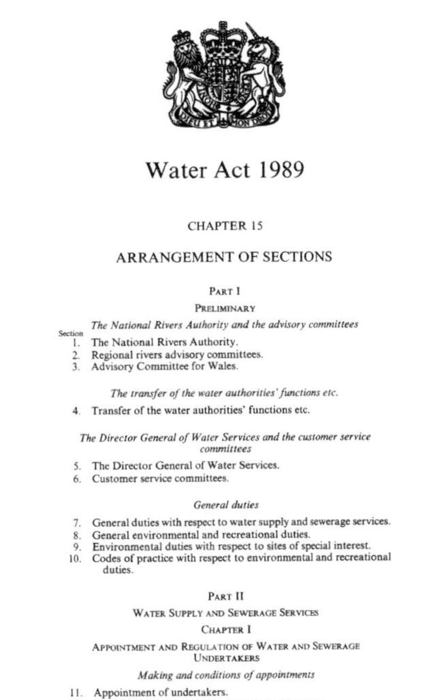

Water Act 1989

CHAPTER 15

ARRANGEMENT OF SECTIONS

PART I

PRELIMINARY

The National Rivers Authority and the advisory committees

Section
1. The National Rivers Authority.
2. Regional rivers advisory committees.
3. Advisory Committee for Wales.

The transfer of the water authorities' functions etc.

4. Transfer of the water authorities' functions etc.

The Director General of Water Services and the customer service committees

5. The Director General of Water Services.
6. Customer service committees.

General duties

7. General duties with respect to water supply and sewerage services.
8. General environmental and recreational duties.
9. Environmental duties with respect to sites of special interest.
10. Codes of practice with respect to environmental and recreational duties.

PART II

WATER SUPPLY AND SEWERAGE SERVICES

CHAPTER I

APPOINTMENT AND REGULATION OF WATER AND SEWERAGE UNDERTAKERS

Making and conditions of appointments

11. Appointment of undertakers.
12. Restrictions on making replacement appointments.

The Development of Regulation and the Periodic Review Process

Office of Water Services (Ofwat)

In the period leading up to privatisation, the Government had decided that price limits would be set for a 10-year period. However, the new 25-year water supply licence, required by the Water Act 1989 and issued to each company, provided for a possible five-year review in 1994. Financial regulation and the monitoring of each company's customer service standards were delegated to a newly created organisation, the Office of Water Services (Ofwat).

National Rivers Authority/Environment Agency (NRA/EA)

Following the reorganisation of the Water Industry in 1974, responsibility for the management of water resources had been vested in the regional water authorities, but it became clear that the newly privatised companies would be unable to fulfil the role of both 'poacher' and 'gamekeeper'. Instead the NRA was established with specific responsibilities not only for the management of water resources, but also for the control of water pollution, flood defence, land drainage, fisheries and, in certain areas, navigation. By 1995, the Authority's brief was widened to include waste regulation and wider pollution controls; as a result, the EA came into being.

Drinking Water Inspectorate (DWI)

The EC Directives for drinking water quality led to the UK's implementation of the Water Supply (Water Quality) Regulations 1989. These set down standards for the microbiological, physical and chemical properties of water supplied for human consumption, along with strict standards for the sampling and analysis of drinking water. The DWI was established to monitor compliance with the new regulations, principally by conducting audits of the methods used and data provided by companies, many of which had their own laboratories. The companies continued to undertake sampling and analysis of treatment works, service reservoirs and customers' taps in designated supply zones. The frequency of sampling was strictly controlled according to the volumes of water supplied, the specific parameter being measured and previous results from the zone.

Customer Service Committees (CSCs)

In order to give weight to the views of customers, Ofwat established CSCs on a regional basis, with each committee Chairman meeting the Director General of Ofwat at a national level. Regional CSC meetings were held in public at various locations, although few members of the public were ever present to see the conduct of business on their behalf. The committees consisted of people with a range of backgrounds, who carried out their part-time duties on a voluntary basis. A representative of each company was expected to attend to respond directly to any questions raised about its performance. The CSCs also audited each company's customer service activities. Debt, disconnections and customer complaints were their main areas of concern.

Ofwat Reporters

To be able to monitor the performance of the companies on a regular basis, Ofwat set up a system of annual reporting and, to ensure that the data submitted was accurate, they required the companies to appoint 'Reporters' who would work to strict Ofwat guidelines.

Since the 1989 'privatisation', two Reporters have provided Ofwat with independent views on the Company's annual and periodic review submissions. Brian Rofe, Senior Partner of Rofe, Kennard & Lapworth (RKL), fulfilled this role from 1989 to 1999, assisted by his colleague Alastair Elder. RKL was absorbed into Arup as RKL Arup in 1998. Alastair Elder himself, now of Jacobs UK, has been the Company's Reporter since 1999.

The Asset Management Plan (AMP)

Having agreed charging limits with the DoE in 1990 for the 10 years ahead, work began on prioritising the AMP1 investment programme. A substantial programme of pumping station and treatment works refurbishment was compiled, setting out a detailed list of work along with costs and timing, with the largest stations or those with the oldest plant to be tackled first. In addition, a method for prioritising mains renewals was determined using burst records and information about the varying corrosive effect of local soils on buried iron pipes.

The Periodic Review 1994

Anticipating that charging limits set in 1989 for the following ten years would remain unchanged, the Company continued to operate in much the same way as it had for many years before. Regulation seemed to be something that had to be endured rather than embraced and so, in the early years, Company staff had minimal contact with the regulators. In fact the regulators themselves were still finding their feet.

In the early years, there was relatively little interference from Ofwat, but it soon dawned on the Company that the Director General possessed, and would use, considerable muscle. Quite soon, Ofwat decided that, although the DoE had set charges for ten years in 1989, it would review water charges in 1994. A timetable was set and companies were required to prepare business plans to detail their needs for the period 1995-2005. In contrast to the AMP1 submission, the Company was able to include a detailed programme of treatment works and pumping station refurbishment, along with an assessment of how much mains renewal was required, all based on additional studies carried out in 1991/92. Other aspects, such as growth in demand and the implications for water resources, reservoirs and trunk mains capacity, were also examined.

The main difference between the AMP1 and AMP2 submissions was the vast increase in the amount of information required by Ofwat in 1994, compared to the DoE's requirements in 1989. The Company was not fully prepared for this, but by using a combination of manual calculation and desktop computer analysis, it completed its submission by the due deadline of 31st March 1994.

When Ofwat announced its determination of water charges for 1995-2005, the Company was shocked to find that, despite its charges already being the lowest in the country, reductions in charges were required for the 10 years ahead. Moreover, there were problems with Ofwat's assumptions about future revenue from commercial customers and these concerns raised doubts for the Company about future financial viability. The Board decided to refer Ofwat's determination to the Monopolies and Mergers Commission (MMC), where the Company was joined by South West Water, one of the companies with the highest charges!

MMC referral

Thus, soon after the intense activity on the AMP2 submission had finished, there began a further busy period in preparing for the forthcoming MMC hearings. City advisers and lawyers were appointed to help the Company in this task and a detailed case against Ofwat's determination was compiled in the autumn of 1994. Meanwhile an MMC panel came to Portsmouth Water on the first of two fact-finding visits, while its staff sent requests for information. Three hearings took place at the MMC's offices at Carey Street, London. On each occasion, a group of Company Directors, staff and advisers attended for a 'grilling' about every aspect of the case being made. The hearings, which were very formal, took place in a large, somewhat dilapidated room, with the MMC panel and staff facing the Company's delegation and stenographers typing every word spoken! The transcript of each hearing was sent to the Company later for any corrections of fact to be made.

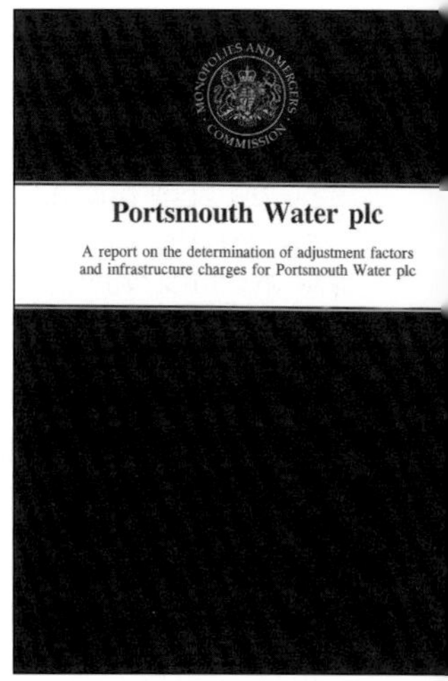

Eventually the MMC decided to uphold Ofwat's price determination for the five years to 1999/2000, but to ease the reduction for the second five-year period to 2004/05. This was only a pyrrhic victory for the Company, because shortly afterwards Ofwat announced that they would be carrying out another five-year price review in 1999.

The Company then had no choice but to seek to significantly reduce its operating costs. Fortunately it proved possible to achieve this by reducing staff numbers gradually, through a policy of not replacing those who left or retired, unless this was absolutely essential.

National Issues affecting the Industry

Water Resources in the South East

The 1989-92 droughts caused significant problems in parts of Sussex and Kent and the water companies in those areas were forced to impose restrictions, principally hosepipe bans, in order to maintain supplies. The fragmented nature of the companies prompted an attempt by the French owners of South East Water and Folkestone & Dover Water Companies to mount a takeover bid for the Mid Kent Water Company, which had more plentiful water resources.

The bid was referred by Ofwat to the MMC, which concluded that a merger was not necessary to rebalance the inequalities in water resources between the companies. Their report recommended that bulk supplies between the companies could resolve those inequalities and the regulators were urged to institute such arrangements. Consequently an initiative by all the water companies and regulators in south-east England called 'Water Resources in the South East' (WRSE) was formed in 1997.

The Group prepared a regional strategy for resolving supply problems in the most economic manner. This eventually led to the Company agreeing in principle to the provision of a bulk supply to Southern Water's Sussex North Resource Zone from Littleheath Reservoir. The development of the supply is covered in more detail in the next chapter.

Drought in Yorkshire (1995) and the Water Summit

Before the WRSE Group came into existence, there was a very hot, dry summer in 1995. Fortunately, it followed a relatively wet winter so that, although peak demands were very high, groundwater levels at Portsmouth were above average at the beginning of the summer and the Company did not need to impose supply restrictions. The residents of West Yorkshire were not so fortunate; Yorkshire Water's surface water storage reservoirs came very close to being completely emptied and, in fact, had it not been for a massive tankering operation from Northumbrian Water's Kielder Reservoir, West Yorkshire's customers would have had to collect their drinking water supplies from standpipes in the streets! The shortage was only relieved by a wet winter, but it led to a great deal of criticism of the

Water Industry, not least because there was a perception that the companies were making vast profits and executives were being paid 'fat cat' salaries.

Eighteen months later and within a month of the election of a Labour Government in May 1997, the new Deputy Prime Minister, John Prescott, called senior executives of the companies to a 'Water Summit'. He was in no doubt that he wanted to impose stricter controls upon the Industry and he put forward a '10-point action plan', which set in motion a number of Government reviews, requiring companies and regulators to take a more active role in leakage control and water efficiency.

The Water Act 1999

By the late 1990s, there were considerable concerns about the ability of many customers to pay their water bills. Until then, all companies had the legal power to disconnect supplies to those who did not pay. Portsmouth Water had always taken a firm stance on debt and, despite its efforts to encourage all to pay, it disconnected significant numbers of customers, taking the view that the burden of debt would otherwise fall upon the responsible paying customers. A number of companies began to relax their policies on disconnection in an attempt to be 'customer friendly'. The Government seized upon this opportunity and the Water Act 1999 was passed, banning companies from disconnecting domestic customers. Unsurprisingly, the level of debt began to rise.

Since the early 1980s, domestic customers had been able to pay for their water by meter. It was usually small families in large properties with high rateable values who took advantage of this option. They made substantial savings over the unmeasured charge, which was based upon the rateable value of the property. Savings were also made on their wastewater charges for the same reason. To ensure that sprinkler users, who used large quantities of water in the summer, paid their fair share, the Company had introduced a policy of requiring such customers to hold a sprinkler licence. A licence was only issued once the customer had a meter.

National Metering Trials carried out in 1989-90 had shown that, whilst metering did save water, the savings were dependent upon a number of factors. Many water companies did much to encourage their customers to opt for meters, but Portsmouth Water believed that, with its low charges, the financial incentive for its customers to save water was not very attractive.

The Water Act 1999 brought about significant changes, since it permitted all households to opt for a meter to be installed free of charge. In addition, customers could revert to the unmeasured tariff after twelve months, if they were unhappy with the measured charges. Whilst the installation and reading costs were notionally 'free' to customers, the Company's installation, reading and maintenance costs were being recovered from the whole customer base through the tariff-setting process at each five-yearly price review by Ofwat.

Company Structure and Finances

Having converted to a plc to enable it to diversify its activities, the Company very soon realised that a vehicle would be needed to separate diversified activities from the regulated water supply operation. As a result, Brockhampton Holdings plc was formed as a holding company and it acquired the entire share capital of Portsmouth Water plc. Whilst this book is concerned with the history of Portsmouth

Water as the principal business within the Brockhampton Group, some Brockhampton matters are also covered where they are relevant.

The Board and senior staff, 1990. Back row, left to right: David Rock, Hugh Pringle, George Slater, Fred Bailey, John King (Chief Engineer), Tim Jackson, John Batty (Secretary & Treasurer). Front row, left to right, John Glanville, David Childs OBE (Chairman), Eric Guymer

The Involvement of the Pension Scheme

It was always the intention of the Pension Scheme Trustees to hold their investment in the Company for the long term, to safeguard the interests of members and help to preserve the traditions of Portsmouth Water, at the same time benefiting from its future prosperity. The Scheme's investment in the Company and others in the Industry delivered such an outstanding financial return that it created a pension fund surplus, which remains today, even though a great many other pension schemes are in deficit.

The investment in the water company was so successful that it grew to represent a high percentage of the Scheme's portfolio. Whilst not initially a problem, in late 1992 regulations under the Social Security Act were introduced, prescribing limits to the levels of investment by pension funds in their sponsoring companies. Although not entirely happy, not least because of the valuable income from dividends that would be lost, the Trustees had to find a way to reduce the level of 'self-investment'. In anticipation of the new regulations, the Trustees had already begun to restructure their investment and, over a three-year period, a number of disposals of various groups of shares were undertaken. By July 1994, the Scheme held 57% of the voting equity, which represented just 19% of its total investment value.

At that level, the Trustees believed that there was a very low risk in self investment and that its holding would continue to represent a material source of income. However, the National Association of Pension Funds was pressing the Government to ensure that pension investments were being properly protected and it came to light that a Pensions Bill was being prepared, which would limit self-investment to no more than 5% of a total fund value. Foreseeing the potential for problems, the Trustees lobbied the Government officials drafting the legislation to try to modify the provisions and at first it appeared that they were willing to give the proposal consideration. Robert Maxwell's disappearance from his luxury yacht off the Canaries and the extent of the financial irregularities of his dealings with the Mirror Group Pension Scheme quickly changed matters. As soon as legislative space could be found, the Pensions Act 1995 was passed and the 5% self-investment limit imposed without any modification. Fortunately for the Trustees, the Act incorporated a lead-in period and this enabled the investment to be reduced before the new provisions took effect on 1st April 1997.

The Development of Employee Shareholders

Like many other water companies, the Company was keen to increase the commitment of staff to its objectives. In 1992, therefore, Brockhampton established a 'Sharesave' scheme, enabling staff to fund the purchase of shares at a reduced price through regular savings from salary. It was so enthusiastically taken up that five further schemes were set up in the years that followed.

In addition, as part of the 1996 pay deal for staff, Portsmouth Water negotiated an arrangement with its holding company, Brockhampton, enabling it to set up an Employee Share Ownership Trust. The Trust was established as an incentive to employees, by tying potential benefits to the future performance of the Company and the underlying increase in value of its shares. Members of staff and trade union representatives were elected as Trustees to manage the Trust.

Growing Discontent amongst other Shareholders

During the early 1990s, there had been some consolidation within the Industry, with a number of the smaller companies merging or being taken over, especially where there were common owners. In 1992, the Board received an approach from East Surrey Holdings, suggesting that there might be economies from the two companies joining forces with the Sutton and District Water Company. The Brockhampton Board declined the offer, although East Surrey did, in due course, merge with Sutton.

Brockhampton's share structure consisted of voting and non-voting shares, not an uncommon arrangement in the 1980s. By the 1990s, a large number of companies had enfranchised (given voting rights to) many non-voting shares. A significant body of Brockhampton's non-voting corporate shareholders were just as keen to see it enfranchise its shares, so that they could exercise greater influence over the activities of the Group. Some pressure came from existing voting shareholders, but it also came from those who had deliberately purchased non-voting shares in the expectation that, in time, the shares would be enfranchised, realising significant additional value in the process. The difficulty for the Board was that, for enfranchisement to take place, the voting shareholders would need to receive a sizeable premium in return for giving up their control, something which was not expected to be supported by shareholders as a whole!

As it would be difficult to satisfy all shareholders in any rearrangement, the Directors resisted the pressure for change, instead focusing upon the financial performance of the Group. However, as time progressed, the frustrations of individual groups of shareholders became more apparent and these came to the fore at the Annual General Meeting (AGM) of Brockhampton in 2000; until that time,

AGMs had been relatively quiet affairs. It was not until late 2000 that matters really came to a head and this is covered in the next chapter.

The Management Structure

At the beginning of the decade, Portsmouth Water's management structure was much as it had been for some time, John Batty being Secretary & Treasurer, with Nick Roadnight his deputy, while John King was Chief Engineer, with Tim Jackson his deputy. Both John Batty and John King became Directors in 1990.

In 1992, John King retired as Chief Engineer although, as was usual practice, he continued as a non-executive Director. At that time, a significant change in structure occurred, as John Batty became the first ever Managing Director of the Company. Tim Jackson became Chief Engineer and Nick Roadnight Financial Controller; there were no longer any deputies! To deal with the rapidly expanding capital investment programme being driven by the new regulatory regime, a new post of Capital Works Manager was filled by Andy Neve, the then Supply Engineer. Nigel Rowley, who had joined the Company in 1990 from Dwr Cymru Welsh Water, became the new Supply Engineer and several more engineering staff were recruited to deliver the expanding programme. In 1994, Nick Roadnight and Tim Jackson joined the Board as Finance Director and Technical Director respectively.

The Brockhampton Board, 1996. Standing, left to right: Hugh Pringle, John King, Fred Bailey, Martin Copp. Seated, left to right: John Glanville, George Slater (Chairman), John Batty (Managing Director).

Further changes were to occur five years later in 1997 when, just before John Batty's retirement, George Slater vacated the Chairman's position, after serving a total of 47 years with the Company. John Batty became Chairman, Nick Roadnight was appointed as the new Managing Director and Tim Jackson decided to leave the Company. John Cogley was appointed to the new post of Customer

Services Director, responsible for both the Distribution and Customer Accounts functions, while Andy Neve was appointed Technical Director. The post of Finance Director was filled by Neville Smith, who was recruited from Roxspur plc in 1998.

At management level, John Harvey was appointed Customer Services Manager following the retirement of Tony Perry, Mike Hedges took on the new role of Planning & Capital Works Manager, while Dave Lang was appointed Facilities Manager, with responsibility for stores, purchasing, transport and building maintenance. Other managers in post at the reorganisation were Alan Day (Management Accountant), Sue Halford (Company Secretary), Brenda Monnery (Computer Manager), David Rock (Chief Accountant), Nigel Rowley (Supply Manager) and Bill Thomas (Water Quality Manager). The three Distribution Managers were Ken Baldwin (Fishbourne), John Stein (Maindell) and Mick White (Havant).

New Resource Development

Following the dry winter of 1988/89 and only 65% of average rainfall in the remainder of the year, groundwater levels at the end of 1989 were close to a record low. Although no restrictions were necessary to meet customer demands, the yields of several sources were considerably reduced. A number of stand-by sources were brought into use and this spurred the Company to begin the process of investigating new resources.

Slindon and Tangmere

As a result of reduced yield at Eastergate, a scheme was approved in November 1989 for two new trial boreholes at Slindon and Tangmere. The Company already owned land at Slindon Pumping Station, but at Tangmere the Company had to reach agreement with landowners.

Low rainfall continued to strain the Company's resources during the summers of 1990 and 1991. Meanwhile, the new borehole at Slindon was test pumped, producing 11 million litres per day during continuous pumping of 28 days and over 13 million litres per day during a three-day extension of test pumping. The Company was confident of a successful licence application, but the NRA immediately expressed its concerns that Swanbourne Lake, a spring-fed artificial lake created within Arundel Park in the 1700s, might be affected by the Slindon abstraction, even though Slindon was some 4 miles to the west! The Lake had dried up in the autumn of 1989 and the newly formed NRA believed that, despite the very low rainfall, water supply abstractions might have been responsible.

More extensive test pumping and groundwater monitoring was carried out during the winter of 1990/91. Despite limited impacts upon groundwater levels at all monitoring sites, the Company was only granted a short-term licence to utilise Slindon, and then only as part of the Eastergate group licence, which already incorporated the original Slindon borehole and the sources at Westergate and Eastergate. The NRA decided that it needed to undertake a more detailed investigation of the whole of the so-called Chichester Chalk Block. This is a section of the South Downs running from the River Ems near Emsworth to the banks of the River Arun at Arundel. The Company appealed against this decision and engaged the consultants, W S Atkins, to prepare the supporting case. They even proposed some trials for pumping additional water into the Lake, but the NRA and Southern Water, who have a borehole at Arundel, did not support the proposal.

Confident of the long-term future of such a reliable source, the Company began the refurbishment of the site at Slindon, incorporating a brick and flint building in the style of a Sussex barn. The new building, designed by James W Harper & Associates, won favour with the planners at Arun District Council. Henry Jones Ltd of Havant was the building contractor and the structure housed the new controls and disinfection equipment, as well as those for the Slindon boosters serving Slindon Reservoir. As the new borehole pumped to Littleheath Reservoir only, final monitoring of the treated water from Slindon was carried out at a remote kiosk on the boundary of the reservoir site.

Slindon Water Treatment Works

At the same time, a further exploratory borehole was put down at Chestnut Farm, Easthampnett, just east of Tangmere and close to the head of the valley that forms the Aldingbourne Rife. Unfortunately the test pumping produced no more than 2 million litres per day and so the Company abandoned the trial and observation boreholes.

Aldingbourne

Having been unsuccessful at Easthampnett , the Company continued the search by conducting a short test pumping exercise at one of the NRA's observation boreholes, at a site adjacent to the Aldingbourne Rife, just west of Aldingbourne village. The test proved to be quite promising and, after extensive negotiations with the landowner, a 600mm diameter borehole was drilled and successfully test pumped at 10 million litres per day in the autumn of 1992, a time when groundwater levels were again close to an all-time low.

The NRA's study of the Chichester Chalk Block was finally published in 1994, but criticism from both Southern Water and the Company resulted in further studies not made public until mid-1995. The studies concluded that Southern Water's borehole abstraction at Madehurst and the new borehole at Slindon had a significant impact on Swanbourne Lake. Despite the Company's protests, it was clear that the NRA would not be persuaded otherwise. Eventually the Company applied for the inclusion of the Aldingbourne and Slindon sources within the Eastergate group licence, incorporating an increase in the peak licensed capacity, but no change in the overall annual total. It was not until the middle of 1996, by which time the NRA had become the Environment Agency, that the application was finally approved. Disappointingly, the new licence contained no changes to either the overall annual or peak licence quantities and,

Aldingbourne Water Treatment Works

whilst it did include the new source at Aldingbourne, the temporary licence for Slindon was withdrawn and the peak daily amount reverted to its original 2.5 million litres per day limit.

Consequently, the Company conceded defeat, concentrating its efforts on the development of the Aldingbourne Works, which, like Slindon, was constructed in the brick and flint style of a Sussex barn.

Major Supply Improvements

Havant & Bedhampton Springs Refurbishments

In the late 1980s, the Company had undertaken limited refurbishment of the springs on the Head Office site at Havant. Enclosed basins had been constructed around the springs in the old eastern basin, which was then abandoned.

Enclosure of Havant Springs, 1997

In 1997, the remaining open springs basins were enclosed. This provided better protection against malicious interference, minimised airborne pollution and prevented the adverse effects of wildfowl and weed growth on water quality. P Trant Ltd was awarded the contract to cover the channel and enclose the remaining basins. The two large collecting ponds, originally constructed to store water for the steam engines in earlier years, were finally disconnected from the supply system to Farlington; they were, however, retained as ornamental features. Some years later, an island was constructed in the high level pond to encourage birds to nest.

Four years previously, a similar scheme had been carried out at Bedhampton. The Blue Hole Stream, a wide channel forming the original collecting basin for the steam-driven pumps of the Bedhampton No. 1 Pumping Station, was in particularly poor structural condition. It was replaced by a reinforced concrete tank to supply the suction wells of the pumping station, with water from new spring enclosures being piped to the new tank. Connections were also provided from the suction tank to Havant Pumping Station as well as Bedhampton No. 2 Pumping Station, which had been relegated to stand-by duty.

The now redundant Blue Hole Stream provided the Company with a significant opportunity. The demands of highway authorities for higher standards of trench reinstatement by utilities had generated more surplus excavated material, which had to be disposed of in landfill tips. With the increased expense of landfill tipping, the Blue Hole Stream provided sufficient tipping space for many years and, having obtained the necessary licences, the Company began to dispose of all surplus inert excavated materials at Bedhampton.

New high lift pumps, River Itchen Works, 1999

River Itchen Works Refurbishment

By the mid-1990s, the River Itchen Treatment Works was more than 20 years old and much of the plant and equipment was in need of refurbishment. A staged programme of modernisation was devised.

One of the first requirements was to improve the early warning of poor quality water in the river. Instruments to measure various important parameters, such as a hydrocarbon monitor to detect oil, were installed at the intake. To inhibit the continuing problems of algal growth in Highwood bankside storage reservoir, plant was installed to dose algal coagulants into the reservoir when the temperature favoured the growth of algae. Other chemical dosing and control systems were replaced at the same time.

In 1997, the Company began a major scheme to refurbish the upward flow clarifiers and rapid gravity filters. New electric valve actuators, penstocks and automatic de-sludging equipment were fitted throughout. A new computer-controlled operating system was also installed.

In 1999, the pumps and control systems in both the Low and High Lift Pumping Stations were renewed, while the flat roof on each building was replaced with a pitched roof. The screens at the river intake were refurbished and new high voltage switchgear was installed. New disinfection and chemical dosing equipment was provided and a new control room was built within the main Works building to house control computers and instruments.

In all, the 1990s modernisation of the works cost £3.6 million, only just less than the £4 million original cost of the works.

Refurbishment and Improvements at Farlington Treatment Works

By the late 1990s, the need for improvements to the control equipment at Farlington was becoming apparent.

Until this time, the Farlington Treatment Works had relied on the service reservoirs to provide sufficient contact with chlorine prior to water entering supply. However, more rigorous regulatory consideration of the disinfection of water led to the decision to provide a separate chlorine contact tank at the works. The tank, of 2,500 cubic metres capacity, was completed in 1999 by Dean & Dyball at a cost of £1 million, and included facilities to distribute the works output more evenly between the Farlington Service Reservoirs.

At the works itself, a study by Binnie, Black & Veatch recommended a number of improvements. Consequently, the rapid gravity filters were completely refurbished with new valve actuators and controls and the filter media in the original 1965 filters was replaced. The works stand-by generator was replaced with a larger unit and improvements were made to the disinfection dosing system.

Binnie, Black & Veatch carried out these improvements at a total cost of £1.7 million, whilst total expenditure on the 1990s refurbishment at Farlington and Havant & Bedhampton Springs came to £3.05 million.

Additional Reservoir Storage

The Company's first Corporate Plan in 1986 had set out the policy for minimum reservoir storage. However, as greater transfer capabilities were being developed within the supply network, further storage was needed at several important sites to provide greater security of supply during emergencies.

In 1990, the Board approved the construction of No. 3 Reservoir at ***Hoads Hill***, a site which was an important part of the supply for Fareham and Gosport. It also contained booster pumps for the transfer of water to Nelson Reservoir, serving Waterlooville, Cowplain and Portchester. It was decided to maximise available storage on the remaining land at the site by constructing an irregular-shaped reservoir. The scheme incorporated a new chamber allowing water from the River Itchen, Meon valley and Hamble valley sources to be blended at the inlet of the reservoirs, thus alleviating a previous water quality concern. The former Shellabear Price Company, now taken over by Biwater, was awarded the contract for the design and construction.

Construction of Hoads Hill No.3 Reservoir, 1990

The Farlington Reservoir Zone was, and continues to be, the Company's largest zone, with a population of over 200,000 and other important commercial supplies, such as the Naval Base and the Continental Ferry Port. With that in mind, the Company decided, in May 1991, to construct a further service reservoir at ***Farlington***, with a capacity of 40 million litres. The new No. 7 Reservoir was connected to No. 6 Reservoir, the eastern wall becoming the dividing wall between the two. For the sake of economy, the Company broke with tradition, obtaining competitive design-and-construct tenders from suitable contractors. Biwater Construction was the successful tenderer. The scheme did not progress quite as planned. The Company found that, for the first time, it was obliged, following changes in planning law, to apply for planning permission; until then reservoirs had been exempt under permitted development rules. Moreover, the sloping site meant that there would be far more excavated chalk than was needed to backfill the walls after construction. Residents of Woodfield Avenue, to the south of the site, were unhappy with the proposal to accommodate the surplus material in a steep embankment between the reservoir and the site boundary. The planning application was refused and the Company eventually agreed to remove a significant volume of the surplus chalk to the site of the abandoned slow sand filters.

Further delays occurred when an error was discovered on the drawings submitted with the planning application, requiring revised plans to be submitted to the City Council for approval. Matters did not improve when excavation finally commenced. The chalk on the southern portion of the site was far more fractured than it had been on the site of the No. 6 Reservoir and the foundations for approximately one third of the reservoir floor had to be piled. Moreover, during the very hot summer of 1992, a number of fine cracks appeared soon after the thin floor and roof were cast, as a result of thermal contraction during the curing process. The cracks had to be laboriously sealed to ensure that the structure was watertight.

In July 1992, the Board approved a scheme to add a third reservoir at ***Lavant***. The existing reservoirs formed the principal storage of water for Chichester, Selsey and the Witterings, and could also support Bognor Regis in times of emergency. For these reasons, the storage at Lavant needed to be increased to two days' average demand. Negotiations began with Goodwood Estates, the owner of land adjoining the Chalkpit Lane site on the South Downs, with a view to purchasing some more land. Plans were submitted to Chichester District Council for a traditional flat-topped design, much the same as for the other two reservoirs on the site. The application was refused, owing to the sensitive location of the reservoir in an Area of Outstanding Natural Beauty. Eventually, with the assistance of planning adviser, Richard Stubbs, and after reviewing options with consultants Morgan Horne, two alternative options were submitted to the planners. In July 1993, the Council approved the application for a reservoir with a stronger roof, which could be returned to Goodwood Estates for agricultural cultivation after completion. The reservoir was built by Dean & Dyball Ltd of Ringwood and, during construction, the remains of an Iron Age settlement were uncovered. Work had to stop for several weeks while archaeologists carried out investigations. There was considerable coverage of the find, both on local TV and in the press.

Construction of Farlington No.7 Reservoir

Routine tests and inspections showed that the original Nos. 1 and 2 Reservoirs at Farlington, constructed in 1869, were leaking quite badly, even though an earlier scheme to cover the roofs had been relatively successful. In May 1993, the Board decided to demolish these two reservoirs and to replace them with ***Farlington No. 8 Reservoir***. Tilbury Douglas Construction was awarded the design-and-construct contract and, although progress was good, concerns were raised about the disturbingly familiar cracks in the floor and roof. Tilbury Douglas were not too concerned until it came to the reservoir testing; significant leakage was recorded and, after unsuccessful attempts to seal the floor, they eventually constructed a new floor on top of the first one. This required them to cut a large hole in the completed roof to enable them to lower in the plant, reinforcing steel and concrete to complete the work. However, the new floor also leaked and it was not until June 1996 that, after further repairs, the new reservoir finally passed its 'watertightness test' before being commissioned some 18 months late.

Construction of Farlington No.8 Reservoir

Pumping Station Refurbishment and Modernisation Programme

Many of the Company's pumping stations had either been converted to electrical power in the 1950s and 1960s or had been newly developed at that time. By the early 1990s, most of the electrical equipment and controls were more than 25 years old, were relatively unsophisticated and included some important components for which spare parts could no longer be obtained. Therefore, in 1991, the Company began a refurbishment programme, under which virtually all its source and treatment works were modernised over the following 13 years.

For these refurbishments, an important policy was established, requiring that all pumping stations with disinfection by simple chlorination would incorporate at least ten minutes' contact time with chlorine before the treated water left the site. This development led to a change of title from 'pumping station' to 'treatment works'.

The first site to be tackled in 1991 was ***Woodmancote***, north-east of Emsworth, which had been taken over from Chichester RDC in 1963. The building was in particularly poor condition and a new one was constructed, incorporating new controls and disinfection equipment, before the old one was demolished. A contact main, providing ten minutes' contact time, was also laid around the site.

In the same year, the redevelopment of ***Soberton*** was proposed. Immediately prior to considering the Company's planning application to demolish the extended Edwardian structure that had once housed the steam-driven pumps, Winchester City Council designated the site a Conservation Area without any reference to the Company. Despite its objections, there was no means of appeal and the planning application within the Conservation Area was refused. Eventually, a scheme drawn up by the architects, James W Harper and Associates, was approved, in which the former coal shed at the rear of the pumping station building was converted to include the new control panel, disinfection equipment and Fir Down booster pumps, together with a small office. The building contractor was John Hobden Ltd, of Southampton.

Walderton Water Treatment Works

At ***Walderton***, constructed in the 1960s, there were modest improvements that left the existing building intact. With a potential maximum output of 36 million litres per day, a very considerable length of contact main would have been needed on the site to ensure 10 minutes' contact time. Use was therefore made of the existing pumping main between Walderton and Racton to provide adequate contact time. A remote kiosk containing monitoring equipment was constructed at a point 10 minutes down the main at the maximum pumping rate from the works. The chlorine content was measured by instrumentation at the kiosk and a signal was sent back to the works by telemetry cable. The control panel and disinfection equipment were also replaced and the scheme was completed in 1993.

The ***Northbrook*** site had already been extended in previous years, a 1960s flat-roofed building having been constructed alongside the 1940s building over the No. 1 borehole. While the 1960s building was in relatively good condition, its flat roof was letting in rainwater. The refurbishment in 1994/95 provided for a pitched roof to the 1960s extension and the demolition of the 1940s structure, together with a 1200mm diameter contact main and new controls and disinfection plant.

In 1995/96, the buildings at ***Worlds End*** were provided with pitched roofs and the disinfection plant and pump controls were replaced. As Worlds End pumped directly to George Reservoir, a small kiosk was constructed on the pumping main further along Apless Lane at a point providing ten minutes' contact time, the controls being routed back to the works via cables in ducts. In the same year, refurbishment began at ***Lavant***, where the building had already been modified some years before and no major building works were therefore necessary. New controls and plant were installed, along with a 1000mm diameter contact main for disinfection.

Worlds End building with new pitched roof

In 1996, the Board approved the refurbishment of ***Havant Pumping Station*** in two stages. The first stage consisted of the overhaul of the motors installed in 1959, together with new electrical controls and disinfection equipment for chlorinating the spring water on its way to Farlington Treatment Works. The second stage was the refurbishment of the main engine house and replacement of the

Lavant Water Treatment Works

stand-by power generator. The engine house, dating from 1927 and built in traditional waterworks style, had been suffering from ingress of rainwater for a number of years. A contract was therefore let to Henry Jones Ltd, the local Havant building contractor, to completely refurbish the roof, guttering and drainage arrangements.

The work at Havant was followed by the refurbishment of ***Bedhampton No. 1 Pumping Station*** in 1996/97. As was now becoming the norm, a pitched roof was installed over the 1964 flat roof and new electrical controls and disinfection equipment were installed. Work at ***Westergate*** began in the same year, the unusual sloping fascia with cedar 'shingles' being retained and new electrical controls and disinfection equipment being installed. In anticipation of the new nitrate blending arrangements at Littleheath Reservoir, which would require Westergate to pump directly to the reservoir, the existing pumping main was used to provide ten minutes' chlorine contact and a remote monitoring kiosk was installed in Littleheath Road, just north of the A27.

In 1996/97, ***West Meon Pumping Station*** was modernised, with the provision of 10 minutes' contact time and replacement of electrical controls. A new 200mm ductile iron main was laid to link the previously isolated West Meon Reservoir Zone to Fir Down Reservoir. This main henceforth became the primary means of supply to West Meon, although the West Meon source itself continues to be used from time to time. The new main was laid to West Meon via Warnford, and properties in the village were connected to the new main; thus they ceased to rely on a local private supply, which the owner wished to downgrade for his sole use.

The new building at Funtington

In 1997/98, ***West Street***, near Soberton, was the next source to be modernised. Constructed in the 1960s with flint-faced concrete panels, this was another site with a flat roof and, as at several other sites, a pitched roof was added to minimise future maintenance. As well as the usual replacement of electrical controls and disinfection equipment, a contact main was laid on the site. In the same year, refurbishment of the ***Funtington*** Works, a site first developed by the Chichester Corporation in the 1940s, was also begun. Here a new building was built alongside the existing one and, once the new controls and disinfection plant had been commissioned, the old building was demolished and covers were installed over the wells and boreholes on the site. This development was designed for the Company by James W Harper and Associates and undertaken by E A Chiverton Ltd, of Bognor Regis.

In 1999, the refurbishment of the ***Lovedean*** Pumping Station was commenced. Superchlorination and dechlorination with sulphur dioxide had already been installed there in 1996. The principal work undertaken, therefore, was the replacement of electrical controls. In the same year, new pumps and a new control panel were installed at ***Hoads Hill Booster Station***; the flat-roofed building had a new pitched roof added.

New pumps at Hoads Hill Booster Station

Distribution Network Improvements

Mains Renewals

Having begun a regular programme of mains renewals in 1987, after privatisation the Company focused on the need to invest heavily in the upkeep of the mains network. By 1990/91, the programme had grown to 38 kilometres per annum. Initially many mains in poor condition could easily be identified by their substantial burst history and there was no difficulty in selecting mains for renewal.

During the 1970s and 1980s, it became fairly apparent that the rate of bursting of cast iron mains was strongly linked to the nature of the soils in which they were laid. However, until 1991, there was no

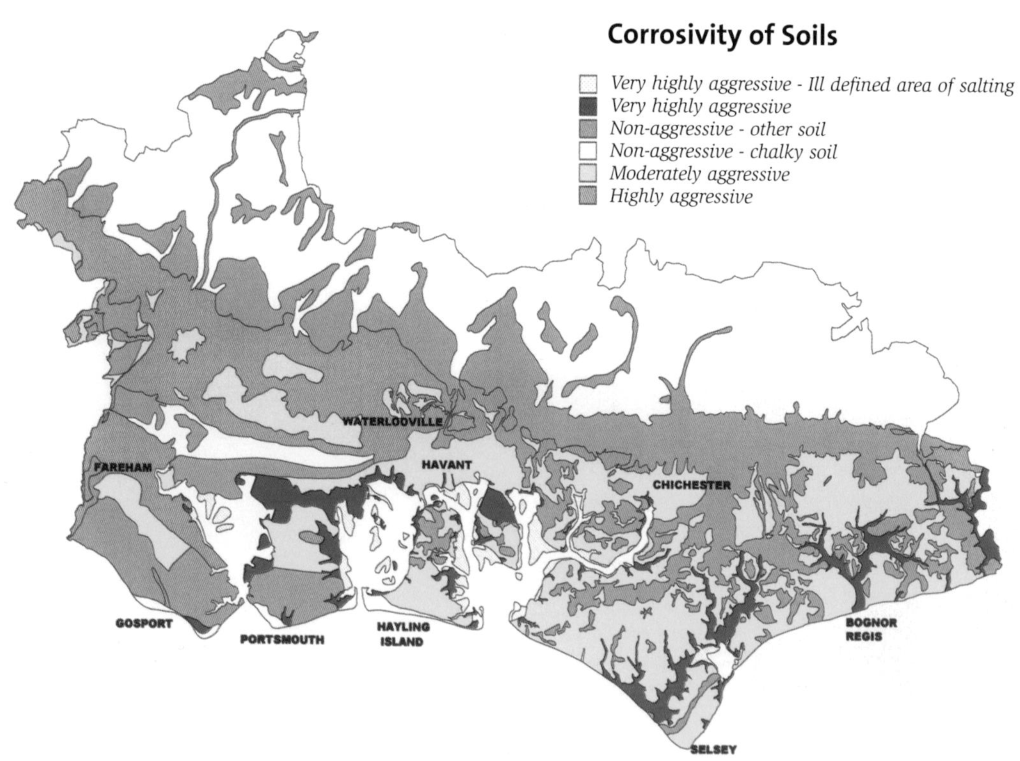

scientific basis on which the degree of risk to mains could be assessed. Matters improved when Mike Hedges, the Technical Services Engineer, asked the Soil Survey and Land Research Centre to provide information that could determine the risk to a cast iron main in any part of the Company's area of supply. The end product was a map showing the corrosivity of the shallow soils across the area; the map was based on the type of soil, (e.g. clay or chalk), the presence or absence of shallow groundwater, the redox potential (likelihood of corrosion) and results from soil surveys carried out in the past.

Corrosivity arises from a weak electrolytic action (rather like the effect of a car battery) that occurs when an iron pipe is laid in wet clay. Perhaps unsurprisingly, the soils categorised as being more corrosive were found to coincide closely with areas where cast iron mains had burst frequently in the past. Portsmouth Water was the first company to carry out risk assessments in this way.

A fragment of corroded cast iron water main

In order to develop a programme for renewal, an empirical scoring system based on a number of critical factors, such as burst rate, soil corrosivity and age of the main, was created. The empirical scores were used to produce a list of mains renewal schemes in priority order. This method was used throughout the 1990s and into the 2000s with little modification. After a few years of renewing mains using this selection method, the number of bursts fell and was maintained at a stable level.

Mains renewal in Southsea

The target length for mains renewal was 1% of the network (or 32 kilometres) per annum and this was broadly achieved during the 1990s.

During renewal of distribution mains, the opportunity was taken to replace all lead and galvanised steel communication pipes (the section of pipe from the main to the stopcock) with MDPE service pipes. A new combination stopcock box, incorporating a meter housing, was also provided, so that if the customer wished to pay for water on a measured basis, a meter could simply be screwed in without any further excavation or reinstatement.

As well as dealing with bursts, it became apparent that there were areas of the network where a high level of maintenance, not only on water mains, but also valves, hydrants, service pipes and stopcocks, was adding significantly to everyday operating costs. In 1990, the Company noted that the worst performing distribution area for both leakage and distribution network maintenance was the New Road waste district in Portsmouth. Consequently, a 'blanket mains renewal' scheme was carried out, in which all the mains, valves, hydrants, communication pipes and stopcocks were renewed in this waste district. The whole process took some considerable time to organise, with local meetings held with highway authority representatives, councillors and other local community groups. The work was undertaken by A H Ball Ltd, of Farnham.

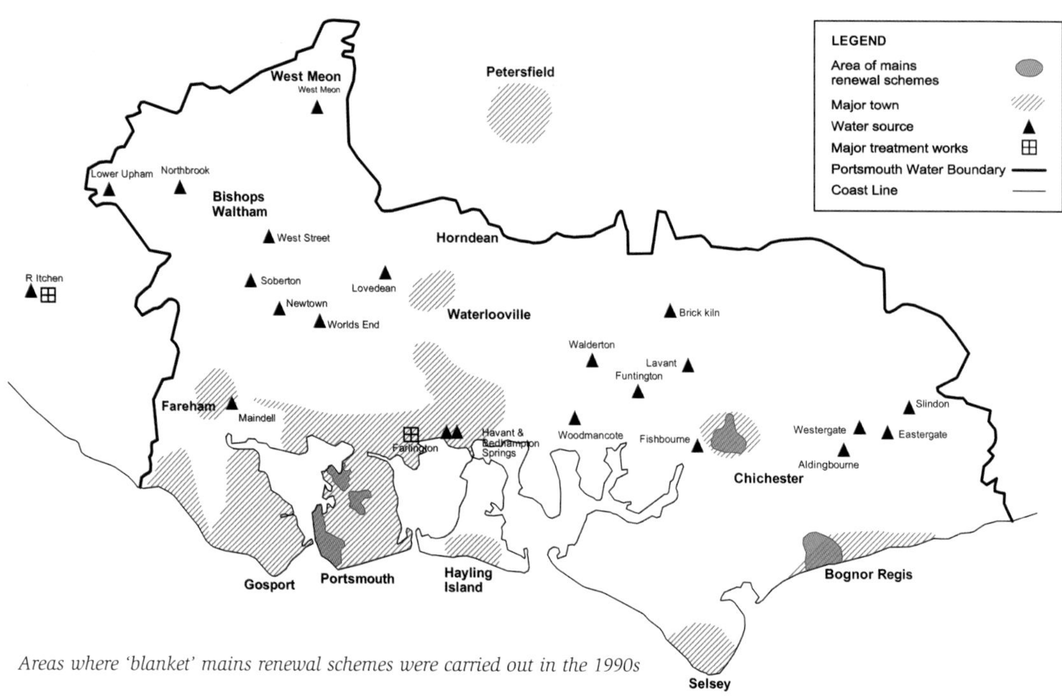

Areas where 'blanket' mains renewal schemes were carried out in the 1990s

Although considerable disruption was inevitable, the work was phased to minimise inconvenience. Overall, it was so successful that further 'blanket mains renewal' schemes were undertaken in Old Portsmouth, the Kent Road area of Southsea, the Derby Road area of Stamshaw, Bognor Regis town centre and Chichester city centre, followed by the Whyke and Summersdale areas of Chichester. Despite the fact that work took place in several sensitive areas, such as the main shopping centres of Southsea, Bognor Regis and Chichester, careful planning and co-ordination with the respective councils and chambers of commerce ensured that little criticism was received.

Water mains renewal in Bognor Regis town centre, 1997

Hilsea Mains Renewal

From the early 19th century until the Second World War, the only route on to Portsea Island for mains supplies was through the Hilsea Tunnel and under Portscreek to Portsbridge, at the northern extremity of the Island. As additional capacity was required to meet increasing demands, so further mains were laid south of the Hilsea Tunnel along London Road. This was also the major road access into Portsmouth and so maintenance of these mains was extremely difficult to undertake.

Laying of 1000mm main at Hilsea, 1991

Leakage from several of these mains had continued for some time, with the Company unable to locate and repair the leaks. Thus, in 1991, these trunk mains were replaced by Solent Excavations Ltd with a single 1000mm diameter steel main encased in concrete. Although it was usual policy to protect steel mains with a cathodic protection system, the presence of so many other utility services in this location meant that a concrete surround was a preferable form of protection.

Although the single main provided less capacity than the combination of the original trunk mains, demand on the Island had fallen in recent years and the Company's computer network model had shown that foreseeable peak demands could be met without significant pressure losses. It also had the benefit of producing an immediate reduction in leakage on Portsea Island of 1.5 million litres per day!

View upwards in one of the Hilsea Tunnel shafts

Hilsea Tunnel Refurbishment

The Hilsea Tunnel between Portsbridge and Hilsea was constructed under Portscreek in 1903/04, at a time when the Admiralty was asking the Company for more water and was also considering deepening the creek to enable ships to pass between Portsmouth and Langstone Harbours. The 600-foot long tunnel contained two 36-inch and two 20-inch diameter mains. Whilst frequent routine mains inspections were carried out, a full structural inspection of the tunnel was only conducted on a 10-yearly basis. An inspection in 1995 revealed that, although the cast iron segments in the tunnel and the vertical shafts at each end were in remarkably good condition, the mains themselves, steel pipes with lead socketed joints, were extensively corroded. Hydraulic calculations showed that the mains were considerably oversized. The four mains were therefore replaced with two new coated steel mains and access arrangements were also improved. The scheme was undertaken by P Trant Ltd of Southampton in 1996/97.

Pressure Control Schemes

For more than 20 years the Company had paid particular attention to leakage reduction. In the early 1990s, the Industry's research body, WRc, published new guidance highlighting the fact that leakage rates were greater at night, owing to the higher night-time network pressures. Thus, if pressures could be minimised at night, there could be a significant leakage saving, perhaps accompanied by some reduction in overall demand.

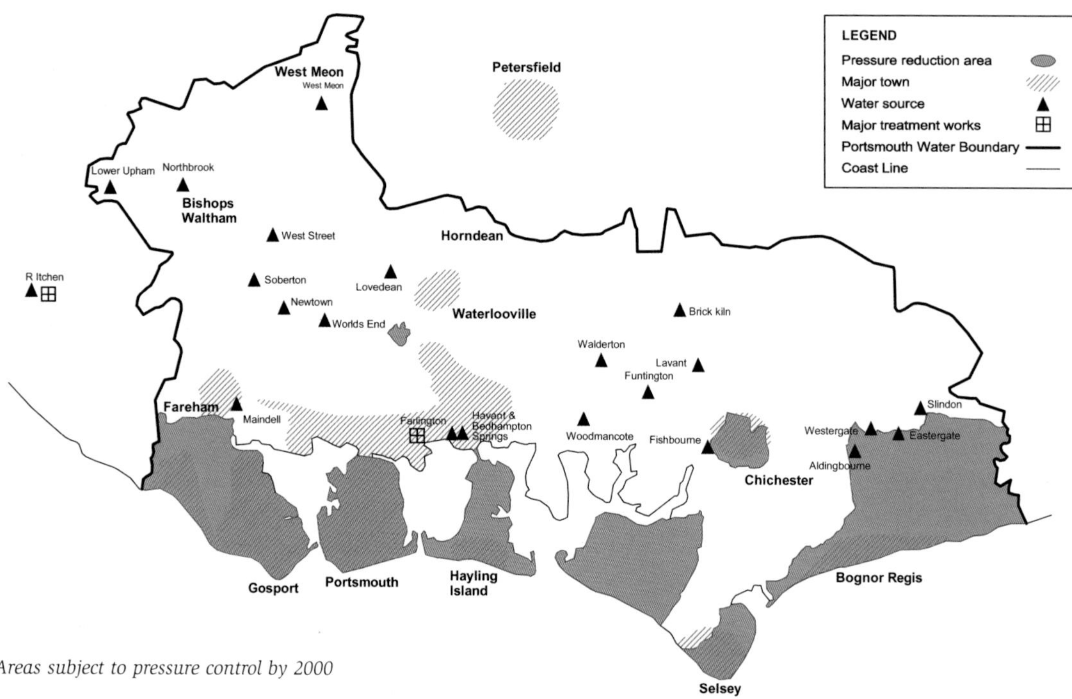

Areas subject to pressure control by 2000

With just two main supplies to Portsea Island, the provision of pressure control in 1994 was a relatively straightforward scheme. A pressure control valve was installed at the southern end of the Hilsea Tunnel and immediately upstream of the newly laid 1000mm diameter Hilsea trunk main. Downstream pressure monitors were installed and a computer model was used to confirm that the chosen valve settings would provide sufficient pressure at the network extremities in Eastney and Southsea. A telemetry outstation was installed to send electronic flow and pressure data and alarms to the Operations Centre at Havant.

Eventually the 36-inch main adjacent to Eastern Road was throttled to provide only a 'sweetening' flow. After the new valve was commissioned, it was estimated that overall demand on the Island, including leakage, had reduced by 3.5 million litres per day.

The scheme was so successful that further pressure control valves were installed on the supplies to Bognor Regis, Chichester, Selsey, the Witterings, Hayling and Gosport. By the end of the decade, some 65% of the Company's supplies were covered by similar controls. In total, it was estimated that the demand savings amounted to a further seven million litres per day.

Nitrate Blending

Rising nitrate levels in drinking water had already been identified as a cause for concern in the 1980s. Nitrates from fertilisers used in intensive farming since the Second World War were believed to be the major cause for the rise. In 1995, there was an exceedence of the permitted concentration of nitrate in treated water from the Eastergate source. The nearby Westergate source also exhibited a nitrate trend that regularly approached the permissible limit of 50 milligrams per litre. The Company therefore decided to blend water from these two sources at Littleheath Service Reservoirs with water of lower nitrate concentration from Slindon.

The first stage of the scheme was to carry out trunk main modifications to ensure that water from Eastergate and Westergate was blended with water from Slindon before reaching customers. To do so, Solent Excavations Ltd laid a new 800mm welded steel gravity distribution main from Littleheath to connect with trunk mains serving the Bognor Regis area at Westergate. The changes were completed by adding local cross-connections to some trunk mains and capping off others.

Water with a lower nitrate concentration from Slindon was, in due course, supplemented in 1997 by water from the new source at Aldingbourne, also pumped to Littleheath for blending. However, it was apparent that supplies from Aldingbourne and Slindon (especially now with a reduced abstraction licence) would, with a rising nitrate trend at Eastergate and Westergate, be insufficient to produce a blend of water that would contain nitrate within the maximum permitted concentration. Two further links from other networks were therefore carried out in 1996 and 1997.

The first was the laying of a 600mm ductile iron trunk main from service reservoirs at Lavant to those at Littleheath. This main, which incorporated a control valve at Boxgrove, allowed water with a lower nitrate concentration from sources at Lavant, Brickkiln and Funtington to be transferred for blending to Littleheath. The scheme also incorporated the pumping main from the new source at Aldingbourne that connected to the Lavant to Littleheath main at Boxgrove. The mains were laid in 1996 by P Trant Ltd.

The second scheme permitted still more blending water from the Walderton source in the Ems valley to be transferred to Lavant Service Reservoirs. A new 600mm ductile iron main was laid by Solent Excavations Ltd to the Lavant Reservoirs from East Ashling in 1997.

The two schemes provided an excellent west to east trunk main 'spine', which was to prove even more valuable in later years when Southern Water requested a bulk supply of water from the Company.

During mainlaying, archaeologists were employed to check for artefacts as mainlaying progressed and some interesting archaeological finds were uncovered. On the Lavant to Littleheath main, a number of Roman coins were found, along with a Bronze Age skeleton. However, on the Funtington to

Aerial view of the 'henge' at Lavant

Lavant main, a remarkable prehistoric 'henge' was discovered just west of Chalkpit Lane; this was first revealed when the chalk surface, exposed after topsoil stripping, revealed a number of concentric earth 'rings'. These proved to be shallow, earth-filled trenches and, in the outer trench, a number of deer antlers were found. The henge was believed to have been the site where the body of an important chieftain had been placed on his death, with the deer antlers symbolising regeneration, in this case of the chieftain's spirit. The henge was thoroughly investigated and recorded by archaeologists. Although there were no objections to laying the main through the site afterwards, the decision was taken to divert the main around the henge to avoid inhibiting possible future investigation.

Wickham Trunk Mains Replacement

Since the mid-20th century, an important component of the supply to Fareham and Gosport was provided by Northbrook and Hoe sources. Treated water was pumped to Shedfield Reservoirs, from where it flowed by gravity along one 18-inch and two 15-inch trunk mains to Hoads Hill Reservoirs and then on to Fareham and Gosport.

The 18-inch trunk main had burst six times between 1989 and 1998, on one occasion in August 1993 flooding part of Wheatley's Yard at Wickham. In November 1998, it burst by the bridge over the River Meon in Fareham Road, an awkward location for the repair, which was successfully carried out by Solent Excavations.

Following this latest burst, the decision was taken to replace all three mains with a single 800mm welded steel main between the Wickham Community Centre in Mill Road and the northern foot of Hoads Hill, adjacent to the A32. The work, again carried out by Solent Excavations, was relatively straightforward, but in order to avoid any adverse impact on fisheries, the main was laid below the bed of the River Meon by jacking a steel tube underneath the river and then inserting the 800mm pipe through the tube.

Archaeologist holding a Roman coin found at Wickham, 1999

In the early summer of 1999, with archaeologists present, the stripping of topsoil in advance of mainlaying began immediately behind the houses along the east side of School Road, Wickham. Desk studies had shown that Roman remains might be found, as Wickham lies on the route of a Roman road between Chichester and Bitterne, Southampton. The name itself originates from the Old English 'wicham', meaning a small Roman town or villa complex, and previous work in the vicinity had revealed Roman ditches and pits. By the end of the first morning, a concentration of Roman remains had been exposed. These were centred on the site of a small Roman single-chambered, open-flue kiln, which was surrounded by many fragments of Roman pottery. Portsmouth Water, on the advice of the archaeologists, decided to halt work along this section of main to allow time for the archaeology to be fully recorded. In addition, part of the known site of an 11th century manor house was exposed and investigated. The discovery had confirmed what the historians had suspected for many years!

By the time investigations were completed, nearly 400 features had been recorded and excavated over two months. 2,600 litres of soil had been taken for sieving and further analysis and 4,322 fragments of pottery had been recovered. Further excavation revealed two more kilns of a similar type to the first one. All three kilns had been located within a circular structure made of wooden posts, probably a roofed hut. Archaeomagnetic dating showed that two of the kilns were in use between 185 and 225 AD. A copper alloy coin bearing the profile of the Emperor Hadrian was found, along with an enamelled copper alloy brooch. Within the soil samples were found the burnt remains of wheat and barley grown nearby in the same period.

Life at the Company in the 1990s

The Single Table Agreement

Having left the national negotiation arrangements behind in the late 1980s, the Company set about improving its industrial relations procedures. There were differing sets of working terms and conditions and these were not conducive to harmonious working in such a small company. Deputy Chief Engineer, Tim Jackson, set about the task of bringing all the Company's staff under a set of common conditions.

The 1992 'Single Table Agreement', which had initially been proposed in 1989, provided not only a single set of conditions, but also a no-strike clause, coupled with a commitment from both management and trade unions to seek resolution to disputes as a last resort by 'pendulum' arbitration. Since its inception, pendulum arbitration has been used only once, in 1993, to settle annual pay negotiations.

Computer Disaster Recovery

By 1997, it had become apparent that the Company was very heavily dependent upon its computer systems for its everyday business. It was not just the customer billing that needed computer systems but also purchasing and stock control, accounts payable, the management of distribution operations, highway notification systems, payment of invoices and management accounts. All these systems were run on the mainframe computer at Head Office, Havant. In the event of a major power failure or, worse still, a fire, a lot of important information could have been lost and the Company would have suffered significant disruption.

Initially the Company bought a 'disaster recovery service' from a specialist supplier, but the costs were significant, so much so that Computer Manager, Brenda Monnery, persuaded the Board that the provision of the Company's own 'stand-by machine' at another location would be more economic. Fortunately, a building on a remote site was available and was converted for the purpose. Not only was another computer installed, but also a number of workstations, which would enable essential systems to operate in the event of a major disaster at Havant. To date, it has not been used 'in anger'.

Water Quality Issues

In the 1990s, even greater attention was paid to drinking water quality. Even at the beginning of the decade, compliance with the new Water Quality Regulations 1989 was very high, but the DWI demanded yet higher standards, both for compliance and the analytical techniques used in laboratories. The first report of the Chief Inspector found that, during 1990, of the 15,339 samples taken by the Company, 99.7% complied with the regulatory standards. By 1999, that pass rate had risen to 99.91%, following a number of improvements.

Lead

There is no lead in any of the Company's source waters, but lead pipes were used from the early 1800s until the 1960s for service pipes, which connect each property to the mains in the street. When water remains static in lead pipes, small quantities of lead can be dissolved, leading to elevated levels of lead in drinking water at customers' taps. Lead is a toxin known to accumulate in the body and impair the development of the brain.

The 1989 Regulations led to a halving of the lead standard from 100 to 50 micrograms per litre and the Company was obliged, along with all other water undertakers, to investigate the potential for the new standard to be achieved. In the three Portsmouth zones and the Havant zone, there was a 'risk of failure to meet the standard in a significant part of each zone'. The Company was therefore obliged to enter into a legal Undertaking with the Secretary of State to install phosphate dosing at the Farlington Works, which served the four zones. The controlled dose would deposit a thin layer of relatively insoluble lead phosphate on the inside of all the lead pipes. In 1993, one of the old sandwashing sheds at Farlington was extended to accommodate the orthophosphoric acid storage and dosing facilities.

Subsequently, two compliance samples from the Worlds End zone failed the standard in 1996 and a further two from the Chichester zone in 1997. The Company was required to submit further legal undertakings to the Secretary of State to install three dosing plants, at Worlds End, Fishbourne and Lavant, the latter also treating water from Brickkiln and Funtington.

Orthophosphoric acid dosing plant building at Lavant Water Treatment Works

Polycyclic Aromatic Hydrocarbons (PAHs)

A group of compounds called PAHs occur naturally, mainly in decomposing organic matter and also in the atmosphere due to the burning of wood and garden refuse. Fluoranthene, a soluble PAH, was used in the coal tar lining of cast iron pipes laid prior to 1976.

The new regulations of 1989 imposed standards for total PAHs, as well as individual compounds, such as fluoranthene. In several zones, samples occasionally contained levels of fluoranthene exceeding the standard. In most cases, flushing resolved the problem while, in others, short sections of main were renewed and no further exceedences occurred.

However, high PAHs were consistently a problem in the Highdown zone, which included the villages of West Dean, Singleton and Charlton, to the north of Chichester. The Company was obliged to submit a legal Undertaking to the Secretary of State to scrape and reline the existing pipes with a special epoxy resin mortar. The work was undertaken by Pipeway Ltd in 1993/94.

Pesticides

Pesticides in drinking water were not a significant concern for the Company. The new 1989 Regulations incorporated a standard that was, at that time, based upon the limitations of the analytical equipment used to detect the chemicals. This meant that no water sample from customers' taps should contain any traces of pesticides.

The wide variety of pesticides in use meant that the Company had to assess which pesticides were used most frequently and then sample for their presence; in fact, just one commonly used pesticide, atrazine, was occasionally found in samples. There were concerns that the Havant & Bedhampton Springs might be particularly susceptible to pesticides, both from surface water infiltration in the upper parts of the catchment and airborne contamination entering the springs basins. The latter risk was dealt with by enclosing the basins, whilst national controls on the use of pesticides resulted in far fewer failures. The Company was therefore not required to undertake the high levels of investment in pesticide removal required of many other companies.

Trihalomethanes

New standards for trihalomethanes were introduced by the 1989 regulations and there was considerable concern that the River Itchen water, which had elevated levels of organic compounds even after treatment, would, in combination with the chlorine used for disinfection, exhibit elevated levels of trihalomethanes.

These concerns led to the inclusion of a blending chamber in the new Hoads Hill No. 3 Reservoir in 1991. This allowed water from the Itchen Works to be blended with that from sources in the Meon and Hamble valleys.

Cryptosporidium

The cause of an outbreak of cryptosporidiosis, an infestation of the gut causing sickness and diarrhoea, in Oxfordshire in 1989 was ascribed to drinking water supplies containing small numbers of the microscopic parasite, cryptosporidium. The Government asked Sir John Badenoch to chair an investigation into the outbreak and, in due course, the Badenoch Committee made a number of recommendations on water treatment practice. These included the installation of turbidity meters on the outlets of all rapid gravity filters to monitor their performance (subsequently carried out at the Farlington and Itchen Works) and new procedures to minimise the risk of the organism entering drinking water supplies. At the time, it was principally surface water sources that were implicated.

Several more major outbreaks occurred across the UK during the 1990s and concerns were expressed by the local Health Authority about the performance of the River Itchen Works. Sampling was conducted during the spring, when run-off from fields in the upper parts of the catchment into the river would contain excreta from young calves and lambs, thought at that time to be the most likely cause of elevated levels of the organism. So concerned were the Company and the Health Authority that, on several occasions, the Itchen Works was temporarily shut down, either when occasional positive samples were obtained or when an outbreak of cryptosporidiosis occurred in the community. As it was the Company's second largest source, shutdowns of the Itchen Works led to a number of operational difficulties.

In 1997, an outbreak of cryptosporidiosis occurred in South Hertfordshire and North London, an area supplied from a groundwater source operated by Three Valleys Water. Customers had to boil their water for a number of days and the subsequent investigation by the Bouchier Committee, the successor to the Badenoch Committee, concluded that cryptosporidium could infiltrate those groundwater sources prone to surface water infiltration. Spurred on by a further outbreak at Torbay, Devon, the Government introduced new regulations in 1999. These required water companies to undertake risk assessments in each catchment and, where the source was classified as at 'significant risk', to conduct continuous 24-hour sampling using a new and more accurate analytical technique.

Work for the Company by the British Geological Survey identified five sources at significant risk, these being Farlington, Lovedean, Soberton, Maindell and Fishbourne. The River Itchen Works was already deemed to be at significant risk, owing to it being a surface water source with limited bankside storage. At all sites, on-line turbidity monitors were installed, with alarms linked to the Operations Centre at Havant. For Farlington and Lovedean, sites known for past turbidity problems, the Company included proposals for membrane filtration plants in its 1999 Business Plan submission to Ofwat. At the remaining works, the Company had to undertake continuous monitoring to very exacting standards, using 'chain of evidence' bags, which could potentially be used in a criminal court, were a failure of the new treatment standard to occur.

A raw water turbidity meter at Lovedean

Microbiological Problems at Lavant Water Treatment Works

Until the mid-1990s, the Company had regarded the Lavant Works as one of its more reliable sources. However, occasional microbiological failures, principally of the treated waters, suggested that all was not well and so improved disinfection using superchlorination and dechlorination was installed.

Despite this additional treatment, the failures continued and the DWI threatened to take action against the Company. To avoid this, the Company submitted a legal Undertaking to investigate the potential causes.

The exhaustive investigation resulted in the replacement of sample taps and sample lines, and new sampling procedures. Cool boxes and refrigerated vans were used to transport samples at the optimum temperature.

To this day, the Company has not been able to determine the cause of the original failures, but the actions taken have ensured that more rigorous procedures are in place for sampling, transportation and the analytical processes adopted in the Laboratory. The problems have not recurred at Lavant since the new procedures were implemented.

The Maindell Incident

Maintaining thorough disinfection processes at all treatment works had been a priority for the Company for many years. Chlorine residuals were monitored in treated water and, if the residual fell outside certain high and low limits, the pumps would be shut down and alarms would be relayed through the telemetry system to the continually manned Operations Centre at Head Office. Appropriate action would then be taken to rectify the fault before pumping recommenced.

Thus, when on the morning of 9th December 1998, it was reported by the area supply staff that water had been pumped into supply from Maindell Works for almost twelve hours without disinfection, there was an element of disbelief in the report. However, within the hour, it had been confirmed and an Incident Response Team was assembled. Unfortunately, Maindell Works was one of the few that pumped directly into supply, the majority of other works pumping first to service reservoirs. Moreover, Maindell pumped into the Fareham area of the Hoads Hill Reservoir zone, a zone supplying over 50,000 households.

As the microbiological quality of the water within the zone could not be guaranteed, the Incident Response Team decided that, as a precaution, customers in the zone should be advised to boil their supplies until satisfactory microbiological quality could be confirmed. The Distribution Department immediately planned a major exercise to deliver notices to every household in the area. Not only were all the Company's distribution inspectors and mains and services staff involved, but also contract main layers and employees from the Stores, Drawing Office and Supply section. In total, around 120 delivery staff worked through a long and wet day to deliver notices; even staff from Southern Water helped out. The deliveries started at around 1 pm on 9th December and were largely completed by midnight. John Stein, then Distribution Manager at the Maindell Depot, masterminded the delivery operations. He recalls, "One of the most difficult problems was maintaining communications with everyone, as

Residents told to boil their tap water

By Neil Durham
The News

Havant-based Portsmouth Water was today warning 60,000 households to boil drinking water after a failure at one of its treatment centres.

The problem at the firm's Maindell water treatment plant at Wallington, Fareham, means some water may not have been treated with chlorine.

This could mean bacteria exists in unchlorinated supplies provided to homes in the Gosport, Lee-on-the-Solent and southern parts of Fareham.

John Cogley, Portsmouth Water's customer services director, said a stomach upset was likely to be the most severe reaction to drinking untreated water.

He added: 'The probability is that everything will be safe. But we do not want to take any risks and want to keep the public informed.'

Portsmouth Water is to deliver leaflets to all 60,000 homes warning them to boil drinking and cooking water.

Mr Cogley said an investigation was today under way into what caused the problem.

It was spotted at 8am today and may have happened at 10 or 11 last night. It meant that water not treated with chlorine may have entered supplies.

The plant supplies up to one fifth of the water in the area affected but it would mix with treated water as it went out.

Courtesy The News, Portsmouth

they did not all have radios and there were relatively few mobile phones in those days. It was impossible to know how long it was going to take each individual to deliver the notices and, once they had completed their work, they found it difficult to get through to us from telephone boxes. However, the most gratifying aspect was that everyone wanted to be involved – no-one wanted to be left out".

Meanwhile, the Company had notified organisations such as the DWI, the Ofwat Customer Services Committee, the Health Authority, local Environmental Health Officers and many others. Press releases and local radio and TV interviews were used to inform the public. The incident was the headline story for the two local TV news bulletins. Customer Services staff played an important role in dealing with many telephone calls from worried customers. The switchboard stayed open until 8.30 pm that evening, as almost all the Company's staff played their part in responding to enquiries.

By the next day, the results of the previous day's samples confirmed that microbiological quality was satisfactory. A further notice lifting the 'boil water' advice was then delivered by hand to customers, this being completed by early evening.

Investigation of the controls at Maindell revealed that a faulty relay had been the cause of the failure. As a result, a scheme was authorised to make improvements to the controls and telemetry systems at all treatment works. In addition, a number of additional checks were instituted at all treatment works to ensure that a similar fault could not recur.

The subsequent investigation by the Drinking Water Inspectorate concluded that the Company 'had not supplied water unfit for human consumption', although it included two recommendations for improvements to procedures. Had the DWI thought otherwise, the Company might have been prosecuted for a breach of water quality regulations for the first time in its history.

New Fluoridation Legislation

Government had imposed new legislation in 1985 hoping to encourage water fluoridation, which was seen as providing improvements in dental hygiene. Unfortunately, progress had stalled since the legislation was not sufficiently prescriptive to guide those who would have to take the decision to promote fluoridation.

In the mid-1990s, the Company was approached by the Portsmouth and South East Hampshire Health Authority, which was keen to see the Company fluoridate supplies. A feasibility study was undertaken by W S Atkins on behalf of the Health Authority, with the Company heavily involved in providing technical advice on the supply and distribution system. Although pressure was applied by the Health Authority for the Company to agree to fluoridate, the Board was adamant that it would not consider such a proposal unless the Health Authority conducted a public consultation exercise to demonstrate whether a majority of customers was in favour. It also sought a number of indemnities from the Health Authority. In the event, nothing more came of the scheme until legislative changes resulted in a further request, as outlined in the next chapter.

Unexpected Challenges

The National River Authority's Low Flows Investigations

In 1992, after a four-year drought in the south-east, the NRA embarked on an investigation of 40 rivers, which it believed suffered low flows caused by water supply abstraction. The rivers Hamble and Meon, in the catchments of which the Company had a number of abstractions, were listed in the Authority's 'top 40' low flow rivers and consultants Mott MacDonald carried out a detailed hydrogeological study of each. The Company was not entirely surprised by the NRA's conclusion that the 1940 Hoe source, close to the springs feeding The Moors at Bishop's Waltham, was found to affect spring flows during periods of low groundwater levels. The NRA also concluded that the Soberton source, in use since the early 20th century, had the potential to adversely affect flow in the River Meon if it were to be operated at its full licensed capacity, something which had not occurred in its entire history.

The Hoe source had been in regular use from the 1940s until 1973, when the River Itchen Works was commissioned. Hoe was then relegated to stand-by use and, for the next 20 years, was only used occasionally, for example if a problem occurred at Northbrook or the River Itchen Works. During that period, the copious spring flows at The Moors and the consequent changes to the biodiversity of the area resulted in its designation as a Site of Special Scientific Importance (SSSI). That designation, along with The Moors' influence at the head waters of the River Hamble, led the NRA and its successor, the Environment Agency, to exert pressure upon the Company to surrender its licence at Hoe. That pressure was resisted for a number of years, but the 1999 Periodic Review included a new project to investigate and develop new sources to replace Hoe. The development of those sources is covered in the next chapter.

From Drought to Floods

Whilst the winters of 1990/91 and 1991/92 were dry and opportunities for groundwater recharge were limited, the summers of 1991 and 1992 were relatively cool. Meeting demands, despite reduced source yields, had not been much of a problem. In fact, in the late summer of 1992, with groundwater levels close to record lows, the Company organised yield tests at Lavant, Soberton, Worlds End and Northbrook. Valuable information was obtained at some sites, but the test at Lavant had to be aborted, because demand was so low that the Lavant Reservoirs had completely filled and there was nowhere to store the full output from the works!

In the winter of 1992/93, normal groundwater conditions returned for a short while. However, the autumn of 1993 was relatively wet and was followed by very heavy rainfall over the Christmas and New Year period. This prompted a further sharp rise in groundwater levels and consequent flooding in the usually dry valleys of the upper catchments throughout the area. The River Lavant, which flows through Chichester, rose to such a level that there was flooding in low lying areas and a significant risk of the collapse of the culverts that take the river under the city centre. Despite the best efforts of the fire services, the EA was forced to divert the flow at Westhampnett, east of the city, and even asked the Company to maximise abstraction at Lavant and Brickkiln in an attempt to reduce the groundwater flow. The flood diversions were in place for several months, leading to considerable traffic disruption.

Digital Mapping/Geographic Information System (GIS)

The use of computerised utility records was first developed in the UK in the mid-1980s. The digitising of water main positions on an electronic Ordnance Survey map, along with important attributes, such as material, diameter, year laid and burst record, promised to provide companies for the first time with a very powerful tool for the rapid analysis of mains data across the whole network. This, in turn, would open up possibilities that water engineers could only dream of in the past; for the first time, spatial information could be used to target activity such as maintenance and investment on a sound footing. The scale of such an exercise using paper records meant that it could not previously have been contemplated.

In the mid-1980s, an exercise had been carried out to improve the quality of the Company's paper records by surveys and checks against other records. Thereafter, the 'as-laid' position of new mains was recorded by surveying more accurately than previously. These records formed the basis of the Company's future digital mapping mains record.

Diane Bourne using the GIS

In 1991, the Company embarked on a pilot exercise to digitise its mains in the Waterlooville area. Alper software was purchased and the digitising was carried out by two temporary staff under the supervision of Chief Draughtsman, Brian Bunyard, assisted by Diane Bourne. The exercise proved very successful and the Company moved quickly to digitise the remainder of its mains network, employing eight temporary staff to do the work. Each map was rigorously checked for errors before it was accepted on to the record. The whole task took 18 months and was completed in December 1993. From then on, every new main was recorded, not on a paper plan as previously, but on the digital mapping system which, with the addition of other data such as land ownership and soil corrosivity boundaries, soon became a full geographic information system (GIS).

In the mid-1990s, the GIS was complemented by the adoption of a computer-aided drawing (CAD) system, on which drawings for contracts and works, reservoirs and pumping stations were prepared electronically. The drawing board became redundant!

Hazleton Farm Landfill Proposal

In the latter part of 1997, the EA advised the Company that the owners of Hazleton Farm, to the south of Horndean, had applied for planning permission for a major landfill facility for domestic refuse. The owners had previously been encouraged by the County Council's Waste and Minerals Strategy to develop the site and initially this had not been resisted by the EA. It was not until the Agency's groundwater protection staff became aware of the proposal that concerns were raised, principally because the site was within the catchment of the Havant & Bedhampton Springs and there were known swallow holes in very close proximity to the site. The Company considered that there was, therefore, a significant risk of pollution of the springs by water leaching from the landfill site.

The application having been turned down, the owners, the Borrow family from Cowplain, appealed and a Public Inquiry was held at Merchistoun Hall, Horndean. Although Tim Jackson prepared the initial representations, his successor, Andy Neve, was called as the Company's expert witness, with Julia Barrett, an independent barrister, acting as counsel for the Company. Despite a number of other objections relating to traffic and other nuisance from local residents, the concerns about the risks to public water supplies were the primary influence in the decision of the Planning Inspector to recommend the rejection of the appeal. Thankfully, the Minister accepted the Inspector's advice.

The Periodic Review 1999

The 1999 Periodic Review submission for the AMP3 period (2000-2005) set out the case for a continuation of the mains renewal programme and the refurbishment of treatment works and pumping stations. One other notable scheme was the planned replacement of Farlington Nos. 3 and 4 Reservoirs, built in 1906, where tests had shown significant leaks from the reservoir floor. The need for future water resources was examined in the Water Resources Plan submitted to the EA and Ofwat, but none were found to be required in the 25-year period of the Plan. However, for the first time, substantial investment was included for improvements in drinking water quality and reduction of environmental impacts.

Cryptosporidium Risk

On the basis of the risk assessment by the British Geological Survey, the AMP3 submission included membrane filtration plants at Farlington and Lovedean Water Treatment Works. It also proposed the installation of continuous monitoring of water at the River Itchen, Soberton, Maindell and Fishbourne works, as required by the 1999 cryptosporidium regulations.

Lead

New regulations provided for higher standards for lead in drinking water. Work in the United States had already demonstrated that the dosing of orthophosphoric acid into drinking water at low concentrations substantially reduced the tendency for lead to dissolve from the walls of service pipes. This had been confirmed by the Company's experience in the Farlington, Worlds End and Chichester zones. Such dosing offered a cheaper and more effective way to meet the new limit for lead in drinking water of no more than 10 micrograms per litre by 2013.

Farlington Treatment Works had been equipped with orthophosphoric acid dosing plant since 1993, and the Company submitted plans for similar dosing at Northbrook, Soberton, Maindell, Lovedean, Hoads Hill Service Reservoirs, Woodmancote and Walderton. These seven dosing plants covered the whole supply area apart from Bognor Regis, where there was a very small number of lead pipes, it having been the local practice of predecessor organisations to use galvanised steel service pipes in place of lead.

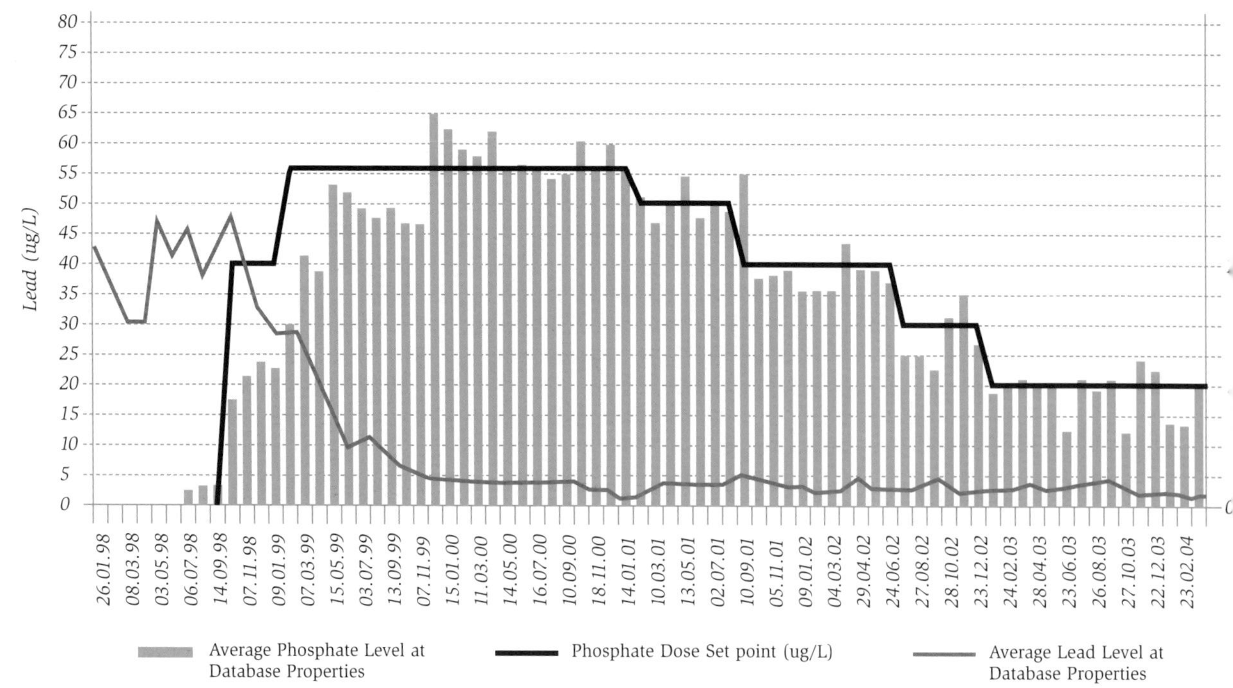

Environmental Concerns

Environmental investigations were proposed into the impact of the Company's abstractions on the River Itchen and Chichester Harbour, including the Fishbourne Channel, as required by the European Habitats Directive. It became apparent that much of the Company's area is contiguous with several sensitive inland and coastal sites. In the case of the River Itchen Special Area of Conservation, the EA set up a steering group to oversee studies into the impacts on the species and habitats. For other sites, either the Company or the EA undertook the work independently. These sustainability studies are covered in more detail later.

A further environmental improvement scheme was the proposal to surrender the abstraction licence at Hoe, where abstraction had been found by the Environment Agency to have adverse impacts on the nearby Site of Special Scientific Interest at The Moors, Bishop's Waltham. The Company included plans to find and develop replacement water resources and to construct the associated treatment works and water mains.

The Outcome of the Review

All the drinking water and environmental quality schemes were accepted by the regulators and included in Ofwat's Final Determination of water charges for the period from 2000-05.

The Company's proposals for refurbishment and maintenance of pumping stations, treatment works and service reservoirs were also accepted, as were its plans for continuing the mains renewal programme. As always though, the amounts allowed by Ofwat included for reductions in the original estimates to drive further efficiencies in the Company's capital investment.

The impact upon water charges and the Company's operations is covered in the next chapter.

2000 - 2007: A Change in Ownership, but Business as Usual

Changes in Legislation and Periodic Reviews of Water Charges

Ahead of the changes imposed by the Water Act 1999, the Company made free meter options available to domestic customers from 2000 onwards. Initially, requests were received from around 2000 applicants each year, considerably less than for most other companies. The Company was heavily criticised by the Environment Agency for not promoting water metering, as it believed this would provide significant savings in water demand.

Until 2005, the Company still offered new households the choice of whether to be metered, a standard licence fee being charged to customers who chose to be unmetered. The Company's Water Resources Plan 2004 identified a potential shortfall in resources by 2020. As part of the long-term strategy for ensuring a balance between supplies and demand, the Company metered all new households from April 2005.

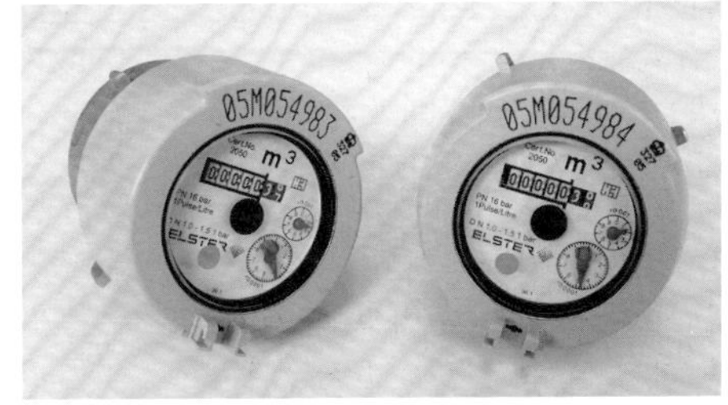

Water meters

The Impact of the 1999 Periodic Review

In the lead-up to the 1999 Review, industry commentators had been predicting a harsh determination by Ofwat and that indeed was the outcome, with an immediate cut in water bills averaging 12.3% across England and Wales. Although prices would rise over the remaining four years, on average they would be 2.1% lower in 2005 than they were in 2000.

Having the lowest charges in England and Wales already, the Company was relieved when it was revealed that the initial price cut for Portsmouth Water would only be 3.0%. However, subsequent cuts over the next four years meant that the average annual bill was expected to fall by 1.4% each year, from £81 to £74. The result was that the Company had to find economies in its operations in the five years ahead.

The Company examined the benefits of outsourcing some activities and one of the first casualties was the Vehicle and Plant Workshop, where it was decided that the maintenance work would be carried out by contract. Two staff were retained to carry out minor repairs and oversee the contract, which was let to Adams Morey of Portsmouth in April 2000. The remaining staff opted for early retirement or redundancy, rather than joining Adams Morey.

Since the major cost involved in the Company's operations was staff remuneration, a review was undertaken by Managers and Directors to see if economies could be found. As a result, for a short period, the Pension Scheme Trustees were persuaded to waive pension reduction penalties for those retiring early and, in 2002, 15 staff departed, many with very long service.

At the beginning of the AMP3 period, 2000-2005, the Distribution Department operated three depots covering separate geographical areas. The Maindell Depot covered the area of the old Gosport and Fareham undertakings, while the Fishbourne Depot was responsible for the areas of the four former West Sussex undertakings. The Portsmouth, Havant and Waterlooville area was managed from a depot at Head Office. Whilst additional travel would be involved if distribution operations were centralised, there were significant administrative economies to be gained. Thus, in June 2000, the Maindell Depot closed and staff transferred to Havant, while the same fate befell the Fishbourne Depot in October 2002.

Throughout the remainder of the period, the Company continued to seek economies in its operations by any means possible.

The 2004 Periodic Review

As the third Periodic Review approached, the Company felt that the preparation of Business Plans was becoming a 'production line process'. Ofwat had other plans, however, deciding that on this occasion the Company should prepare a draft Business Plan, to be submitted in August 2003, almost two years before new charges would come into effect. Moreover, as decisions on the requirements from the other regulators, the EA and the DWI, were not finalised, it seemed at first that Ofwat wanted companies to produce three separate plans for differing investment scenarios. Following pressure from companies, Ofwat relented and a single plan was prepared, albeit with three sets of costs!

After submission of the draft Plan, Ofwat published Draft Determinations giving indicative charging limits for the AMP4 period, which would run from 2005 to 2010. Yet again, Ofwat proposed that charges should fall and it transpired that several key projects had not been incorporated for one reason or another. After the submission of the final Plan in April 2004 and further justification for some additional security measures, the Final Determination, setting out charging limits for the next five years, resulted in an initial reduction in charges followed by modest rises in later years. Overall, average annual household charges would rise by just 3.9%, from £77 to £80, over the five-year period. By 2010, the only customers in England and Wales with average household water charges below £100 per year will be those supplied by Portsmouth Water!

The main elements of the capital investment programme in the AMP4 period are outlined elsewhere in this chapter.

More Fluoridation Legislation

The debate on the rights and wrongs of water fluoridation has continued from the 1960s through to the present day. Those with a responsibility for dental health have long argued the benefits of fluoride for young people from fewer decayed and filled teeth, citing the experiences of those in Newcastle and Birmingham, where supplies have been fluoridated for many years. However, many pressure groups are very much opposed to the proposal since, as well as its connotations of 'mass medication', there are concerns about other potential medical side effects. Thus, for many years, there has been a debate on whether or not companies should fluoridate their supplies.

In 1985, Parliament passed legislation intended to relieve the impasse, but the drafting left loopholes that were not closed until 2003. Further legislation was passed, which enabled Strategic Health Authorities to make the final decision on whether to fluoridate, but only after public consultation had been carried out in accordance with new regulations. There was also a requirement for water companies to be indemnified against any liabilities for fluoridating. At the time, it was thought that the new legislation would result in firm proposals to fluoridate, but the Portsmouth City Teaching Primary Care Trust decided in August 2006 not to ask the Strategic Health Authority to conduct a joint feasibility study with the Company.

Diversification at Brockhampton Holdings

After the changes in share structure to create the parent company, Brockhampton Holdings, in the early 1990s, the Board of Brockhampton had taken a cautious approach to any diversification from the core activities of Portsmouth Water. It had seen a number of the large water and sewerage companies carry out major expansion of their activities, only to see them retract within a short time because of significant financial losses. The significant reduction in water charges at the 1999 Periodic Review, however, led the Brockhampton Board to more actively seek new activities that would increase profitability, but would be closely aligned with the core business of the water company. Most of them were relatively small-scale operations.

Seven Springs

With large quantities of spring water normally available at Havant and Bedhampton and the rapidly growing market for 'water coolers' in commercial premises, Brockhampton, with the help of consultancy advice, set up a brand new bottling facility within the old Bedhampton No. 1 Pump House. At the same time, a sales and service centre was established at Head Office, Havant. Finance Director, Neville Smith, oversaw the operation, with newly recruited staff managed by Anita Damron, who was experienced in sales and

marketing. Whilst sales growth did not match the projections forecast by the consultant, Seven Springs, as the company was named, quickly established itself among many other small competitors in the south-east of England.

However, by 2001, following the restructuring of Brockhampton, a decision was reached to focus on core activities and the search for a buyer commenced. An attractive offer from Chateau d'Eau International was received and the water cooler business was sold in August 2002. Within a few months, the supply and administrative operations moved elsewhere.

Portsmouth Water Lillywhites

Soon after privatisation, a number of larger water companies had set up their own plumbing subsidiaries, convinced of the prospects of using their reputation to provide a successful additional service to customers. Many of these initiatives were relatively short-lived.

In 2000, the Directors of R H Lillywhite Ltd, a long established plumbing company in Emsworth, approached the Board of Brockhampton. They were near to retirement and offered the opportunity to take over their business. The Brockhampton Group believed that offering customers a plumbing service would add value to its water supply operations. Mick White, the Distribution Manager at the Maindell Depot, took on the role of manager of the new business and initially expansion was achieved. Whilst the Company was able to provide both a reliable and assured service, it was unable to match prices offered by self-employed plumbers and the business was wound up early in 2005.

Leakfinder Ltd

In 2000, a member of the Distribution staff, John Shepherd, asked the Board for financial support to produce a prototype leak location device, which he had developed in his own time. Investigations were needed to ensure that the device did not breach any patent rules. Leakfinder Ltd, as the company was named, then contacted potential distributors for the device, initially in the UK, but in due course worldwide.

The business continues to operate on a small scale and 88 Leakfinders had been sold by the end of 2006.

Commercial Services

In anticipation of increased competition in the Water Industry, the Company decided in 2001 that it would develop its own commercial consultancy service, principally for commercial customers. The services provided are leak detection and repairs, data logging from the Company's meters and a design and installation service for new mains on sites. To date, additional annual income of more than £60,000 has been generated each year since its launch.

Company Structure and Finances

Further Pressure from Shareholders

As has been outlined in the previous chapter, Brockhampton shareholders were beginning to express their displeasure publicly at the apparent unwillingness of the Directors to reorganise the share structure of the Company. The matter came to a head in 2000, when an Extraordinary General Meeting (EGM) was requisitioned by two shareholders, together holding more than 10% of the voting stock. The meeting was held on December 15th and 44 shareholders were present to debate a resolution, prepared by the two shareholders, to enfranchise the non-voting shares. It was a vociferous affair, with several shareholders expressing their support for the Directors, but there was also considerable criticism. The dilemma for the Board was that different shareholders had different opinions on how an enfranchisement proposal should be structured. Managing Director, Nick Roadnight, recalls, "At one point, individual shareholders were arguing with such ferocity that they were shouting at each other. There was nothing we could do to stop them!"

The upshot was that the Chairman on the day, Hugh Pringle, called for a poll and shareholders rejected the resolution. The experience did little to satisfy shareholders and the Board recognised that action was going to be needed in the months ahead.

A 'Buy-Out' saves the Day!

Following the EGM, it was clear that the Board could not ignore the feelings of shareholders. Another key factor was that the 1999 Ofwat Final Determination had imposed harsh reductions on water company charges, which were expected to constrain opportunities for continued dividend growth. The Industry was becoming much less appealing to investors and the small water-only companies were seen as even less attractive than the water and sewerage plcs.

The Directors began to look at a number of possibilities, the first being the search for an enfranchisement formula to satisfy the majority of shareholders, which was not an easy task. The possibility of buying back shares was also considered. However, as was the case previously, some groups were initially interested, but others were not!

Finally, in June 2001, Managing Director, Nick Roadnight, and Finance Director, Neville Smith, met Brockhampton's financial advisors, Close Brothers, to discuss further options. It was apparent that, at the time, there existed the possibility of borrowing on the capital market at very reasonable interest rates. It was suggested that, by 'instigating' a buy-out, Portsmouth Water could be taken back into private ownership. The loan required would be paid back by the cashflow generated principally by the core water business. With the Board's sanction, the two Directors made contact with the Royal Bank of Scotland; having made initial contact by telephone at 9 am, so eager were the Bank that they were discussing the proposal in London at 5 pm the same day!

Within days, the proposal was put together, with a new company, South Downs Capital Ltd, being established with a loan of around £72m from the Royal Bank of Scotland, which would enable it to purchase the entire share capital of Brockhampton. Approximately 80% of the loan was to be funded by index-linked debt finance, on which a low, fixed interest rate would be paid. Low interest rates were obtained as a result of the very stable revenues and low risk nature of the Water Industry. The remaining 20% was the subject of a subordinated loan from the Bank, which would also receive dividends during the repayment period. The subordinated loan was to be repaid from surplus cashflow from the Brockhampton business.

A new ownership structure was prepared, giving the Bank the principal controlling interest until such time as the subordinated loan was repaid. At this point, control would be transferred to two groups, the first being the existing water company management team, the second a new Employee Benefit Trust.

As soon as the buy-out Offer was presented to the Board, it meant that Nick and Neville could play no active part in the consideration of it at Brockhampton Board meetings, as they were part of the team planning to acquire the business! Work on the preparations had to take place under strict secrecy, the reason for long evenings and some odd questions to staff being explained under the guise of a 'refinancing arrangement', which to a certain degree it was! Major groups of shareholders were approached and were also sworn to secrecy, as well as being bound by Stock Exchange rules not to trade their shares. The Pension Scheme Trustees and the Trustees of the Employee Share Ownership Trust were included. In all the process of 'due diligence' took four months.

Finally, at 2.30 am on the 24th October 2001 at the offices of City solicitors Linklaters, four Executive Directors of Portsmouth Water signed the documents committing them to the Offer. At 7.30 am, an announcement was made to the Stock Exchange. At 8.30 am, having assembled all staff at Head Office, the Directors were able to reveal the plans. Remarkably staff, although aware that something was afoot, had not guessed that it was a buy-out. They had been aware of the dissatisfaction of major shareholders and feared many of their jobs would have been at stake if the Company had been taken over. On hearing the plans, they were so relieved that they spontaneously applauded the Directors' actions!

The Board, 2007. Standing, left to right: Andy Neve, John Cogley, Neville Smith. Seated, left to right: Robert Sullivan, Terry Lazenby (Chairman), Nick Roadnight (Managing Director), Ray Tennant.

During the next few weeks, offers were sent out to shareholders and Ofwat carried out its public consultation on the change of ownership, the main outcome being the requirement for Portsmouth Water to appoint three new and independent non-executive Directors.

It was on the 19th December 2001 that the offer was declared 'unconditional', meaning that there was sufficient support from shareholders for the buy-out to go ahead. It meant that the new South Downs Group would acquire Brockhampton, with the share ownership arrangements as follows:

A Shares owned by the Royal Bank of Scotland	45%
B Shares owned by Employee Benefit Trust	40%
C Shares owned by Management Team	15%

Neither the Employee Benefit Trust nor the Management Team would receive any dividends until such time as the subordinated loan was paid off. At the time of the buy-out, this was expected to be in 2015. Since then, the Company has been able to accelerate the repayment rate as a result of surplus land sales and, at the time of publication, it now seems likely that the loan might be repaid by 2011.

As a result of the buy-out, the Brockhampton and Portsmouth Directors, John King, Martin Copp and Hugh Pringle, resigned and were replaced on the Portsmouth Water Board by three new independent non-executive Directors, Terry Lazenby, Robert Sullivan and Ray Tennant.

The Chairman, John Batty, remained on the Board until December 2002, when he finally retired after 38 years with the Company. Terry Lazenby succeeded him as Chairman. At the same time, Brockhampton reverted from a public limited company to a privately-owned limited company.

Subsequent Investor Changes

Within months of the buy-out, the Royal Bank of Scotland was involved in a potential purchase of another water company. With a substantial investment in South Downs, this would have led to a Competition Commission referral and so the Bank was forced to reduce its holding. Four fifths of its 45% share in South Downs was transferred to Abbey National Treasury Services in April 2002.

Abbey National's interest lasted a little longer, although its 36% share was sold to the Secondary Market Infrastructure Fund in February 2005.

Engineering Improvements

Farlington No. 9 Reservoir

Routine inspections of the Nos. 3 & 4 Reservoirs, which were constructed at the time of the original Farlington Treatment Works in 1910, revealed that cracks in the floor were leading to unacceptable levels of leakage. Whilst the structural integrity was not at risk,

Demolition of Farlington Nos 3 and 4 Reservoirs

Construction of Farlington No.9 Reservoir

the Company decided that it was wise to demolish the reservoirs and replace them with a single modern reinforced concrete structure.

A contract for the work was let to Dean and Dyball Ltd in October 2003 at a cost of £3.3m. To maximise the available space on the site, one of the Company's largest service reservoirs (capacity just under 45,000 cubic metres) was completed and brought into service in February 2005. During the course of the scheme, over 20,000 cubic metres of concrete from the old reservoirs was crushed on site and transported from site for use as recycled construction aggregate.

Strategic Meters

For many years, the measurement and detection of leakage had been dependent upon the use of Kent waste meters, mechanical devices that usually served areas of the distribution network containing no more than 3,000 properties. These waste districts, as they were called, were not in continuous operation and they had to be set up by District Inspectors closing valves on a regular basis, so that the night-time flow rates into the districts could be recorded. The resulting night flows could be compared with expected rates to identify whether there was any leakage. The assumption was that any significant flow occurring in the 'dead of night' was leakage. If rises were identified, inspectors would then carry out a 'step test' during the night to determine the sections of main where leakage might be occurring. All in all, the process was very labour intensive.

Whilst more sophisticated leak location equipment was being used to pinpoint leaks on individual sections of main, the process of identifying the area containing a leaking main had been largely unchanged for 25 years or more. Many other companies with waste district coverage of their networks were installing district meters, to enable them to calculate the night flows in parts of their networks. The difference was that these new districts were permanently 'set up' and the flow data was recorded by loggers and either collected at some later date or alternatively sent by telemetry to a central recording point. The labour savings were significant.

Left: Supervisor Tony Bird carrying out leakage correlation work with John Shepherd

In 2000, the first scheme went ahead to install 7 strategic meters, which monitored the flows into areas serving between 5,000 and 10,000 properties in the Fareham and Gosport area. This covered the major parts of the distribution network, with only the remote rural areas excluded. The scheme was so successful that, over the next three years, it was extended to cover the majority of the area of supply. In all 54 districts were set up. Data from the strategic meters was recorded on site for transfer by telephone link on a regular basis to Head Office at Havant. Here the data would be analysed on a weekly basis by the Leakage Technician, Martin Trust, and the results used to prioritise the leakage investigations by the Distribution Inspectors.

Brickkiln

At Brickkiln, one of the Company's newest works developed in the 1970s, the mechanical equipment and electrical controls were refurbished. Fortunately the building, in the style of a Sussex flint barn, was in remarkably good condition and so, although some internal building alterations were required, no major works were needed.

Lovedean

The treatment works at Lovedean was the subject of three separate phases of work in the early part of the decade. Having already been modified in the 1990s to improve disinfection capacity, the mechanical and electrical controls were replaced in 2000. In 2005, the adjacent booster station, which delivers water to both Catherington and Clanfield Reservoirs, was updated, with new pumps and controls being installed, along with a generator capable of operating the borehole and booster pumps. The development of a new membrane filtration plant is described later.

Lovedean Booster Station

Water Quality Improvements

In the period immediately prior to the 1999 Periodic Review, the Government had signalled its intention to introduce new water quality regulations to meet the requirements of tighter European directives. Although the regulations were not endorsed by Parliament until 2000, the DWI had set out the requirements beforehand so that companies could incorporate any necessary improvements in their Business Plans covering the period 2000-05. The impacts of all the new regulations are outlined below.

Lead

Having halved the permitted level of lead in water supplies from 100 to 50 micrograms per litre in the 1980s, a new European Directive in the 1990s required member states to further reduce the limit to 25 micrograms per litre by 2003 and to 10 micrograms per litre by 2013. The Company already had some success with orthophosphoric acid dosing to reduce lead concentrations in the Worlds End and Chichester zones, lead levels in the drinking water being lowered to well below the long-term lead standard of 10 micrograms per litre.

Between 2000 and 2002, the Company installed orthophosphoric acid dosing plants treating water for the whole supply area, except the former Bognor Regis UDC area, where it had been the practice to use galvanised steel service pipes in preference to lead. Databases were established to enable the success of the dosing schemes in reducing lead levels to be monitored. Unlike many in the Industry, the Company chose to take regular samples from customers' properties where high levels of lead had been recorded. The customers of these properties were given a 50% rebate on their water bills and, in return, were asked to sample their supply monthly according to strict rules. The results were used to optimise the performance of each dosing plant. When the databases were initially established, it was expected that they would only be needed for about two years. In 2007, some of those set up in 2000 are still running!

Cryptosporidium

Following the introduction of new water quality regulations in 1999, a cryptosporidium risk assessment had been carried out by the British Geological Survey. The River Itchen Works was already deemed at significant risk because of its limited bankside storage and regulatory monitoring was also found to be needed at Farlington, Fishbourne, Lovedean, Maindell and Soberton.

The Company had already included proposals to install membrane filtration plants at Farlington and Lovedean in its 1999 Business Plan. The new regulations and the survey came too late for the inclusion of plants at Fishbourne, Soberton and Maindell. Following regulatory approval, trials on different types of membranes were carried out in 2000 at Farlington and Lovedean to identify those suited to the raw water characteristics at each works. After inviting tenders and obtaining further planning approvals for buildings smaller than originally approved, 'design-and-construct' contracts were awarded.

Gary Hynds checks the new membrane filtration plant at Farlington, 2003

The membrane plant building at Lovedean, 2004

At Farlington, a submerged membrane plant provided by Memcor Ltd was installed by the main contractor, Black and Veatch. At Lovedean, submerged membranes from Memcor Ltd were also selected, the main contractor being OTVB Ltd, of Birmingham. The membranes themselves were shipped from Australia. The membrane building at each works was designed by James W Harper & Associates. Whilst the plant at Farlington was commissioned in June 2003, considerable problems were experienced with high turbidity, which resulted from heavy rain in December that year. Through the replacement of some of the membranes and increased chemical storage, performance improved such that the contract was finally completed in December 2005. The scheme for Lovedean closely followed, with installation completed in October 2003 and final commissioning and 'handover' in May 2004.

At the four remaining 'significant risk' sites, continuous monitoring for cryptosporidium began in 2000, the difficult process of analysis of the cryptosporidium filters having been contracted to South East Water. Whilst cryptosporidium oocysts were rarely found in samples from Maindell and Fishbourne, they were quite frequent at Soberton in small numbers after heavy rain. At the River Itchen Works, the Company installed a separate monitoring filter on the incoming raw water to give a measure of cryptosporidium levels in the river. Their presence in the raw water was a regular feature and, although the treatment process could remove the vast majority, low levels were frequently found in the treated water.

The local Health Authority (subsequently the Health Protection Agency) had, for a number of years, believed that the River Itchen Works was the cause of occasional outbreaks of cryptosporidiosis in south-east Hampshire. During the 1990s, the Company had been obliged to temporarily suspend supplies from the works on several occasions. With continuous monitoring in place and the absence of elevated oocyst levels, the Company felt able to refute such allegations when an outbreak occurred in the autumn of 2002. The Health Authority was not convinced, especially as almost all those affected lived in areas supplied from the Company's Hoads Hill Service Reservoirs, which received treated water from the River Itchen Works, as well as Northbrook, West Street, Soberton and Maindell.

Nevertheless, the 2002 outbreak and the worrying propensity for oocysts to be present in the raw and treated water at the River Itchen Works prompted the Company to incorporate proposals for a membrane filtration plant at the works in its 2004 Business Plan. Until then, the DWI had been unwilling to support proposals for the installation of additional treatment at a conventional two-stage treatment works such as the River Itchen. The Company also proposed membrane filtration plants at Soberton and Fishbourne, as cryptosporidium had been found in samples and there was no filtration system at these works. The DWI supported the Company's proposals and Ofwat allowed a sum of £11.8m for three new plants in the 2004 Final Determination. As at Farlington and Lovedean, pilot trials were undertaken; tenders were then invited for all three schemes in one package to obtain best value. The contracts were awarded to Trant Construction Ltd, of Southampton, with Memcor submerged membranes again chosen on the grounds of suitability and economy. The River Itchen membrane filtration plant is due for commissioning in the summer of 2007, with the Soberton and Fishbourne plants due for completion in 2008.

Unfortunately, before completion of the new plant at the River Itchen Works, a further cryptosporidiosis outbreak occurred in south-east Hampshire in the autumn of 2005 and this is covered later in the chapter.

Nitrates

In the mid-1990s, the Company had been obliged to undertake several major mainlaying schemes to enable it to blend water from the Ems and Lavant valley sources with those at Eastergate and Westergate, and thus avoid exceeding the limits prescribed in the water quality regulations. The Company had urged the Government, through its work with the EA, to set up new Nitrate Vulnerable Zones. These were intended to protect groundwater sources from further pollution by limiting the amount of agricultural fertilisers applied to land. These efforts were only partially successful; in 2003, new zones were established, but they only covered limited parts of the supply area.

A further review of nitrate data, prompted by work on the 2004 Business Plan, identified four more sources that were at risk of nitrate exceedence in the near future. As a result, the Ofwat Final Determination approved the Company's proposals for blending facilities for Funtington, Lovedean, Maindell and Northbrook Treatment Works. Whilst blending facilities at Lovedean and Funtington were provided at low cost in 2006, more extensive schemes for Northbrook and Maindell are not due to be commissioned until 2009 and 2010 respectively.

Farlington Mains Rehabilitation

Between 1997 and 2004, there were five separate incidents in Portsmouth and Southsea when customers reported discoloured water supplies. On each occasion, the cause was attributed to sediment being disturbed in trunk mains by what should have been routine, uneventful valving operations for maintenance purposes. The legal limits for turbidity, iron, aluminium and manganese in drinking water were exceeded for a short time, often by a substantial margin. Extensive flushing of the mains system was needed to clear the problem and one incident in 1997 affected as many as 8,400 customers.

Laying a washout main across Southsea Common, 2006

The cause of the sediment deposits was initially perceived to be either carry-over of aluminium by-products from the treatment process at Farlington, or corrosion of mains causing iron sediment to accumulate, or possibly a combination of both.

Following DWI approval, but in advance of the Ofwat Final Determination, the first stage of the investigation in 2004 involved a computer network model of the trunk mains being built for the Company by local firm HydroCo. This model was used to find those trunk mains and larger distribution

Old main removed to leave space for laying new main, Winter Road, Southsea, 2006

mains where the velocity of flow did not normally exceed 0.3 metres per second, this being generally recognised as the threshold velocity above which particles will not settle in a pipe. The model showed that there were a significant number of mains where this threshold was not reached, even during peak demand. This implied that sediment could be accumulating in these particular lengths of main, which were located in all parts of the Farlington zone, although the worst areas were in southern Portsmouth, where all the incidents had occurred.

The second stage of the investigation was to carry out an under-pressure tapping on each length of main, to enable specialist equipment to withdraw an undisturbed sample of any sediment present on the bottom of the main. The tapping work was carried out by Durkin & Sons Ltd in 2005, along with sample capture and analysis by Mayfield Consulting. Their analysis showed that some mains had quite significant deposits of sediment (as much as 31mm in one main in Winter Road, Southsea). The analysis concluded that the deposits were rust particles from the corrosion of iron mains.

A scheme was included in the Ofwat 2004 Final Determination, and a contract was put together to carry out rehabilitation of all those mains with deposits of sediment exceeding 0.1 millimetres in depth. Rehabilitation itself was carried out by renewal of the main concerned in a smaller diameter (to increase flow velocity), by abandonment of the main or by installation of wash-out facilities to enable the main to be flushed at a high rate at periodic intervals to remove accumulated sediment.

The contract was awarded to Durkin & Sons Ltd and was a lengthy and involved operation, requiring great care to ensure that the very act of rehabilitation did not itself result in sediment being disturbed, when mains were isolated for connections to be carried out. The computerised network model was used to determine the effect of isolating mains and, where necessary, initial flushing to remove potential sediment deposits from mains was done before contract work could proceed. Contingency plans for notifying the public of actions to take in the event of discoloured water were drawn up each time work was carried out on a 'live' main.

The contract started in October 2005 and was finally completed in 2007.

Dave Atkins flushing a water main

Respecting the Environment

Hoe Source Replacement

The Company's Hoe source was initially implicated by the NRA in one of its low flow investigations as having a potentially adverse impact upon The Moors SSSI, near Bishop's Waltham. During the late 1990s, a number of trial boreholes were sunk in an attempt to locate suitable sources to replace the output at Hoe.

Hoe Pumping Station

By 2000, the Company had identified three potential sites where production boreholes were to be drilled, these being at Denmead, Lower Upham, to the north-west of Bishop's Waltham, and Newtown, between Soberton and Worlds End. Whilst none of the sites was capable of producing sufficient water during test pumping to replace Hoe on its own, the two sites at Newtown and Lower Upham did produce a combined total of close to 7.5 million litres per day. These two sites had been identified as being potentially good sources by the British Geological Survey, after it had examined seismic oil exploration records unavailable to the Company owing to commercial confidentiality. Further prolonged test pumping at both sites, together with substantial local environmental monitoring, was required before the Company could submit its application for abstraction licences.

Laying the Newtown pumping main, July 2004

Eventually, in March 2003, the Company submitted applications for variations to its licences at Northbrook and Soberton to incorporate the new boreholes at Lower Upham and Newtown respectively. The resulting licences, which were conditional upon the surrender of the Hoe licence, enabled the Company to retain its existing drought deployable output, but with a reduction in the annual licensed capacity at Soberton; this also resolved an earlier concern of the NRA regarding the 'low flows' in the River Meon.

The Company completed the installation of mechanical plant, electrical controls and connecting pipelines to enable the two new boreholes to be commissioned in 2005.

Hoe had always provided an alternative source in the event of a problem at Northbrook. Thus prior to completion of the commissioning of Lower Upham and Newtown, the Board authorised the laying of a 450mm diameter link main at Hoads Hill Reservoirs to enable a back feed from Nelson Reservoir to maintain supplies to Shedfield.

In addition, to guard against the Hoads Hill Zone being short of water, a booster was constructed at Portchester to transfer up to 10 million litres per day from the Farlington Zone to Hoads Hill. Little did staff realise how soon this emergency supply would be needed; following the shutdown of Northbrook in October 2004 due to an oil spillage and then the isolation of the River Itchen Works in October 2005 due to cryptosporidium, the Portchester Booster was in use for many months.

The 1995 Habitats Regulations Review of Consents

In the early 1990s, the NRA had investigated the impacts of abstraction on the flows in the rivers Meon and Hamble. This had alerted environmental groups to the possibility that groundwater abstractions could be having a significant influence on valuable ecological species and habitats. This became significant when the European Habitats Directive was translated into UK legislation by the implementation of the Habitats Regulations 1995. The NRA's successor, the EA, was charged as the competent body responsible for reviewing all abstraction and discharge consents which might affect sites designated as Special Protection Areas (SPAs) for birds, or Special Areas of Conservation (SACs) for other species and the habitats supporting them. In advance of the 1999 Periodic Review, the EA advised the Company of its concerns about the River Itchen abstraction and also that at Fishbourne, where the abstraction could have been affecting spring flows feeding freshwater into the head of Chichester Harbour. The Company included proposals for environmental investigations at both sites in its 1999 Business Plan and the costs were included in Ofwat's Final Determination for the 2000-05 period.

The River Itchen is a classic chalk stream, renowned for its trout fishing, rising near Alresford in the Hampshire Downs and flowing through Winchester and Eastleigh before discharging into Southampton Water at Woodmill, near West End. The river's natural characteristics are stable temperature and flow and good quality, clear water. As well as their role in sustaining the nature conservation interests, the water resources of the valley are also used for public water supply by both Southern Water and the Company, dilution of treated sewage effluent, fish farms, cress beds, agriculture, fisheries and recreation. There are water supply intakes at Otterbourne and Gaters Mill and groundwater abstractions throughout the catchment. The river has been heavily modified and affected by man's activities over many hundreds of years.

The river's national and European conservation status is recognised by its UK designation as a SSSI and more recently an SAC under European legislation. Parts of the Itchen valley floor have been designated as SSSIs for many years, but the whole river, including its three headwater tributaries, was confirmed as an SSSI in 1997 for its chalk stream habitat and communities of plants, invertebrates, fish, birds and mammals. The main conservation interests of the SAC centred on the salmon, otter, water crowfoot, southern damselfly, bullhead, brook lamprey, white-clawed crayfish and their habitats. These interests are dependent on reliable flows and velocities of high quality chalk-derived water throughout the year.

The SAC designation of the River Itchen required the EA to ensure that no water company activity had an adverse effect on the river and its ecology. The Agency therefore set in train a comprehensive sustainability study of the River Itchen to examine the effects of both water abstractions and sewage works discharges. The work of this study was guided by a steering group comprising the EA, Portsmouth Water, Southern Water, English Nature (later Natural England), Hampshire County Council, Eastleigh Borough Council, Winchester City Council and the Government's Department for Food and Rural Affairs (Defra). Portsmouth Water's interest arose from its licence to abstract up to 45 million litres per day at Gaters Mill, 1.2 kilometres upstream of the tidal limit of the Itchen.

The River Itchen at Brambridge

The study commenced in late 2000 and was finally completed in March 2004. It included the examination of important aspects of the river, namely ecology, fisheries, groundwater flow modelling, river flow modelling, water quality, wet grassland, specific species studies and invertebrate studies.

The study concluded that the abstractions and discharges on the river had significantly adverse effects on salmon migration, water crowfoot and invertebrates. The invertebrates were not themselves designated interests under the Habitats Directive, but nonetheless were essential as food for salmon. Low flows were concluded to be detrimental to all three interests, along with phosphates carried into the river with sewage treatment works effluent.

Following this study, the EA asked its consultant, Atkins, to determine the extent of reductions in abstraction licences required for the status of these interests to be improved to 'favourable', as defined by the Habitats Directive. At the time of publication of this book, the results of the Agency's work were still awaited, although it was anticipated that the outcome might be a loss of deployable output from the Company's source at Gaters Mill during drought periods.

At ***Fishbourne***, the Company argued that the effluent discharge from Southern Water's Apuldram Wastewater Treatment Works, less than a kilometre from the Company's abstraction, was providing a much greater freshwater input to Chichester Harbour than the quantity that could be pumped from the Fishbourne source. The study took on a very local focus, the major concern being the possibility of impacts upon the 'wet woodland', adjacent to the Mill Pond at Fishbourne, where detailed ecological surveys revealed the presence of the rare Desmoulins Whorl Snail. This species is dependent upon damp conditions, although it is not usually present in shady woodland habitats. The EA was concerned that the Company might abstract at its full licensed rate and thereby 'dry out' the snail habitat. Despite further work by the Company and its consultants, Mott Macdonald, the Agency indicated that a reduction in the peak abstraction rate might be necessary. At the time of writing, the outcome of the review has still not been announced.

The EA also considered that the Company's abstractions at Funtington and in the Ems and Lavant valleys might impact upon the freshwater flows into ***Chichester and Langstone Harbours***, both of which were designated SPAs by the Habitats Regulations, principally for over wintering birds. Unfortunately the Company was not notified of this until after the 1999 Periodic Review submission.

Limited study work was carried out by the EA and the preparation of 'Appropriate Assessments' under the regulations was based upon studies carried out elsewhere in the UK. The review 'was not able to conclude that the abstractions did not have an adverse impact upon the environment' and so the Agency has been conducting further studies aimed at identifying what changes are needed to abstraction licences to ensure that the sites are protected for the designated wildlife. Those decisions remain outstanding.

Chichester Harbour at Fishbourne

Other Sites

There are, in addition to those mentioned above, a number of other 'habitats sites', mostly associated with the Solent maritime areas, and the EA is also considering the combined impacts of many sources, such that over 80% of the Company's licensed abstractions could be affected by the review.

Biodiversity Action Plan

Along with a growing environmental awareness among customers, there was a conservation commitment under the Environment Act to further the ecological diversity on many of the Company's operational sites. Thus the Company published its first Biodiversity Action Plan in December 2002, establishing a policy to conserve and enhance the natural environment of operational land and water areas and to preserve historic buildings and equipment.

Adonis Blue butterfly at Hoe Pumping Station site

Like many other water companies, Portsmouth Water owns and operates sites in important conservation areas, such as the valleys of the Rivers Itchen, Hamble, Meon, Ems and Lavant, on the chalk hills of the South Downs and Portsdown Hill and in close proximity to the coast. The rigorous avoidance of using pesticides and weed killers on operational drinking water sites means that many of them have remained ideal habitats for rarer plants and insects.

Bee Orchid on a service reservoir site

In summer/autumn 2000 and again in spring 2001, the Company commissioned Ecosa, of Grateley, to carry out an ecological survey of all its sites. The survey concentrated on establishing the habitat value of the sites and identifying scarce and protected species. Each site was evaluated for the species and habitat types present and graded as low, medium or high conservation value. In total, five sites were identified as being of high value, 16 of medium value and 21 of low value. The high conservation value sites were the River Itchen Water Treatment Works and the service reservoirs at Fort Southwick, Nore Hill, Slindon and Madehurst.

The Biodiversity Action Plan contained a number of habitat action plans, outlining measures to protect and improve hedgerows, trees, woodland, grassland, streams and ponds. Species action plans were devised for bats, badgers, dormice, reptiles, great crested newts and birds. Finally, a number of site-specific action plans were prepared to guide staff in their day-to-day management of the sites.

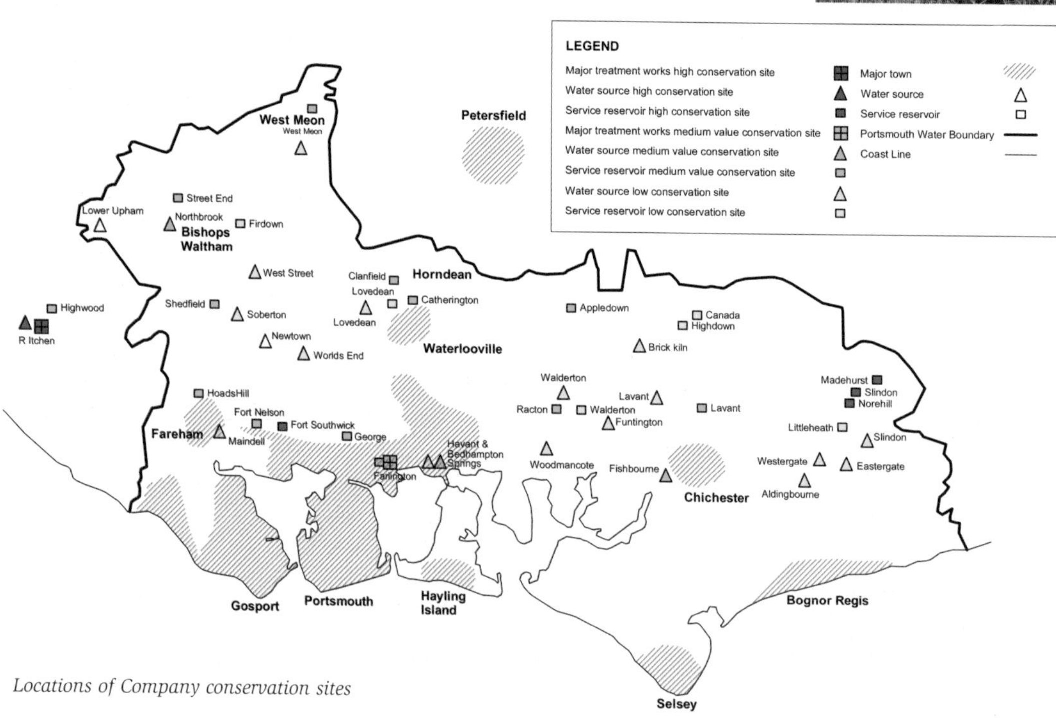

Locations of Company conservation sites

A Bulk Supply to Southern Water

The drought conditions of the early 1990s and 1996 prompted a joint bid by two companies for Mid Kent Water. The conclusion of the MMC Report into the bid led to the creation of the Water Resources in the South East Group, as outlined in the previous chapter.

In preparation for the 1999 Periodic Review, the WRSE Group put forward a strategy to maximise the region's water resources. A key element was the development of a bulk supply from Portsmouth Water to support Southern Water's Sussex North Resource Zone, which serves Horsham and Crawley. Initially reluctant to compromise its satisfactory resource situation, the Company conceded that it could do so, provided that the financial provisions were sufficiently attractive. Having agreed terms in principle in 2001, the companies jointly employed consultants Adams Hendry to prepare the environmental statement needed to support a planning application. This covered a pipeline from Littleheath Reservoirs to Southern Water's Hardham Treatment Works, a new booster station at the Company's Slindon Works and a new 'break pressure tank' at Whiteways Lodge on the South Downs. The Company also had to apply to the EA for an increase in the peak licensed capacity of the Eastergate group licence. It was expected that Southern Water would need to use the supply for a maximum period of three months in only one year in three, but the 15 million litres per day maximum flow would mean that water from the Lavant and Ems valleys would have to be transferred to support the Eastergate sources. The trunk mains laid in the 1990s from Funtington to Lavant and from Lavant to Littleheath would be more frequently used!

It was 2003 before all the permissions and agreements were in place and, within fifteen months, transfers of water had begun. The new break pressure tank was constructed by Dean and Dyball Ltd, as was the new booster station at Slindon, using the Sussex barn style to match the existing buildings on the site. Solent Excavations laid the 450mm diameter main from Littleheath Reservoir to Whiteways Lodge, whilst Southern Water laid the gravity main from Whiteways to their Hardham Works. Black and Veatch Ltd carried out the mechanical and electrical works at Slindon. Initially, the transfer comprised only a 'sweetening' flow, but it was to prove invaluable to Southern Water during the autumn of 2005 and more extensively in 2006, when the region was affected by drought.

Left: the new booster station at Slindon

The capital cost of the scheme is being recovered over a ten-year period from Southern Water, whilst the volumes transferred are charged according to the 2003 agreement.

Unexpected Challenges

Extremes of Weather

After a number of drought years during the 1990s, the winter of 2000/01 was one of the wettest on record, with eight consecutive months of above-average rainfall from September 2000. The year 2000 was the wettest since the Company began collecting records at Havant in 1886. Recharge of the chalk aquifer began with a sharp rise in groundwater levels in October and continuing heavy rainfall led to the Hampshire Lavants appearing in the normally dry upper valleys of the chalk catchments. Prolonged rainfall caused groundwater levels to reach their highest since records began at Idsworth in 1932 and many villages such as Hambledon, Finchdean and Rowlands Castle experienced groundwater flooding for almost four months. The situation caused little inconvenience for the Company and ensured that groundwater reserves were well and truly topped up for the next summer. A repetition of the flooding that affected Chichester in the 1990s was averted by a range of temporary measures installed by the EA. The permanent scheme, which now transfers surplus flows to Pagham Harbour, had not been completed.

By 2003, the opposite extreme was beginning to affect the area and extremely hot weather in August and September was followed by a very dry autumn. Companies in south-east England were beginning to prepare themselves for drought, but wetter weather in mid-winter returned groundwater levels to normal.

It was not long, however, before the companies had to 'dust off' their drought plans. A dry winter in 2004/05 led to supply restrictions being imposed in the early summer of 2005 by Southern Water in Sussex and Kent, South East Water in Sussex, Mid Kent Water and Sutton & East Surrey Water. Groundwater levels in the Portsmouth area were below average, but not low enough to necessitate action other than a request to customers to use water sensibly. The Company did, however, provide additional water to Southern Water through the bulk supply pipeline and was very involved in the regional co-ordination and public communications work.

The situation worsened in the region after a second dry winter in 2005/06, although wet months in October 2005, and March and May 2006, meant that resources were not so stretched for the Company. Several more companies in and around London imposed restrictions and, by midsummer 2006, more than 13 million people were suffering restrictions. The publicity surrounding the drought resulted in a very significant reduction in the expected peak summer demands, despite the fact that very little rain fell between the end of May and the middle of August.

An Oil Spillage at Bishop's Waltham

In the autumn of 2004, an event occurred to the north of Bishop's Waltham, which had a very significant impact. It was on the 5th October that Nigel Rowley, the Supply Manager, received a call from the EA, saying that a domestic oil storage tank had leaked approximately 2,000 litres of kerosene into the ground at Chapel Farm, approximately 1 kilometre 'up catchment' of Northbrook Treatment Works. Since supplies from the works were pumped directly into the local distribution network, it was immediately shut down and water was transferred from Nelson Reservoir to make up the deficit. As the Company's fourth largest source, it was imperative that all other sources were available to make up for the temporary loss of Northbrook.

Granular activated carbon filters at Northbrook, 2005

Initial investigations by the EA revealed that the kerosene had seeped through the subsoil to the chalk aquifer below and that a more extensive borehole survey would be needed to estimate the possible impact upon the Northbrook source. This took several months and so the difficult temporary supply arrangements became more permanent. The additional borehole surveys were unable to identify either the extent or the presence of the kerosene in the chalk; it seemed to have disappeared! Since Northbrook was so important, it was imperative that some form of remediation was put in place.

Activated carbon filters were installed to remove any hydrocarbons, albeit with a capacity of only one third of that of the works. However, the output was enough to supply the immediate locality, but insufficient to support the Gosport and Fareham area. The Company purchased the activated carbon filters second-hand from South Staffordshire Water at a considerably lower cost than new filters and they were also available in a much shorter time! In addition, organic carbon monitoring facilities were installed as a further precaution.

In total, the works remained out of service for almost a year and, to date, oil has not been found in the supplies from Northbrook.

Another Cryptosporidiosis Outbreak

In September 2005, the Company was advised by the Health Protection Agency that there had been a significant rise in cryptosporidiosis cases during the month. On this occasion, there had been significant numbers of oocysts recorded in the samples taken from the treated water at the River Itchen Works, although regulatory standards were not exceeded. The Company temporarily suspended supplies from the works and a major public information exercise, in conjunction with the Health Protection Agency, sought to reassure residents, although the ensuing media stories unfortunately did nothing more than heighten concerns. Whilst the number of cases subsided in the following weeks, the Company quickly instigated an independent review of treatment processes and a number of improvements were implemented at the River Itchen Works. A subsequent investigation by the DWI complimented the Company for its prompt actions, but also produced a number of recommendations. The Outbreak Control Team, set up by the Health Protection Agency, conducted an epidemiological study. This concluded that water supplies were the most likely cause of the outbreak, despite the fact that a large proportion of those affected lived in the Worlds End Zone, which was supplied by a works clear of cryptosporidium!

The Company decided not to recommission the works until the improvements were completed. It did not finally return to service until April 2006, just in time for the summer rise in demand.

The Failure of the Hilsea Control Valve

Much has been said in the previous chapter about the leakage savings that resulted from the installation of a new pressure control valve in the 1990s at Hilsea. Operational staff had always had concerns about what would happen if there was a failure of the valve at a critical period when demands increased. A number of 'fail-safe' procedures and alarms were in place. However, on no less than three occasions, the valve at Hilsea failed, usually early in the morning, each time for a different reason. Each time supplies were quickly restored but not before a large number of customers on Portsea Island had been without water for a short period at the busiest time of day. The resulting experience led to the installation of a stand-by valve on the alternative Eastern Road supply into Portsmouth, along with improved controls at Hilsea.

In an attempt to avoid similar occurrences with other schemes, automatic controls were installed to open a bypass in the event of valve failure.

Planning Water Resources for the future and the Havant Thicket Winter Storage Reservoir

Despite the first proposal for a reservoir at Havant Thicket being put forward in the early 1960s, it was not until Portsmouth Water prepared its 2004 Water Resources Plan that the need for Havant Thicket came once more to the fore. The Plan was submitted to Ofwat and the EA to support Ofwat's review of water charges for the 2005-10 period.

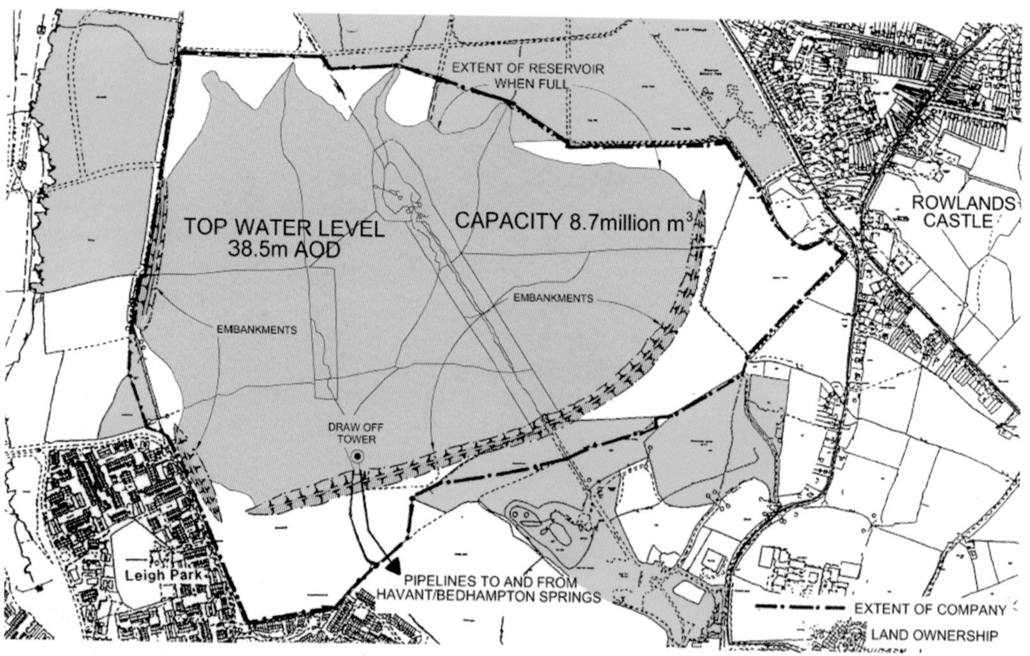

The concept plan developed in the 1970s for Havant Thicket Winter Storage Reservoir

The Plan contained a demand forecast for the 25 years to 2030, which showed that there would be a deficit in supplies by 2021. A number of options were evaluated for meeting the expected additional demand and the final strategy combined a number of measures, including:

- The compulsory metering of new houses from 2005;
- The continued promotion of water efficiency measures, followed by a more active programme from 2018;
- Maintaining leakage at its current economic level, with an active programme leading to reductions in 2018;
- The construction of a washwater recovery plant at Farlington Treatment Works in 2019; and
- The construction of Havant Thicket Winter Storage Reservoir by 2021.

This strategy followed the so-called 'twin-track' approach of combining realistic water efficiency measures with the development of new water resources. It was also the most economic solution, meaning that it would have least impact upon customers' charges.

It was in 1965 that Portsmouth Water purchased land at Havant Thicket for the purpose of constructing a reservoir to store surplus water from the springs during the winter. At the time, water demand from new and existing housing and from industry was growing rapidly and the reservoir was seen as the most suitable way of meeting that extra demand. The water to be stored in the reservoir was intended to come from surplus winter yield from the prolific Havant & Bedhampton Springs, which have been used for public water supply since 1860. In summer, the yield from these springs diminishes because rainfall is lower and percolation of water from the surface to the underlying aquifer is almost non-existent. Conversely, in winter, higher rainfall leads to a higher springs yield greatly surplus to public water supply requirements. The whole of the surplus yield currently flows into the sea and the intention would be to pump some to the new reservoir.

Although demand for water continued to rise during the 1960s, the proposal to build 'Solent City' between Portsmouth and Southampton led to an alternative scheme to build an abstraction and treatment works at Gaters Mill on the River Itchen, near West End, Southampton. The River Itchen scheme was cheaper than building a reservoir at Havant Thicket and was developed as the preferable alternative. It was commissioned in 1972.

However, the Havant Thicket site remained in the Company's ownership and, in the 1960s and 1970s, a number of studies looked at alternative reservoir sites in southern Hampshire and West Sussex. They confirmed Havant Thicket as the optimum site and then focused specifically on the geology and suitability of the site by taking out trial boreholes to analyse the underlying geological strata. All this work underlined the suitability of the site for the pumped storage of water.

In December 2004, Ofwat announced its final determination of water charges for the coming five years, which included funding for the initial stages of the project. Although 2021 seems a long way off in 2007, a further review of the yield, the options, the demand forecast and the engineering aspects has just been completed. The next stage is a development planning study and environmental impact assessment, culminating in a planning application in 2010. Following a possible Public Inquiry, detailed design would then proceed, with construction starting in 2015 and finishing in 2020.

Anticipating the long leadtime, the Company had already commenced preliminary work. Given the breadth of issues involved in the scheme, it was necessary to establish a Stakeholder Group of interested parties to help take the scheme forward from inception to completion. The Group included:

- Environment Agency
- Hampshire County Council
- George Staunton Country Park (in which the reservoir site is situated)
- East Hampshire District Council
- Havant Borough Council
- Rowlands Castle Parish Council
- Forestry Commission (owner of adjacent land)
- Hampshire & Isle of Wight Wildlife Trust
- Consumer Council for Water
- Hampshire Ornithological Society

By early 2007, the consultant, Entec UK Ltd, had completed the first stage of the project and the Company was preparing to embark on the development planning and environmental impact assessment.

The reservoir is expected to be a substantial engineering project; the volume of water held in the reservoir when full is expected to be approximately 9 million cubic metres. The reservoir would be approximately one mile long and half a mile wide.

Aerial view of Havant Thicket Winter Storage Reservoir site, with, right, a conceptual view of the completed reservoir

Life at the Company post 2000

Staff

A tragic event occurred in June 2001, when Bill Thomas, the Water Quality Manager, was drowned on holiday while swimming off a beach in the Gulf of Mexico. Despite being a strong swimmer, Bill was swept away in a strong tidal current while attempting to rescue his son's father-in-law, who also drowned.

Jonty Stead, his deputy, succeeded Bill as Water Quality Manager.

Staunton Country Park Education Centre

Several years before the Government's Water Summit in 1997, the Company had developed a Water Efficiency Plan aimed at encouraging its customers to be conservative in their use of water. It has used its own offices as a showcase for trialling new water fittings and received praise from its regulators for the savings achieved.

In February 2004, with the intention of aiming a water conservation message at the young, the Company made a three-year commitment with the Staunton Country Park to jointly develop an education centre to enable both organisations to host school visits. The Park has employed the staff and the Company has provided much of the equipment in the new centre.

Wall-Mounted Meter Boxes

For many years, the Company has installed a stopcock below ground in a small chamber, usually in the footpath outside each property. In the 1980s, it had decided to standardise upon the installation of a meter combination box, enabling a meter to be relatively easily installed and maintained at a later date. However, the connections to stopcocks and combination boxes have been a persistent source of leakage and a significant maintenance cost.

In anticipation of its decision to meter all new households from April 2005, the Company decided in September 2004 to follow the practice of gas and electricity utilities by installing its stopcock and meter in a wall-mounted insulated box, attached by the builder to the outside wall of every new house. The proposal had benefits for customers who could much more easily read the meter and operate the stopcock, while the benefit to the Company was the absence of pipe joints between the new box and the connection to the main. Whilst the box cannot yet be easily fitted to existing properties, there is expected to be a long-term benefit in reducing overall maintenance costs.

Performance Improvement Projects

Faced with the continuing need to deliver ever greater efficiencies in the Company's operations, Directors and senior managers developed a number of projects in 2003, designed to improve performance. A range of topics was covered, including IT facilities, staff performance and reward, internal communications and health and safety awareness. Project teams, including staff at all levels, were set up and a Steering Group oversaw the development of each project.

The exercise was repeated in November 2004 and three new projects were developed, the most revolutionary being 'Man in the Van', an electronic system that permits much quicker communication between distribution staff and customers. The system also saves considerable paperwork!

A further project, 'Customer First', was developed in 2006 to enable the already high standards of customer service to be further improved.

Health and Safety

A health and safety awareness project highlighted the need for all staff to play their part in ensuring that activities took place in a safe environment. Since then, the Company has completed a number of new initiatives:

- Formal safety awareness for all staff.
- Regular incident briefings to all staff.
- Toolbox talks', ie informal briefings covering a wide range of topics, including health and safety.
- Poster campaigns

The project has achieved a very significant reduction in the number of accidents since its inception. The Company was proud to have received in 2006, at its first attempt, a Gold Award from the Royal Society for the Prevention of Accidents (RoSPA). This success was repeated in 2007.

150th Anniversary Celebrations

In recognition of the Company's 150th birthday in 2007, the Board agreed to authorise some modest celebrations to develop the Company's local identity as well as to highlight the commitment to maintaining high standards of water quality and customer service. The celebrations will incorporate a new educational and information display and DVD, a drought resistant garden and a number of commemorative features which will recognise the staff's contribution to the Company's success.

Portsmouth Water people

Two strong threads have run through the entire 150-year history of Portsmouth Water. The first is the influence of strong leaders, who either guided the Company successfully through difficult times or seized the moment to make decisions critical to its continued well-being and independence. The second thread runs through several generations of families employed by the Company, thus embedding its roots firmly in the local community and establishing loyalty and long service as a characteristic of many of its staff.

This chapter looks at just a few of those leaders and families and their service to the Company.

Portsmouth Water Company men's outing to Reading, 1932. Standing alone at back centre: W. Hobbs. Back row (standing): T. Newman, G. Boyce, unknown, G. Paffet, D. Cummings, S. Goldring, Thomson, D. Cummings, W. Mengham, T. Mengham, H. King, W. Borrows, B. Martin, F. Bridger, F. Bridger, Jeffrey.
Middle row (standing): H. Davis, E. Shipp, W. Millington, G. Parvin, A. Glass, G. Davis, W. Newman, B. Higgins, W. Goldring, J. Huntley, R. Treagust, Warren, McGiffen, J. Mengham, C. Bailey, R. Fowles.
Front row, seated: W. Isherwood, F. Coombs, J. McIntyre, Joshua Dalrymple (Deputy Engineer), David Halton Thomson (Engineer), J. Bennett, W. Phillips, G. Harris, J. Randall, C. Davis, McGiffen.

Richard William Ford (1822 – 1900)

Richard Ford, 1897

As we have already seen, in the mid-1850s there were 14,000 inhabited houses in Portsmouth, but only about 4,500 of these had a piped water supply. The older parts of Portsmouth were fairly well provided with water mains, but few had been laid in the newer roads, where the inhabitants still relied on numerous shallow wells or supplies by water cart. The supply from Farlington depended wholly on a single trunk main six miles long, most of it being only 10-inch diameter and of insufficient capacity to supply the whole district at the same time. The mains serving the various districts had to be opened up in turn for periods of up to two hours, so that some houses received an early supply, others late in the day. The former Portsea Island well was of little use.

To remedy this state of affairs, at a meeting of the Town Council in October 1855, Richard William Ford, a rising young solicitor in Portsea, proposed that an application should be made to Parliament for an Act allowing the Council to buy the water undertaking. His motion was lost by a majority of more than 2 to 1, but this defeat led in 1856 to the first moves for a new company, promoted by some well-known Portsmouth residents. The three leaders in this movement were Benjamin Bramble, a former Mayor, Dr William Engledue, who had inspired the foundation of the Royal Portsmouth Hospital, and Richard Ford himself.

In October 1856, a prospectus was issued for investment in the proposed Borough of Portsmouth Waterworks Company. On 6th December, a well attended public meeting heard Ford and others commend the enterprise. Encouraged by the support received, Ford and his fellow promoters sought a Bill in Parliament to create the company and give it the necessary powers. This became an Act on 13th July 1857. At the first general meeting of the shareholders on 11th August, the new Directors were appointed and Richard Ford became the first Secretary, a part-time appointment which he was to hold for 40 years until his retirement in 1897.

He was the chief adviser to the Board, first during the difficult early years and then onwards to more stable times. His work decisively broke the sequence of ill-fortune and bad decisions that had punctuated the story of the two short-lived rival Portsmouth water undertakers in the early 1800s, and allowed the Company to move forward to a position where it could provide a continuous supply of good quality water to all the population.

By profession, Ford was a solicitor in partnership with his elder brother Henry, in the firm of H & R W Ford, first in Portsea and later in Old Portsmouth. He was a Town Councillor for nearly 30 years, was twice elected Alderman and became Mayor in 1864. Being a keen sanitary reformer, he took an active part in the introduction of main drainage. He retired from the Town Council in 1880 to become a Clerk of the Peace for the remainder of his life.

When Richard Ford died at the age of 78 on 8th September 1900, his passing broke the last personal link with the foundation of the Company. The scale of his contribution was summed up in his obituary in the Hampshire Post: 'it was no exaggeration to say that he was the very life of the undertaking'.

David Halton Thomson OBE (1885 – 1959)

David Halton Thomson, 1937
(Photo courtesy of CIWEM)

David Halton Thomson was educated at Highgate School, London, and then, unusually for the time, at the Technische Hochschule, Charlottenburg, Berlin. In 1903, he entered the University of Cambridge and took the Mechanical Sciences Tripos with honours in 1906.

From 1907 to 1909, he was articled to the consulting engineers, Dr G F Deacon and Sir Alexander Binnie, and remained with their firm as an assistant engineer for a further three years. In 1912, he began his long association with Portsmouth Water Company, being appointed chief engineering assistant to the Engineer and General Manager, Herbert Ashley, whom he succeeded in 1926. He was responsible for the design and construction of the new Havant Pumping Station, extensions to the filtration works and reservoirs at Farlington and the introduction of chlorination.

Farlington Pumping Station was electrified under his direction and the Portsbridge Booster Station was constructed in 1929. He saw through the considerable extension to the area of supply in the early 1930s, when mains water was introduced for the first time into many villages north of Portsmouth. In the 1930s too, he oversaw substantial new works to protect the water supply in case of war.

When the Second World War broke out, Halton Thomson was faced with the heavy responsibilities of restoring water supplies, after heavy air raids caused serious damage to the mains system. He carried this out with great energy and ingenuity, and his successor, the late Reg Hall, recalled how, at the height of the worst blitz on Portsmouth, Halton Thomson walked the two miles from his home to the office through what was a blazing inferno to direct operations. In addition, the water demands of the Navy had to be met, precautions against enemy invasion had to be taken and, later, extra water supplies had to be forthcoming for the invasion of France. At the end of the war, Halton Thomson was awarded the OBE for his services.

After the war until his retirement in 1950, he was occupied with the Worlds End scheme and with the conversion of Havant Pumping Station from coal to oil firing. During his retirement, Halton Thomson wrote *A History of the Portsmouth and Gosport Water Supply*, published on the Company's centenary in 1957. His work has been abridged to form the chapters about the Portsmouth and Gosport companies in this book.

Reg Hall recalled him as being rather reserved in manner, though far from suffering fools gladly; he was tolerant and generous to people less fortunate than himself. When his advice was sought, he would spare no effort to help, and he was particularly keen to assist younger engineers in the right approach to a problem.

David Halton Thomson found his greatest interest in the academic aspects of being an engineer. He was a brilliant mathematician and statistician and wrote a series of papers in the Institution of Water Engineers' Journal about the hydrogeology of the local chalk aquifers. He was President of the Institution in 1936-37.

In the words of Norman Hudson, who joined Portsmouth Water Company in 1947, "DHT was one of the old school, and even had a chauffeur-driven car to take him to and from the office. People would stand to attention when he arrived. Everyone went to his office, including the Company Secretary, not the other way round. He would press a button and you jumped to it! But DHT was a gentleman and was well respected by everyone who came into contact with him."

Eric Norman Laurence Guymer (1909 – 1994)

Eric Guymer joined the Borough of Portsmouth Waterworks Company in March 1927 and served the Company until his retirement as Secretary & Treasurer in November 1974, after which he was a non-executive Director until March 1992. Thus, excluding the war years, he contributed a remarkable 59 years of service, a lifetime's work by any measure.

Eric Guymer at his retirement presentation, November 1974

Eric's earlier years at the Company were spent in the Secretary's department, until he joined the RAF as a fighter pilot at the outbreak of the Second World War, attaining the rank of Squadron Leader. After sustaining a back injury during a heavy landing, he spent the remainder of his RAF service transporting aeroplanes and as a flying instructor.

Resuming work at the Company after the war, he was soon appointed Registrar and, in 1958, became Secretary & Treasurer on the death of Frank King. Two examples illustrate his influence.

In 1964, the Company decided to transfer its Head Office from Commercial Road, Portsmouth, to Havant, following notification by Portsmouth City Council of a redevelopment scheme for the city centre that would include the site of the current offices. Subsequently, the financial impact of the office move was greatly helped by Eric Guymer's success in persuading the Admiralty to accept that its agreement of 1906, which required the Company to supply it with water at a price of 6d per thousand gallons, should be abandoned and that, in future, it should pay the standard Company rate. This provided extra revenue which helped to mitigate the cost of the new Head Office. Eric also decided in 1967 that the Company should buy its first computer.

Eric Guymer was an enigmatic man with a dry sense of humour, who kept his life outside work very private. Fred Bailey, at the time Eric Guymer's deputy and his eventual successor, recalls what turned out to be a vital decision that would be instrumental in keeping the Company independent during the major changes in the water industry in the 1980s and 1990s. At the time of the formation of the large regional water authorities in 1974, the Water Companies' Association (WCA), the trade body of the private companies such as Portsmouth, proposed the amalgamation of all the water companies' pension fund assets into a new joint WCA pension scheme. Reg Hall, the Director and former Engineer, put this to the Board in anticipation that it would accept, but Eric Guymer proposed instead that the Company should continue with its own pension scheme for existing members and that only new employees would be eligible to join the WCA scheme. This latter course was supported by the Board.

The consequences of this decision were far-reaching, as it enabled the Portsmouth Water Company pension fund to continue to grow and, through Fred Bailey's initiative (described later), build up an investment in the Company's own shares until it had a controlling interest. When, in the approach to privatisation in the 1980s and afterwards, attempts were made by French and some British utility companies to buy shares in the smaller water companies, Portsmouth was able to resist these overtures and retain its independence.

George Slater (1921 – 2004)

George Slater, 1996

It was George Slater's habit in later years, when addressing staff at open evenings, to begin his remarks by saying, "For those who don't know me, my name is George Slater". These are perhaps the most superfluous words he could have uttered, because throughout his 47 years of service, there were few employees who did not know George Slater. Just as importantly, and for better or worse, he knew them too!

George Slater was born in South Ferriby, Lincolnshire, where his family had a farm. During the Second World War, he served in the RAF as an engineer. Having obtained a degree in engineering at Sheffield University, he joined the local authority water undertaking in Barnsley and then, in August 1950, he moved south to join Portsmouth Water Company as Engineering Assistant.

Never one to shrink from taking the initiative, he recalled what happened when vans had replaced hand carts in the 1950s. "There were still some hand carts in use in Portsmouth Depot, but these were superseded when a second service layers' van was purchased in about 1953. The hand carts were put in store at Havant and I subsequently sold them for £5 each to Gosport Corporation. When I mentioned this matter to Reg Hall [the Engineer], he complained that neither he nor I had any authority to dispose of the Company's assets and subsequently reported the matter to the Board!"

A strong character, George made his influence felt in the Company as he moved up through the ranks. He was the driving force behind many engineering and operational improvements for more than three decades and his foresight in this area still stands the Company in good stead today. He and Secretary & Treasurer, Fred Bailey, strove to eliminate inefficiency and waste and removed the barriers that had existed for years between the Engineer's and Secretary's 'sides' of the Company, resulting in a more unified management approach.

George was in charge of the difficult move of the engineering and operational staff and their equipment from the Head Office in Commercial Road, Portsmouth, to West Street, Havant, in 1967. Soon afterwards, he took the large River Itchen project forward from inception to completion. He planned and implemented a number of strategic trunk main connections and links between water supply zones and these remain of major benefit today.

When Reg Hall retired as Engineer in 1963, his deputy, Leonard Simpson, became Engineer and

George was appointed Deputy Engineer. When Simpson retired early in 1976, there was no doubt who would be the new Chief Engineer and George Slater was duly appointed.

Many employees have stories about George and his ripostes. When asked if the Company could consider adopting flexible working hours, he replied, "Yes, you can come in early and go home late, I don't mind!" Another employee once asked, "Mr Slater, I don't suppose I could borrow a Company van to use at home this weekend?", only to be told that he had just answered his own question! It should also be said that there are many stories of his kindness to members of staff who found themselves in personal difficulties. He was always interested in, and made a point of speaking to, anyone in the Company, irrespective of their position.

After retirement in 1986, George Slater served as a non-executive Director until 1997, and was Chairman of the Company for the last 5 years. He remained a Trustee of the Company's Pension Fund until his death in 2004.

Frederick Arthur Bailey (1923 -)

Fred Bailey, 2007

Fred Bailey was born in Clerkenwell, London, but his family moved to Watford, Hertfordshire, in 1927. Fred entered the water industry with Colne Valley Water Company in 1940 but, on his 18th birthday in 1941, he enlisted in the Royal Armoured Corps. Finding himself rather unsuited to routine army life, he volunteered for the Special Operations Executive (SOE), although he was at the time unsure of what exactly this would entail. In fact, he joined the 'Jedburghs', a group of three-man SOE teams dropped behind German lines in preparation for the liberation of France. Each team comprised a British or American officer, a national of the country the team was to enter and a radio operator. In this latter capacity, Fred parachuted into southern France in 1944 with two colleagues to organise the French resistance for the imminent invasion by the US First Army. This was extremely hazardous work, as capture while behind enemy lines could result in torture and death. However, he came through that mission safely and was then sent to the Far East for similar missions behind Japanese lines in Burma and Malaya. Fred was awarded the Croix de Guerre and mentioned in dispatches.

After the high of wartime experience, Fred returned to Colne Valley Water Company. Realising that he had to build a career, he became qualified as a Chartered Secretary. In 1962, he was interviewed for the post of Assistant Secretary at Portsmouth Water Company and was shocked to find that the interview was to be conducted by the whole Board of nine Directors! He was successful, but was asked to qualify as an accountant, which he duly did, despite being somewhat annoyed at having to obtain a further qualification.

With the expansion of the Company in 1963, it was decided that Eric Guymer would need a deputy and Fred was appointed to the post. He worked with Eric on the plans to persuade the Admiralty to abandon its favourable water charge, already mentioned earlier.

After Eric Guymer had persuaded the Company to retain its own independent pension fund in 1974, it was Fred who persuaded the Board to take advantage of the powers contained in the Water Act 1945 that enabled the Pension Fund to accumulate a controlling shareholding in Portsmouth Water, thus eventually allowing the Company to retain its independence. This is covered more fully in Chapter 13. Fortuitously, the investment in Portsmouth Water subsequently proved to be the most profitable investment the Pension Fund ever made. Of course, the Fund's over-riding consideration always has to be the well-being of its members, but as things stand in 2007, this has been achieved, the Company's pension scheme being in a healthy financial state and one of the few in which pensions are still calculated on the basis of final or average salary.

Between themselves, George Slater and Fred Bailey generated a creative tension that kept the Company moving forward over the period up to their retirements as Chief Engineer and Secretary & Treasurer respectively. Staff numbers were gradually reduced as employees retired and were only replaced if necessary, resulting in a steady reduction of the payroll between the 1970s and 1990s. By avoiding sudden batches of staff redundancies, two of Portsmouth Water's most important characteristics, those of stability and continuity of knowledge, were retained. Cost saving became, and remains, the watchword in Portsmouth Water. On a day-to-day working level, Fred and George always kept a weather eye on each other's activities and would not hesitate to express a critical view if they thought it was warranted! None of this had any effect on the long-standing friendship between themselves and their two families.

Fred retired as Secretary & Treasurer in 1988 and then served as a non-executive Director until 1999. He remains a Trustee of the Company's Pension Fund.

The Bridger family

The Bridger family has probably devoted the longest service to Portsmouth Water of all the families connected with the Company.

In the period prior to 1958, six Bridger brothers and their father worked for the Company. Once, all six Bridger brothers were working there at the same time and, between them, they totalled more than 220 years' service.

Dave Bridger, centre, explains an old flow recorder to visitors at Farlington

Bert Bridger, a painter, put in 43 years' service, Frank Bridger, a general foreman, 52 years, George Bridger senior, an engine driver, 45 years, Bill Bridger, a stoker, 41 years and Edward Bridger, an inspector, worked for the Company for 38 years. Harry Bridger, who suffered from poor health, worked irregularly as an odd job man.

Of the following generations, George senior's son, also called George, was a turncock at Havant from 1931 to 1973. George's sons, Dave and Pete, carried on the family tradition; Dave worked for the Company from 1959 to 2002, retiring as Works Superintendent at Farlington. Pete joined Portsmouth Water Company in 1972 and retired in 2005 as Supply Superintendent for the East District.

Thus the Bridger family has probably contributed at least 350 years' service to the Company!

The Peters family

John Peters, 2007

John Peters, now employed as a Sampling Supervisor in the Company's Laboratory, joined as a 16-year old apprentice carpenter in 1959. He recalls the working hours as 7.30 am to 5.30 pm on weekdays and having to work on Saturday mornings too! He worked for a few years at Farlington in the 1970s, before joining the Laboratory in 1976. John has completed 48 years of service.

John's father, Fred Peters, was employed first as a mainlayer, then as an engine driver at Farlington and finally as a lorry driver, for 40 years between 1935 and 1975. John's uncle, Harold 'Boy' Peters, was a mainlaying ganger at Havant and completed 30 years of service, retiring in 1976. John's maternal uncle, Harry Hedgecock, was a lorry driver and worked for the Company from 1947 to 1970.

On John Peters' aunt's side of the family, there was George Biss who was employed as a turncock at Havant from 1946 to 1984. George's son David was a mechanic in the vehicle maintenance workshop at Havant from 1964 to 2000.

John's brother-in-law, Ray Loader, was employed as a labourer and storeman for 36 years, retiring in 2000, while Ray's son Steve works at Farlington Treatment Works, having joined the Company in 1977. Steve's wife Christine worked at the Company as a secretary for 20 years.

Finally, there was John's grandfather, Charles 'Skimps' Peters, who worked for the Company for many years from the 1930s. 'Skimps' Peters is famous in Company folklore for putting a brand new motor mower into one of the Havant Springs ponds in the 1940s. Ken Bailey was a witness to what happened:-

"'Skimps' Peters had just been taught how to drive a new 'Dennis' ride-on motor mower to cut the very large area of grass around the natural spring ponds at Havant. He thought his new machine was getting hot so, in order to check this out, he raised himself out of his seat and bent over the engine to spit on the top of the cylinder. His mistake was to be right over the spark plug, from which the rubber cover was missing. With a bang, the electrical charge from the plug shot straight to his mouth via his spittle, the shock causing his false teeth to fly out of his mouth as he shot backwards out of the mower seat.

As he dragged himself to his feet, he watched in horror as the now driverless mower headed straight towards the large pond, down the bank and into the water. Panic-stricken, he ran as fast as he could to our workshop for help.

When we arrived on the scene, we quickly saw the funny side of what had happened. However, the true significance of the problem began to reveal itself for, as we watched, we could see signs of petrol and oil forming on the water, all coming from the sunken machine.

The spring in this pond produced water that was pumped up to the Farlington filtration plant for public supply. Oil in drinking water would have been a disaster, but was avoided by some prompt action. The pond outlets were quickly diverted and other pumping plant brought on line, just as we had practised during the war. Powerful mobile pumps were set up to pump the contaminated water away by using local ditches connected to Langstone Harbour, so as to drop the level and allow the mower to be retrieved. When this had been done, it was decided to clear the pond of its accumulated weed growth.

With the pond empty, it could be seen that the muddy floor was full of wriggling, squirming eels, some very large. Those in the pond grappled with these fish and hurled them up on the banks, where they were killed with shovels and poles. The largest eel when measured was almost six feet in length and over fifty pounds in weight."

No such near-disasters at work befell the subsequent generations of the Peters family. John and his close relatives have worked for a combined 330 years or so for the Company!

There are many other families who have worked for the Company down the generations and have long periods of combined service.

The end of the story...so far!

This concludes the story of how Portsmouth Water has developed from the incorporation of the Borough of Portsmouth Waterworks Company in 1857. Over the past 150 years, it has amalgamated with Gosport Waterworks Company, the water undertakings of Fareham UDC, Bognor Regis UDC, Chichester Corporation and Chichester RDC, and Selsey Water Company.

Through all that period the Company has concentrated on the fundamentals of being a water supplier, namely providing a first class service to customers at a low cost. In more recent years, it has also embraced the principles of conservation and environmental sustainability.

Clear, decisive leadership and the efforts of loyal, committed staff have enabled the Company to adapt to changing legislation, while maintaining its focus on securing safe and reliable water supplies for customers. Through careful planning and the development of its staff, it has retained its independence throughout the last 150 years.

By continuing these traditions, it will serve its customers well for many more years in the future.

Glossary

Terms in italics have their own separate definition in the Glossary.

Abstraction licence
A legal permit to pump water from an *aquifer* or watercourse.

Acidisation
The dissolving of pulverised chalk from *fissures*, often after drilling a *borehole*, by the injection of a concentrated acid, usually hydrochloric acid. The process can increase the *yield* that can be pumped from the *borehole*.

Activated carbon
A form of carbon that has a very high surface area, enabling it to adsorb large quantities of organic compounds.

Actuator
A mechanical device for opening and closing a *valve* or penstock. Normally powered electrically or pneumatically.

Adit
A tunnel driven laterally into underground strata from a vertical *shaft* or *well*. In water supply, an adit can enable more water to be obtained by intercepting more fissures in the surrounding aquifer. Can also be referred to as a heading.

Algal growth / algae
Algae are single- or multi-cellular plants, with no true leaf, stem or root, which can grow in water in large masses. Their growth rate is increased by elevated concentrations of nutrients in the water coupled with higher exposure to sunlight. Algal by-products can cause an unpleasant taste in drinking water.

Alum
Aluminium sulphate, a *coagulant* widely used in water treatment to force fine particles to coalesce or *flocculate*, enabling them to be removed by *filtration*.

Aquifer
A water-bearing underground stratum of rock, such as chalk.

Asset management plan
A document that sets out the future capital and operating costs for providing and maintaining operational assets, such as water *treatment works*.

Bankside storage reservoir
A reservoir built alongside a river near a *treatment* works to provide a temporary reserve of *raw water* that can be drawn upon for treatment if the river suffers short-term pollution.

Booster station
A structure containing pumps used for delivering treated water from a lower level *zone* to a higher *zone*.

Borehole
A vertical hole or shaft drilled into an underground water-bearing *aquifer*, containing *submersible pumps* to deliver water to the surface.

Catchment
An area of land from which water falling as rain collects and enters an *aquifer* or a river.

Cathodic Protection
A means of protecting buried steel water pipes from corrosion, such that, by electrolytic action, a metal more reactive than steel corrodes in preference to the steel itself.

Chloramination
A means of disinfection water using a mixture of *chlorine* and ammonia. Chloramines tend to provide longer lasting disinfection than *chlorine* and are thus suitable for very large mains *networks*.

Chlorine
A highly reactive gas which kills many organisms very quickly and is thus ideally suited to disinfecting water for human consumption. Injected into water in solution form.

Clarifier
A structure used in *water treatment* to allow *flocculated* particles to settle out, leaving clearer water to flow out of the top of the structure for further treatment.

Coagulation
A chemical, such as *alum*, which by a weak electrolytic action forces small particles in water to *flocculate*, or coalesce in larger masses. See also *flocculation*.

Coliform
A type of bacterium found naturally in soil and faeces.

Combination Box
A fitting used on service pipes that incorporates both a *stopcock* and a housing for a water meter.

Contact Tank/Main
A tank or pipe designed to provide sufficient time, after the injection of *chlorine*, for water flowing through it to be *disinfected*.

Corrosivity
The degree to which a weak electrolytic action occurs when an iron pipe is laid in wet soil and corrodes.

Cryptosporidium
A micro-organism that inhabits the gut of animals and humans and, when ingested by humans, can cause unpleasant and prolonged bouts of sickness and diarrhoea.

d
An acronym for 'old penny', a coin used before decimalisation of British currency in 1971. Actually an abbreviation for 'denarius', a Roman coin denomination. There were 240 old pennies in one pound.

Disinfection
The process of killing harmful organisms in water to make it fit for drinking. Usually carried out by adding *chlorine* to the water.

Distribution
The process of conveying drinking water to customers along a network of pipes, or mains.

Drought
Defined by the Meteorological Office as a period of at least fifteen consecutive days without measurable rainfall. In practice, a drought becomes critical for water supply after a much longer period of low rainfall, in which *groundwater* and surface water flow reduce to a point where there may be insufficient water available to supply customers normally.

Ductile Iron
A modern form of cast iron that contains magnesium and thus, in contrast to 'traditional' cast iron, is not brittle. Used for manufacture of modern iron water mains, which are also given an internal and external coating to protect them against corrosion.

Faecal
Derived from the faeces of animals or humans.

Fibre Reinforced Cement
A material once used for the manufacture of water mains, comprising cement reinforced with asbestos fibres. Its use was discontinued in the mid-1990s.

Filtration
In *water treatment*, the process of removing particles from water, usually by passing it through a bed of sand and gravel. Removal is achieved by the combined actions of straining and electrolytic attraction.

Fissure
A gap or discontinuity in rock such as chalk.

Flash Mixer
A tank in a water *treatment works* where *raw water* is mixed with a *coagulant* to cause the *flocculation* of fine particles into larger masses that can be removed by *filtration*.

Flocculation
The result of *coagulation*, in which the addition of a coagulant chemical to water causes fine particles to coalesce, or flocculate, into larger masses that can be removed more easily by filtration.

Fluoridation
The process of increasing the fluoride content of water to provide protection against tooth decay.

Flushing
The process of inducing water to flow at a higher than normal velocity along a water main and out through a *hydrant* to clear deposits of sediment (often from iron corrosion) that may have accumulated in the main.

Foot
An imperial measure of length, equivalent to 304.8 millimetres.

Gallon
An imperial measure of volume, equivalent to 4.545 litres.

Geographic Information System (GIS)
A system of recording spatial information about physical features, such as water mains, on an electronic map, ie a 'digital map', that incorporates attributes, such as water main diameter, year laid, material, burst history, etc, as well as the physical position. Enables analyses of these attributes to be carried out for many purposes, such as planning future maintenance investment.

Groundwater
A body of water that exists underground in permeable rocks, such as chalk or sandstone.

Heading
See *adit*.

Horsepower (HP)
An imperial measure of power, equivalent to 0.746 kilowatts.

Hydrant
A fitting on a water main that allows water to be discharged from the main in a controlled manner, eg for *flushing* or fire-fighting.

Hydrocarbon

A chemical containing hydrogen and carbon in combination, such as oil, petrol, kerosene etc.

Inch
An imperial measure of length equivalent to 25.4 millimetres.

Intake
A structure on a river where water is *abstracted*.

Leakage
The uncontrolled loss of water from *mains*, *service pipes* or reservoirs.

Main, Distribution
A main, usually less than 300 mm diameter, which distributes water within a local area and to which individual service pipes to properties are connected.

Main, Gravity
A main along which water flows by the force of gravity alone.

Main, Pumping
A main along which water can only flow by being pumped.

Main, Trunk
A main, usually 300mm diameter or more, which conveys water in bulk between service reservoirs and large geographical areas.

Membrane Filtration
The process of filtering water through the walls of very fine, artifical hollow tubes. Can remove very small organisms, such as cryptosporidium.

A submerged membrane filter is one in which the membranes are located in a tank containing the water to be filtered, the water being drawn by suction from the outside of the membrane fibre to the inside. It is more economical to construct and operate than pressure membrane filtration, in which water is forced by pumping through the membrane fibre wall from the inside to the outside.

Metering
The installation of equipment for measurement of the flow of water.

Network

A system of interconnected water mains.

Nitrate

A family of chemicals which contain oxidised nitrogen. Used as an agricultural fertiliser, among other uses. When present in significant quantities in water, can cause methaemoglobinaemia, or 'blue babies', in very young children.

Observation Borehole

A small-diameter *borehole* drilled into underground rocks, or other geological strata, to enable the measurement of the effect on groundwater levels of pumping from an *aquifer*.

Oocyst

An egg-like micro-organism, such as *cryptosporidium*.

Orthophosphoric Acid

A chemical used in water treatment to reduce the *plumbosolvency* of water passing through lead pipes.

Periodic Review

The review by the Office of Water Services of the charges imposed by water companies for their services. Currently carried out every 5 years.

Pesticide

An organic compound used to kill agricultural pests. Water quality regulations prescribe extremely low permitted thresholds of pesticides and herbicides in drinking water, typically one ten millionth of a gram per litre.

pH

A measure of the acidity of a liquid, such as water. The 'p' stands for 'potenz' (ie the potential to be) and the 'H' for hydrogen. The acidity of a liquid increases with the amount of hydrogen it contains.

Plc

Public limited company, ie one whose shares can be bought and sold on the stock market.

Plumbosolvency

The degree to which lead (Latin 'plumbum') is dissolved by water as it passes through lead pipes.

Pumping Station

A structure containing pumps that deliver raw, partially treated or treated water to a higher level.

Rapid Gravity Filter
A bed of graded sand and gravel layers designed to remove particles from water as it passes through the bed by gravity at a relatively rapid rate.

Rateable Value
The rateable value is an assessment by a local authority of the annual rental value of a property, last carried out in 1973. Prior to 1st April 1990, general rates, which were payable to the local authority, were based on the rateable values of properties. General rates have now been replaced by the Council Tax. Most domestic customers who do not have a water meter receive an annual bill for water and sewerage charges that is based on the rateable value of their property. At Portsmouth Water, properties built after 1st April 1990 that do not have a water meter for billing purposes are charged on the basis of a licence fee.

Raw Water
Water that has not been subjected to treatment to render it fit for consumption.

Recharge
The refilling of *aquifers* by rainfall that has permeated through the ground from the surface.

Reinforced Concrete
Concrete used for building structures, in which compressive stresses are born by the concrete and tensile stresses are born by steel bars cast into the concrete at the time of construction.

Reinstatement
The restoration of the surface of a pipe trench in fields, verges, footpaths or roads to match the surrounding surface in appearance, material, strength and other physical properties, eg skid resistance on a road.

Residual
The small quantity of a chemical, usually *chlorine*, left in drinking water after treatment to protect water from the risk of contamination between the *treatment works* and customers' taps.

Resources
Sources such as rivers, springs, *wells* or *boreholes* that can be used for the *abstraction* of water.

Run Lead Joints
A system of pipe jointing, no longer used, in which molten lead was poured into the joint sockets of cast iron mains to provide a watertight seal.

Sampling
The act of taking a small quantity of water from a main or a tap to measure its physical, chemical or microbiological properties by analysis in a laboratory.

Screen
A device used in *water treatment* to remove larger debris from the *raw water*.

Sediment
Fine particles in water that are deposited by their own weight on the base of a pipe or tank.

Service Pipe
A pipe connecting a property to a water main. The section of the service pipe in the public highway between the main and the property boundary is called the communication pipe. The section within the boundary of private property is called the supply pipe.

Service Reservoir
A reinforced concrete structure containing drinking water. Often abbreviated to 'Reservoir'. It provides a reserve of water to:-

- meet fluctuations in demand during the day.
- provide a reasonably consistent pressure for customers.
- maintain supplies during short-term plant failure and maintenance.
- in some cases, allow cheaper off-peak electricity to be used for pumping at night.

Shaft
A vertical hole in the ground, usually lined, giving access to a tunnel or *adit*.

's' or shilling
A shilling was a coin used before the 1971 decimalisation of British currency, equivalent to 5 pence today. Abbreviated to 's'. There were 12*d* (old pennies) in a shilling and 20 shillings in one pound.

Slow Sand Filter
A bed of graded sand designed to remove particles from water as it passes thorough the bed at a relatively slow rate. Removal is achieved by the combined actions of straining and electrolytic attraction while, in addition, some micro-organisms are killed as they pass through the uppermost layer of the sand. No longer built today, owing to the high cost of regularly cleaning the uppermost sand layer and the area of land required.

Source
A feature such as a river, spring, *well* or *borehole* that can be used for the abstraction of water.

Spigot and Socket
A system of joining pipes together to give a watertight seal, in which the plain end of one pipe fits into the cup-like socket of its neighbour, with a rubber gasket sealing the gap between the two.

Stopcock
A *valve* or tap on a *service pipe* that can be closed to prevent water flowing. Usually installed on the property boundary.

Submersible pump

A pump driven by an electric motor that can operate under water, eg in a *borehole*. The pump motor and cable joints are sealed against the ingress of water.

Sulphur Dioxide

A gas injected in solution to remove excess *chlorine* during the *water treatment* process of *superchlorination*.

Superchlorination

A means of disinfecting water by injecting a high dose of *chlorine* in solution, allowing a period of contact with the water and then removing excess *chlorine* (or dechlorinating) using sulphur dioxide to achieve a lower *residual* before the water is supplied to customers.

Swabbing

The act of passing a foam sponge, or swab, along a water main, using water pressure, to clean deposited material, usually from a new main, before it is *disinfected*.

Swallow Hole

A natural geological feature that provides a rapid route for surface water to enter the underlying *aquifer*, by-passing the natural filtration properties of the subsoils and rocks. Can cause pollution of water supplies unless appropriate *water treatment* is used.

Telemetry

A means of electronically transmitting instrument measurements and alarms from a remote site to a central monitoring point.

Test Pumping

The pumping of water from a *well* or *borehole* at varying rates and periods to establish its probable *yield*.

Treatment Works

A site at which a series of processes takes place to treat *raw water* to render it fit for drinking.

Trihalomethanes

A form of methane in which three of the four hydrogen atoms in the methane molecule are replaced by three atoms of a halogen, usually chlorine [the other halogens are fluorine, bromine and iodine]. Harmful if present in drinking water in sufficient quantities.

Turbidity

'Cloudiness' in water. Turbidity that is normally invisible to the naked eye can nonetheless be unacceptable for drinking water.

Undertaking
A utility organisation that operates under statutory authority.

Valve
A fitting on a water main which, when closed or partially closed, prevents or controls the flow of water.

Washwater
Water used to clean accumulated particles from filters and thus prevent blocking of the filter.

Water Efficiency
Means of reducing the amount of water supplied. Can include leakage reduction, use of domestic appliances and toilets with lower water use, displacement devices in toilet cisterns, re-use or recycling of water, making use of rainwater instead of tap water (eg by using water butts to collect garden water), and many other measures.

Water Hammer
The noise induced by the shock wave created when a moving body of water in a pipe is suddenly stopped by the closing of a *valve* or, less frequently, when a stationery body of water in a pipe is suddenly accelerated, eg by starting a pump or opening a valve.

Waterbar
A rubber strip that is cast into concrete at a joint to prevent the leakage of water from a concrete structure.

Well
Essentially a large diameter *borehole*.

Yield
The minimum amount of water that can be reliably obtained from a water *source*.

Zone
A geographical area that is supplied with all its water from a single *service reservoir* or *treatment works*.

Index

A

B

C

D

G

H

M

N

O

P

R

S

T

Y

Z